Island Life

The Natural History Press, publisher for The American Museum of Natural History, is a division of Doubleday & Company, Inc. Directed by a joint editorial board made up of members of the staff of both the Museum and Doubleday, The Natural History Press publishes books and periodicals in all branches of the life and earth sciences, including anthropology and astronomy. The Natural History Press has its editorial offices at The American Museum of Natural History, Central Park West at 79th Street, New York, New York, and its business offices at 501 Franklin Avenue, Garden City, New York.

ISLAND LIFE

A Natural History
of the Islands of the World

SHERWIN CARLQUIST

Illustrations by Sherwin Carlquist,
Jeanne R. Janish and Charles S. Papp

Published for the American Museum of Natural History

THE NATURAL HISTORY PRESS/GARDEN CITY, NEW YORK 1965

AT first glance, the animals and plants of an island seem merely the animals and plants of a different region. As one moves closer, compares their forms and habits to those of mainland relatives, and reads observations of biologists, a new picture emerges. The island worlds prove to be agents for intricate and un-expected patterns, patterns which fascinated Charles Darwin and which will continue to fascinate both professional and amateur biologist.

The "syndrome" of island-life phenomena long ago attracted my attention, but I found it presented only as scattered notes or observations, often tucked away in the most unlikely corners of biology's archives. This book attempts to collate these scattered data into pictures of the directions and destinies of island or-ganisms. Because there is very little precedent for such a focus, the task has been both difficult and challenging. In the process, I have continually noticed how very little, really, is known about most island plants and animals.

Few scientific laboratories exist on island areas, so this lack of knowledge is understandable. As travel becomes easier, biologists have increased the pace of their visits. Some of the most surprising discoveries about island creatures have emerged only within the past decade. Ironically, this comes at a time when extinction of native floras and faunas is proceeding rapidly, owing to man's spreading influence and demands on island lands. Thus a note of urgency is added to the inherent excitement of studying island life.

Our poor knowledge of insular animals and plants means that many issues are unresolved, and statements are often difficult to make. Today, few biologists have the breadth which Darwin and Wallace did, and I apologize for the myopic touches which may result from the fact that one trained as a plant anatomist attempted this book.

The paucity of information presented to the public at large on island floras and faunas can be explained in part by the low fund of scientific information available and in part by the fact that island organisms, unfamiliar to many readers, are difficult to describe. Please be patient if the names in these pages are not ones you have encountered before. I believe that many island plants and animals deserve a greater currency in print than they have previously enjoyed. Scientific names are not intended for your intimidation, and contrary to popular belief, there is no uniformity among biologists in their pronunciation —indeed, it is doubtful if some of them were ever intended to be pronounced. I have included scientific names not only because many creatures lack popular names but because they are the only sure key to finding further information. To have omitted them would have been to slam the door on whatever further curiosity about island life you may have.

The references given at the end of the book will likewise permit further reading. They also document my sources, and thereby my indebtedness to the painstaking studies of many biologists. There may be some new contributions in this book, but my heavy dependence on others should be evident. In addition to the inspirational starting points offered by Darwin and Wallace, I owe much to Philip Darlington's indispensable *Zoogeography*, a modern classic. Also influential was Zimmerman's fine introductory volume of *Insects of Hawaii*. The rational thinking of my colleague Dr. Robert F. Thorne has been of great assistance.

Many have contributed information or photographs for my use. Photographs are mine unless other wise indicated, but even these would have never been taken without the good offices of those who have aided my field work. Among those who have helped me in various ways and deserve thanks are: Mr. and Mrs. Roy M. Bauer (Santa Barbara), Mr. Edwin Bonsey (Makawao, Hawaii), Dr. Lincoln Constance (Berkeley), Dr. Winifred Curtis (Hobart), Dr. Selwyn Everist (Brisbane), Dr. John S. Garth (Los Angeles), Dr. George Gillett (Honolulu), Dr. Gunnar Harling (Stockholm), Mr. E. E. Henty (Lae), Dr. John Thomas Howell (San Francisco), Mr. Fred W. Humphrey (Perth), Mr. H. D. Ingle (Melbourne), Mr. and Mrs. Robert Jancey (Sydney), Mr. Tadayuki Kato (Kapaa, Hawaii), Mrs. Andre Millar (Lae), Dr. Lucy Moore (Christchurch), Dr. Reid Moran (San Diego), Mr. and Mrs. Hiroshi Murai (Ashiya, Japan), Mr. John Parham (Suva), Dr. Werner Rauh (Heidelberg), Dr. Pieter van Royen (Lae), Dr. Harold St. John (Honolulu), Dr. William L. Stern (Washington, D.C.), Dr. Robert F. Thorne (Claremont), and Dr. Robert Virot (Paris).

I would also like to acknowledge the skill of my artists. Mrs. Jeanne R. Janish did most of the plant drawings, and Mr. Charles S. Papp drew most of the animals. I have contributed other drawings, chiefly those of a mechanical nature.

Appreciation is also expressed to Dr. Dean Amadon, who read the manuscript and offered helpful suggestions.

SHERWIN CARLQUIST
Claremont, October 1964

Contents

Color Plates

Island Life

1 The Island Condition

THE history of island creatures begins with isolation, and the train of consequences begun by separation hovers over and guides the peculiar destinies of all island plants and animals. In the chapters which follow unfold the many and unexpected effects isolation brings, effects which surprise and still puzzle the most sophisticated biologist. Island isolation dictates evolutionary problems in heightened form. Not immune from the romance of remote lands, biologists remain attracted to the many unsolved curiosities in the island museums toured in this book.

Any evolutionist, however, will say that isolation is not restricted to islands. Indeed, without isolation new species might never evolve anywhere. If a plant or animal species formed one large interbreeding population without distinctive ecological pockets, changes would likely be wiped out and little progress toward new adaptations could be made. This is, apparently, rarely true, for all species are spread over areas crisscrossed by many or actual potential barriers: mountains, rivers, zones too wet or dry. Separation of a species into groups of individuals takes place incessantly, and in such new groups mutations can be established and spread. The effectiveness of this process is parallel to development of languages: the many languages, some similar, some completely unlike, which now separate nations and ethnic groups are products of continual isolation of peoples as events of history push them into separate avenues.

If isolation is the key to biological diversity, it obviously happens both on continents and islands, continually, everywhere. How, then, are islands exceptional? Aren't places spaced far apart from each other isolated whether those separations are by land or by sea? Certainly. Cool alpine regions are, in fact, nothing more or less than islands of the upper air. If we look at a list of plants found on Africa's highest mountains, such as Kilimanjaro, we find species which appear—unafrican. A member of the mustard family, for example, *Thlaspi alliaceum* (1–1), grows on Africa's equatorial Alps, and on the higher mountains of Ethiopia, but also on the Transylvanian Alps and the Apennines of Europe, mountains separated from African peaks by land (admittedly narrow and circuitous strips of land), but land which is unthinkable as a site for an alpine plant. I have collected, at twelve thousand feet in New Guinea, buttercups and gentians which have counterparts in the Alps, the Rocky Mountains, and the Himalayas, but which certainly have no relatives in the steamy rain forests which stretch down from the frigid peaks of higher New Guinea.

1–1. Mountaintops are like islands of the upper air: this plant (*Thlaspi alliaceum*) and others are restricted to widely spaced peaks of Europe and eastern Africa.

Likewise, there are a surprising number of Californian plants either the same as, or closely related to, plants from central Chile although these species are absent in intervening regions (1–2). These two areas have a Mediterranean climate, unlike the long stretches of subtropical and tropical lands which separate them. In this case, similarity in plants has been achieved by long-distance dispersal, perhaps by means of seeds carried by migratory birds which are known to fly this route.

When we think in these terms, many other kinds of "islands" can easily be named. Within the ocean, there can be islands of water. One curious island is formed by the shallow tropical waters on the west coast of North, Central, and South America. Limited by land on the east, colder waters on the north and south, and colder waters on the west (1–2), this strip is an island for the fish which inhabit it, and they are different from those of other regions. A recent author calculated that the land barrier on the east is 98 per cent effective in preventing immigration of species from the east coast of tropical America. The "East Pacific Barrier" (the limit of the shelf of shallow water on the west) is 86.3 per cent effective in keeping out species from other parts of the Pacific.

Mention of alpine peaks as islands suggests that the inverse, the deep trenches of the ocean, are islands for organisms adapted to great depth and pressure. Just as extreme cold, bright sunlight, and excessive drying by winds are conditions alpine plants and animals must withstand, fishes in oceanic trenches must have ways of coping with darkness and a food supply very different from that above. Little wonder that the curious lantern fishes (1–3) described by Beebe and other writers have evolved in these extreme niches. Similarly blind fishes and insects which inhabit caves have evolved with respect to special conditions and to an isolation just as effective as that on islands.

Fresh water fishes offer an example of insular isolation, for streams of fresh water are watery islands for fish adapted to them. Some groups of fishes are versatile, able to withstand salt water as well as fresh. Such fishes can be found in fresh water streams on islands, for they can change from a salt water ancestry. Other fresh water fishes are completely intolerant of salt water—the so-called "primary division fresh water fishes"—and are thus entirely restricted to fresh water streams and lakes of the world's continents—or islands which were once part of these continents.

Other "islands" are the host plants or animals on which parasites live. For a flea, a dog is just such an island, and not surprisingly, the fleas which inhabit dogs, cats, and humans are three distinct species. Isolation is told in the irreversible evolution in which parasites indulge. For example, two families of flies which parasitize bats, Nycteribiidae and Streblidae, have evolved winglessness and eyelessness, specializations much like those discussed in this book. "Islands within islands" can result in this way. A family of lice, Nesiotinidae, occurs only on penguins on the tiny Kerguelen Islands. There is a peculiar fungus, *Trenomyces*,

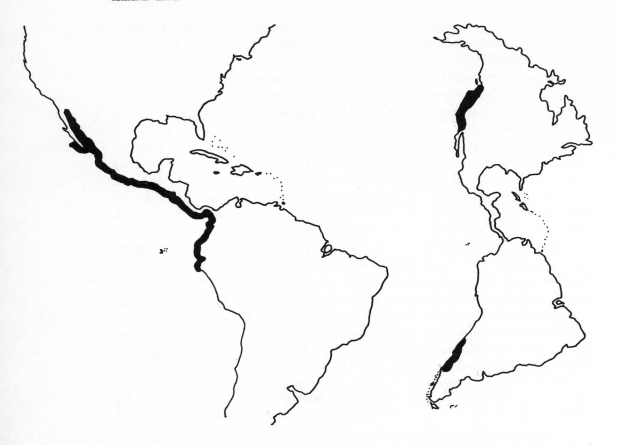

1–2. Island-like situations: At left, a shelf of warm shallow water on the central Pacific coast of the Americas makes an "island" formed by the "East Pacific Barrier" for many fish. At right, a pair of far-flung "islands" similar in climate and connected by a bird migration route is home for *Sanicula crassicaulis*. Many other plants show this curious western North America-central Chile distribution pattern and are absent in intervening regions.

one species of which has been found only on certain hippoboscid flies which live only on lemurs, which live only on Madagascar.

But these "islands," intriguing as they are, are side issues. Islands in an ocean differ from these peculiar cases of isolation in various ways. True islands usually offer not just a few, but a variety of habitats, comparable to those of continents—shores, mountains, and forests, whereas a cave or an alpine peak is a single extreme environment. The broad ecological gamut found on many islands offers unparalleled opportunities for whatever migrants manage to traverse the sea separating them from continents.

Islands in oceans are separated by the most effective barrier of all: salt water.

1–3. Ocean deeps are inverted watery islands to which fish such as the lantern fish *Melanocetus* are restricted.

Although alpine peaks are often decidedly isolated from each other, land birds could travel from one to another and would be afforded stopping places along the way, whereas oceans offer no such advantages. Seeds floating in wind across land might drop, but a breeze can carry them aloft again without damage. Contact with sea water would be fatal for windborne seeds. Most importantly, true islands offer continued isolation for long periods of time. The varied effects of such intense isolation are so intricate that this single feature ramifies into many unexpected consequences. Some facet is seen in each of the chapters which follow.

In addition to isolation and some degree of ecological diversity, islands sometimes offer a feature not generally appreciated. A small area of land completely surrounded by ocean has a noticeably more even climate. Temperatures are more uniform, with fewer sharp extremes, than an area of the same latitude in a continent. This may promote certain changes in the island members of a group of organisms which occurs both on a continent and on an island.

Isolation, ecological opportunity, and to a lesser extent climatic moderation have, over long periods of time, created remarkable designs. Untrammeled by the constant cross-currents of migration, predation, and competition, the smaller number of groups present on islands reveal patterns of evolution as though in a laboratory. Islands are at the same time the experiment stations and archives of evolution. Here is what one writer says:

"The natural history of these islands is eminently curious, and well deserves attention. Most of the organic productions are aboriginal creations, found nowhere else; there is even a difference between the inhabitants of the different islands; yet all show a marked relationship with those of America, though separated from that continent by an open space of ocean, between 500 and 600 miles in width. The archipelago is a little world within itself, or rather a satellite attached to America, whence it has derived a few stray colonists, and has received the general character of its indigenous productions. Considering the small size of these islands, we feel the more astonished at the number of their aboriginal beings, and at their confined range. Seeing every height crowned with its crater, and the boundaries of most of the lava streams still distinct, we are led to believe that within a period, geologically recent, the unbroken ocean was here spread out. Hence, both in space and time, we seem to be brought somewhat near to that great fact—that mystery of mysteries—the first appearance of new beings on this earth."

This statement was made concerning the Galápagos Islands by Charles Darwin, in whose *Voyage of the Beagle* are recorded the "eminently curious" nature of Galápagos plants and animals. H.M.S. *Beagle* dropped anchor off Chatham Island in the Galápagos on September 15, 1835. Although almost twenty-five years were to elapse before the appearance of Darwin's *On the Origin of Species,* we might date the origin of the theory of evolution from that landfall. Biologists agree that the clarity of evolutionary patterns and the strange diversification of those "few stray colonists" which originally stocked the Galápagos Islands permitted Darwin to discern the patterns of evolution and crystallize their workings into his theory as few other experiences could have. And yet the Galápagos are not even the most remarkable group of islands with respect to their flora and fauna: the Hawaiian Islands show the same phenomena, but surely exceed the Galápagos in richness and peculiarity of organisms. Appreciation of island beings came to fruition with the publication by a friend of Darwin, Alfred Wallace, of *Island Life,* a book which alerted generations to the dramatic possibilities islands offer for study of life. Even today, biologists follow the Darwinian precedent, and rarely refuse an opportunity to join an expedition to the Galápagos—or any other islands. Results of these travels may be expressed in evocative scenarios such as those William Beebe offered in his *Arcturus Adventure* or *Galápagos—World's End,* the feelings of a biologist surrounded by and reacting to the curious organisms he studies. Or the almost romantic appeal islands have for biologists may be masked in pages of formal descriptions, technical text, and figures which fill the austere, gray-bound papers emanating from museums, scientific academies, and universities. Even clad in the language—or languages—of biology, the fascination of island-life phenomena can be found, as the pages which follow hopefully will show.

At this point, I apologetically append what in most books is termed a glossary, placed in the last pages of a book, and thus is easily avoided. Discussion of island plants and animals requires use of precise terms covering patterns of origin, dispersal, and evolution, and common parlance alone does not cover all of the situations presented here. Also, concepts of nomenclature and of geological time are basic to understanding of island floras and faunas. Because even professional biologists sometimes misuse some of the terms listed below, this vocabulary seems best introduced at the beginning, rather than at the end of a book.

Continental island; oceanic island. Continental islands are assumed once to have been connected with a mainland, oceanic ones to have arisen from beneath an ocean surface. Unfortunately the matter doesn't stop there, as the next two chapters indicate.

Classification, nomenclature. If scientific names are unfamiliar to you, you are in good company. Probably no biologist has a clear visual image of the appearance of plants or animals included in much more than a fraction of the many families and genera, the names of which seem to make biological literature so esoteric. Books and articles which deliberately avoid or omit scientific names deprive the reader of a valuable tool for further reading and reference. Besides, scientific names are relatively precise, uniform, and universal; attempts to use common names exclusively result in the absurdity of using names by which plants and animals have rarely if ever been called. Scientific names are often familiar, as the examples below show.

FAMILY: in animals, names of families end in -idae; in plants, in -aceae or -ae (Hominidae; Rosaceae; Compositae).

GENUS (plural: genera): the first of a binomial (genus+species); always capitalized and written in italics (*Camellia, Hippopotamus*).

SPECIES (plural: species): the second name in a binomial, italicized and not capitalized in animals, usually not capitalized in plants (*Camellia japonica*).

SUBSPECIES: a unit below the level of species, if more than one unit within a species merits naming. If so, a trinomial results (*Partula suturalis vexillum*).

Native: (=indigenous), not brought by man, intentionally or accidentally. The opposite is *introduced.* The term "native" can include the special cases designated by the next three terms.

Endemic: restricted to, found exclusively in, a given named region.

Autochthonous: having evolved within the island or region where it (a species, genus, etc.) is native.

Relict: persisting in a region after becoming extinct elsewhere; or a surviving member of a group other members of which have become extinct.

Migration: usually, in this book, a tendency of a group to expand into a new location; also, a seasonal movement, as in migratory birds.

Barrier: a geographic, climatic, or ecologic deterrent to migration.

Phylogeny (adj.: phylogenetic): the history of evolutionary change in a group. Descriptions of phylogeny often involve the next five terms.

Differentiation, divergence: a change from an ancestral condition. The term *convergence* is not opposite, but is used to describe two different groups which evolve in a similar fashion, resulting in "look-alikes": convergent evolution.

Radiation: diversification of a group into a variety of new habitats, habits, or forms.

Adaptation: evolution of a group to suit a particular condition.

Primitive: an early member of an evolutionary series; or a particular feature of an early plant or animal which is still present in one living today. The opposite term is *derivative.*

Specialized: having mechanisms, forms, or physiology which represent a high degree of adaptation for particular conditions, markedly changed from ancestral forms. The opposite is *unspecialized* (not *primitive*).

Geological time:

Name	Years Ago (approx.)
Cenozoic	
Pleistocene (ice ages)	1 million
Pliocene	15 "
Miocene	30 "
Oligocene	40 "
Eocene	50 "
Paleocene	60 "
Tertiary	
Cretaceous	125 "
Jurassic	150 "
Triassic	180 "
Paleozoic	
Permian	205 "
Carboniferous	225 "
Devonian	315 "
Silurian	350 "
Ordovician	430 "
Cambrian	510 "
Pre-Cambrian	more than 510 million

Contemporary floras and faunas of islands—especially those of oceanic islands—are most strongly influenced by events relatively recent in the geological time scale. Relicts, however, date their history from earlier periods.

2   Getting There Is Half the Problem

GETTING there is no problem at all, of course, if a plant or animal is already there. This is what happens on so-called continental islands. The British Isles had a dry-land connection with France, but during the Pleistocene, the isthmus became submerged, and the inhabitants of the islands and the mainland have gone their separate ways since, to be sure with some interchange. This example is a relatively clear one; other islands have been separated for a much longer period of time. If a continental island has lain isolated for a very long period of time, thus, the plants and animals have arrived mostly across water and the assemblage which the island hosts will be much like that of an island which arose from the ocean floor without a pre-existing connection with a continent. Often geologists cannot offer much help in telling us the extent of antique land connections, if any, of islands. Most frequently, the best evidence is in the kinds of animals and plants present, if we can perceptively interpret these living archives. Patterns on oceanic islands differ from those on continental islands—with the usual proviso of "all other things being equal." But all things are never equal; time blurs the history of floras and faunas, and just as geologists are not of one mind in reading the history of particular islands, biologists differ in interpreting the flora and fauna. The views I present in this book will be shared by many, but certainly not all. Answers to some island problems will never, perhaps, become clear, but biologists, always optimistic, like to think that most problems will gravitate into that zone where one interpretation becomes much more probable than another.

In unraveling island histories, one must disregard accidental or intentional introductions of plants and animals. In particular cases, this is no easy task, and biologists try to reconstruct the motives people may have had for bringing what seem like poor food plants to islands, or they will speculate what chances a rat may have had traveling on a Polynesian voyage as a stowaway. Fortunately, when the catalogue of an island's species is sorted, relatively few remain in the residue dubbed "dubiously native" or "possibly introduced." The patterns of introduced species are usually clear: weeds which grow only around a village or large mammals such as the pig which lack any means of long-distance dispersal other than man.

There is still disagreement among biologists about whether particular islands once did have a land connection with a continent, or whether they arose from the ocean floor, or whether they are remnants of larger islands. The species which inhabit an island ought to be a living history of the island. We cannot always be certain how or when they arrived, however, and there will always be some latitude in interpreting the story of the world's islands. The species which are not only native but also endemic would seem an excellent clue to island history. But even using these, controversy develops. How, ask land-bridge proponents, could these distinctive endemic species have arrived via chance dispersal, how could they evolve on limited island areas? Easy, says the oceanic-island partisan: the ancestors did have ability at long-distance dispersal and through evolutionary change, the island population became distinct. Obviously such an argument hinges on whether or not long-distance dispersal can suffice for populating an island far from a source area. Biologists increasingly seem to believe that it can. We know that some groups of plants and animals travel much more easily than others, so the relative proportion of good-dispersing versus poor-dispersing sorts on an island should be a clue. That is for the next chapter; first, I must convince you that long-distance dispersal is indeed a fact of island life. By definition, long-distance dispersal occurs by chance and is very rare, and so seeing a dispersal feat is virtually impossible. Indeed, if long transport by natural means were commonplace and therefore easily witnessed, the plants and animals of islands would be like those of continents, and all continents would be alike. Lacking witnesses, we must rely on various sorts of circumstantial evidence.

The best evidence for long-distance dispersal would be afforded by the appearance of a bare volcanic island from the ocean floor, such as the island in 2–1. Such an island should be large, so that it would form a good target for chance immigrants, it should have a favorable climate, it should not be part of a pre-existing island, and it should be neither too far or too near a source area for dispersal. This is asking a great deal—too much, in fact, for these conditions have not been fulfilled within historical time. Krakatau came close. An island lying in the strait between Java and Sumatra (2–2), Krakatau violently erupted in 1883, and after the spectacular convulsion which scattered dust all over the world via the upper atmosphere and reddened sunsets in distant countries, four small barren islets resulted. No sign of life was detected on the Krakatau islets and, although some controversy exists as to whether any living seeds remained, we can say that the land, which consisted mostly of heaps of volcanic ash, was quite effectively laid bare. Humans do not seem to have played any but a minor role in bringing plants and animals, some skeptics to the contrary. The Krakatau islets are separated from Java by twenty-five miles, from Sumatra by fifty miles at the nearest points. The highest islet attains twenty-four hundred feet, and in this region about ninety-eight inches of rain fall annually, providing a suitable climate for many immigrants. One could wish, however, that Krakatau were more distant from neighboring islands, as are Hawaii or the Galápagos, so as to provide a better replica of isolation.

Studies of the revegetation of Krakatau prove that the few species which may have survived the eruption have not affected the picture of immigration;

2–1. A volcano which breaks, steaming, through the surface of the ocean after build-ing up from the sea floor is the means of origin for many oceanic islands. This new island was discovered south of Japan (31° 58′ N. Latitude, 139° 57′ E. Longitude). (Official U. S. Navy photo.)

that the few species introduced by human agencies can mostly be discovered and discounted easily; and that although Krakatau is near Java and the time since 1883 is short compared with geological times involved in population of most islands, revegetation of Krakatau is much like an accelerated version of what has happened on distant islands. Krakatau's repopulation by animals shows a rapidity of successful colonization much like that of the plants.

Plant immigration to Krakatau has proceeded rapidly in the years since 1883, as the graph in 2–2 indicates. In the fifty years to 1933, 271 plant species had arrived and succeeded in establishing themselves. Establishment is the critical event, because mere transport without establishment means effectively that noth-ing has happened.

Other islands like Krakatau have occurred. In 1911, Volcano Island in the middle of Lake Bombon in the Philippines erupted, extinguishing nearly all of its plants. Although not a spectacular story, the report of revegetation makes rather interesting reading. In 1952, San Benedicto Island, in the Revillagigedo

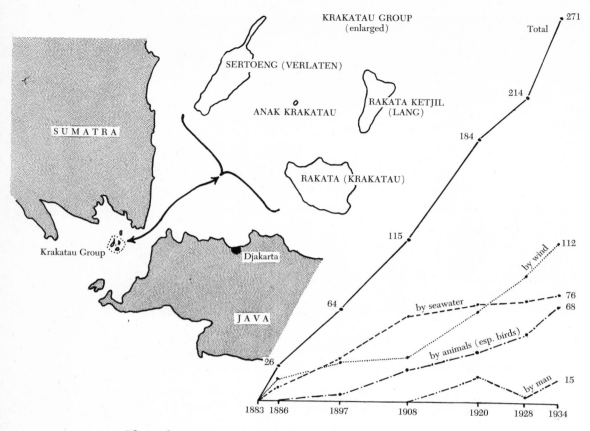

2–2. The violent eruption in 1883 of the volcano Krakatau in the strait which separates Java from Sumatra left four completely bare islands. Gradual repopulation of these islands and the means by which species have arrived have attracted the attention of biologists in the decades following the devastation.

Islands, Mexico, nearly doubled its size by an eruption (2–3). The original vegetation consisted of few species, and fewer than half were extinguished. Nevertheless, the patterns and speed of recolonization on altered soils help us to estimate how volcanic islands are affected by repeated eruptions, and the simplicity of the situation may prove valuable. A volcanic island named Surtsey which arose from the ocean floor near Iceland in November 1963 is now under study by Icelandic scientists. Despite its newness, Surtsey has already been colonized by several plants and a mosquito, and birds have paid visits. Nevertheless, Krakatau remains the best example, despite regrets by some that it was not studied more exhaustively in the years immediately following the eruption.

Those unwilling to believe the rather spectacular evidence of successful natural migration and establishment at Krakatau, or to believe that it applies to Hawaii

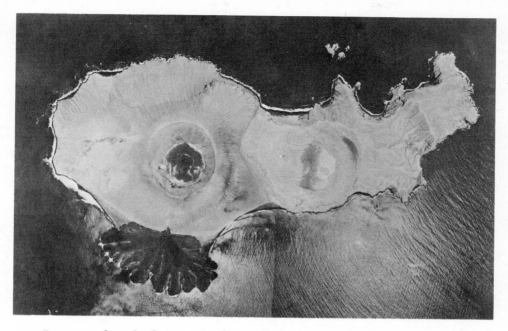

2–3. In 1952, the island San Benedicto off the west coast of Mexico suffered a tremendous volcanic eruption which doubled the size of the island and covered most of the vegetation. This aerial photograph shows the appearance of the large new crater and lava flow (below) as seen from 10,000 feet. Geologists and botanists will watch bare areas of ash and lava such as these for clues to how oceanic islands become populated by plants and animals. (Official U. S. Navy photo.)

or Tahiti or St. Helena, must imagine land bridges and vanished continents to account for present-day distribution patterns. Often a biologist believes that long-distance dispersal is perfectly possible, but not in the particular group *he* is studying. For example, one author imagined an entire continent in the south-western Pacific to account for the distribution of a single genus of land snail, corresponding to the map in 12–2. Although some biologists still cling to land bridges, others opt for continental drift—the gradual drifting apart of continents and islands. When viewed side by side, the various theories of land bridges and of continental drift offer hilarious discrepancies. Even used by a single person, a system of crisscrossing land bridges emerging and sinking with remarkable speed and agility, or a land bridge curiously selective in the immigrants it bars or allows to pass, or continents fragmenting, rejoining, and migrating with seeming abandon would be necessary to account for contemporary distributions of animals and plants. As we will see, a few land bridges, such as that connecting the Greater Sunda Islands of Indonesia with Southeast Asia, have occurred. If continental drift has occurred it would have been, very likely, at such a remote period that present-day distributions of island plants and animals would show no effects of it. Long-distance dispersal is, in fact, by far the easiest hypothesis to believe except for those islands which were clearly formerly united to continents, were portions of islands once much larger, or were islands close to continents. These cases usually can be distinguished without difficulty.

MEANS OF DISPERSAL

How does long-distance dispersal actually happen? The catalogue of adaptations for dispersal is, in fact, fantastic. A magnificent book, *The Dispersal of Plants Throughout the World* by H. N. Ridley, testifies to the endless variety of intricate mechanisms plants have achieved for securing transport of seeds and fruits, even stems and other parts. But are plants ever adapted for exceptionally long-distance dispersal—say, one thousand miles or more? Isn't adaptation to long-distance dispersal, in fact, improbable, since it would be extremely wasteful? If most of a plant's seeds were blown far away, they would mostly land in unfavorable situations; if they land near the parent plant, they are more likely to find a suitable habitat. But many plants compromise, it seems, in their dispersal mechanisms. In the natural course of affairs, most seeds *will* drop nearby, but a few will travel a few yards, and a very few much farther. Some plants are capable of virtually no long-distance dispersal; others, although not primarily adapted for long-distance dispersal, are quite capable of it. This is true for animals, also.

Interestingly, the organisms best adapted for long-distance dispersal could be called "weedy" plants or animals because organisms which inhabit new, pioneer situations must have better dispersal so that they can reach unstable new situations that are constantly opening up. Species adapted to stable environments like forests would do better to stay there by means of short-distance dispersal— and such plants do seem usually to have limited dispersal ability. Just as dandelions or flies are notoriously successful at dispersal, they also occupy "new" disturbed places. Should it come as a surprise that dandelions and flies have, in fact, managed long-distance dispersal and are the sort of species which have arrived on islands and evolved there whereas oaks and elephants have not? The "weediest" plant species are probably beach species, and these are perhaps the only organisms uniformly and exceptionally adapted to long-distance dispersal; this is entirely appropriate, for beach habitats are the most far-flung of all.

Sea water Flotation. The easiest means of transport to an island would seem to be flotation by ocean currents. Ironically, it is all but impossible for land animals to be immersed directly in sea water, constantly swimming, and arrive alive, but for a number of plants it is all too easy. Many plant species are so well adapted to dispersal by sea that they are perpetually introduced and reintroduced on beaches all over the world. To see which species are dispersed by sea, a visit to a beach is usually sufficient, because most beach plants are both adapted to growing there and to dispersing by sea water flotation (2–6). Examination of the low, sandy atolls of the Pacific reveals a monotonous similarity among the lists of plants native to each atoll. These atolls, of course, are little more than beaches. One might expect that being good colonizers, beach species might evolve into new habitats and develop into mountain species. But dispersal by sea water is so easy that the same dozen or so species are continually introduced and reintroduced, and reintroduction prevents the first immigrants from changing and evolving into new species. New immigrants "swamp out" whatever changes may take place, and re-establish the original qualities of any species. For this reason, most beach species always stay beach species.

There are some exceptions to "once a beach species, always a beach species," but these examples prove the rule, so few are they. Clarion Island, in the Revilla-gigedo Islands, is low and therefore much of the flora consists of beach species. One of these is a morning-glory, *Ipomea cathartica*, which is distributed on many beaches in the warm tropics. On Clarion Island, however, another morning-glory may be seen clambering over the lava blocks near the beaches. It is *Ipomea halierca*, and differs from *I. cathartica* in such features as the very hairy stems and leaves (2–4). There seems little doubt it was derived from *I. cathartica*. Perhaps after the first introduction of *I. cathartica*, enough time elapsed before reintroduction so that the original population did develop into this new species.

A similar example is the coral tree of Hawaii, *Erythrina sandwichensis*. The bean-like seeds of this leguminous plant are well adapted to floating, although perhaps less so than the typical beach plants (2–5). *Erythrina sandwichensis* has progressed inland considerably from the beaches, and as a species is distinct from other Erythrinas. It may now be found in valleys and slopes on volcanic soil, rather than on sandy beaches. Interestingly, there is a closely related species,

2–4. The hairy beach morning-glory at right (*Ipomea halierca*) is restricted to the rocky shores of Clarion Island, off the west coast of Mexico. It was probably derived from another beach species, *I. cathartica* at left, which also grows on Clarion but is widely distributed throughout the Pacific.

 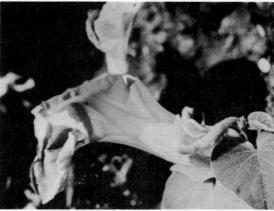

2–5. Ancestors of these two native Hawaiian trees must have grown from seeds floated up on beaches. At left, the coral tree *Erythrina sandwichensis;* right, the koa, *Acacia koa.*

once thought to be the same as the Hawaiian coral tree, *Erythrina monosperma* of Tahiti. Perhaps the Hawaiian coral tree was derived from it—or something like it—during the sea water migrations of this plant across the Pacific. The koa, a leguminous tree of Hawaiian forests (*Acacia koa*), is the dominant tree of drier Hawaiian forests (2–5). Curiously, the koa is virtually identical to a species a great distance from Hawaii—*Acacia heterophylla* of Mauritius Island in the Indian Ocean. Both of these are probably descendants of seeds which floated into the Indian Ocean and the Pacific, respectively, from Australia, where flat-leaved (phyllodial) acacias abound.

Sea water-floated seeds belong to species and genera of many families. Far from being an unusual phenomenon, this topic receives no fewer than ninety-two pages in Ridley's book on seed dispersal, and sea water flotation forms the main focus of H. B. Guppy's fascinating volume *Observations of a Naturalist in the Pacific.* Both of these authors describe the many interesting adaptations for flotation, such as an air space between the embryo and the seed coat, a device found in legumes. An outstanding example of this is the huge "sea bean" *Entada,* a tropical vine the seeds of which often wash up on European shores. Buoyant seed coats, corky floating husks as in the coconut, or buoy-like fruits, as in *Scaevola sericea* (2–6) are among the many adaptations. These mechanisms are a world in themselves and cannot be described fully here. Do they work? Darwin carried on experiments to see how long seeds would float in sea water and if, after various lengths of time, they would still germinate. The results are surprising because some of the species tested, such as potato seeds, are those one would never suppose to be sea water-distributed yet they survived quite unharmed. Recent experiments have shown that such an unlikely candidate for

2–6. Plants dispersed by sea water usually grow near the shore. *Scaevola sericea,* which has white buoyant fruits, forms seaside hedges on Kauai in the Hawaiian Islands, as well as elsewhere in the tropical Pacific.

sea water travel as cotton seeds are borne in floatable capsules and can withstand prolonged sea water treatment. Cotton plants native to the Galápagos Islands may have arrived from South America in this way.

Nevertheless, the conclusion of the great British biogeographers, such as Darwin, Wallace, Guppy, and Ridley is a disappointing one, hinted at above: the sea water-distributed plants account for only a constant and monotonously uniform minority of island plants. But, although ocean-floated seeds may play an unimportant role in the flora of high islands, where other means of immigration predominate, they do play a major part in the low islands. As if to remind us of their importance, they litter the shores of the world in truly enormous quantities.

Rafting. This somewhat elegant term is applied to debris, varying from a log to a floating island, which traverses oceanic stretches. An event too rare or insignificant to be worthy of attention? Here is what one biogeographer, Elwood C. Zimmerman, has to say:

"Large rafts or masses of debris making up 'floating islands' are commonly washed out to sea from islands from Fiji westward. It has been shown that such masses may carry with them a varied assortment of plants and animals. Mr. C. E. Pemberton told me that while out of sight of land on a voyage between Macassar, Celebes and Sandakan, Borneo, many 'floating islands' were seen. These mats of vegetation were lush and green, and palm trees 20 to 30 feet high stood erect on the floating masses. A survey of these rafts probably would reveal that numerous plants and animals were riding them. Although such rafts are probably broken up by rough water, it is possible that some of them, on rare occasions, could travel more or less intact for many hundreds of miles and deposit at least part of their living cargoes on foreign shores. I have seen large trees washed from stream sides during a storm in Tahiti and have seen them floating out to sea with their large branches riding high out of the water. The large, heavy trunks, great root masses in which are entangled stones and soil, and the submerged limbs may act as keel, ballast and stabilizers and hold a part of such floating trees permanently out of the water. Some of the branches may be held 20 or more feet above the waves. At rare intervals, colonies of animals and seeds may be able to survive lengthy journeys in such perches. It is conceivable that over a period of several millions of years a few such floating trees have been beached . . . and that from them there escaped ancestors of insects, terrestrial molluscs and plants."

Another observer, S. S. Visher, notes:

"The floods caused by the excessive rainfall associated with hurricanes influence the dispersal of land forms. There are numerous records of the fall of more than sixty inches in three days. Under such conditions streams normally small may become great rivers and carry to sea vast quantities of driftwood. The river banks are eroded badly, and many trees are undercut and are carried out to sea. During the excessive rains, large masses of dirt and loose rock upon steep hillsides may slip, sometimes damming valleys. If the dam breaks, the sudden rush of water does its part to contribute natural rafts of driftwood with their load of land animals and seeds. Hence, the absence of long rivers flowing to the sea should not lead us to the assumption that natural rafts of considerable size and biological dispersing possibilities are lacking in the Pacific."

What are the odds that a raft-traveler such as shown in 2–7 will arrive? W. D. Matthew, in *Climate and Evolution*, has estimated the effectiveness of rafting as follows:

"Three hundred miles drift would readily reach any of the larger [Pacific] islands except New Zealand. Assume as one in ten the probability that the raft drifted in such a direction as to reach dry land within three hundred miles.

"In case such animals reached the island shores and the environment afforded them a favorable opening, the propagation of the race would require either two individuals of different sex or a gravid (pregnant) female. Assume the probability of any of the passengers surviving the dangers of landing as one in three (by being drawn in at the mouth of some tidal river or protected inlet), of landing at a point where the environment was sufficiently favorable as one in ten, the chances of two individuals of different sexes might be assumed as one in ten, the alternate of a gravid female as one in five. The chance of the two happening would be 1/10 plus 1/5=3/10. The chance of the species obtaining a foothold would then be 3/10 times 1/3 times 1/10 equals one in a hundred.

"If then we allow that ten cases of natural rafts far out at sea have been reported, we may concede that 1,000 have probably occurred in three centuries and 30,000,000 during the Cenozoic. Of these rafts, only 3,000,000 will have had living mammals on them, of these only 30,000 will have reached land, and in

2–7. This lizard is hopeful of arrival on an island by means of the log raft on which it has inadvertently become a traveler.

only 300 of these cases will the species have established a foothold. This is quite sufficient to cover the dozen or two cases of Mammalia on the larger oceanic islands."

One might easily argue with the above entirely arbitrary probabilities, but the reasoning does give an idea of the processes and likelihoods involved. But do such rafts, in practice, really work? Wallace tells us of one instance:

"A large boa constrictor was once floated to the island of St. Vincent [West Indies], twisted round the trunk of a cedar tree, and was so little injured by its voyage that it captured some sheep before it was killed. The island is nearly two hundred miles from Trinidad and the coast of South America, whence it almost certainly came."

Examples of plants, and live termites and ants found in logs washed up on islands have been reported. A traveler in the islands of Indonesia has reported: "On the shores of Little Kei Island I found, on the beach above the reach of the waves, a large mass of the pseudo-bulbs of an orchid with its roots complete. It was partly buried at the foot of a tree, and seemed quite lively. It had evidently been washed up by a storm."

Biologists know little about why some animals may be better adapted to rafting than others. The evidence from distribution affirms that snakes and especially lizards are successful, because they turn up in the faunas of oceanic islands, except for the most remote ones. Reptiles seem to have a physiology better suited to this sort of travel, perhaps because they can go for longer periods without eating or drinking fresh water. The reptile skin resists desiccation well, apparently. Recent experiments by Dr. Walter Brown of Stanford University show that lizard eggs are not harmed by soaking in sea water. Beebe reports forcing a Galápagos tortoise to swim in sea water and found that it was, despite its enormous size and weight, quite able to swim. Indeed, the Galápagos Islands possess an iguana termed "marine." Although not truly a sea-living creature, this giant lizard can swim, a fact which aids it when it feeds at low tide on seaweed. Recent observations show that the iguana can dive to 35 feet.

Mammals are poor travelers but some have, in fact, crossed short oceanic distances if we can judge from distribution patterns. If the Hawaiian rat came to the Hawaiian Islands as a stowaway in the canoes of Polynesians, as it must have, surely small mammals can travel on natural rafts, at least for limited distances. Because small land molluscs, such as snails, do have some capability for resisting desiccation, there is considerable reason for believing that natural rafts have contributed to their dispersal to islands. Rafting is certainly the best hope for long-distance dispersal of many types of animals, and the evidence, scanty as it may seem, does seem to confirm the effectiveness of this method.

Air Flotation. We fail, merely because of our own weight, to realize the tremendous effect winds can have on distribution of organisms. Indeed, it is difficult to imagine how winds must feel to small insects, which can be ripped away and swept to great heights and distances in a gust.

Increase of surface improves air transport markedly, even for such a weighty object as a human: any parachutist or sailplane pilot who has been in a thunderstorm will testify to this. Transportability by wind increases geometrically with decrease in weight, and similarly with increase in surface. An animal or plant disseminule (that portion of a plant—or animal—capable of reproducing it) which is both small and winged possesses a double advantage (2–8).

Is wind transport really effective for such disseminules? Recently, attention has been called to previously unappreciated wind effects. We need not restrict our thinking to the lower altitudes. The upper air is more important because air movement is more rapid there; objects carried there are likely to stay aloft longer and travel farther. The ultra-rapid currents of the high air, the so-called "jet streams," are relatively common and would be ideal for transport. Some note that volcanic explosions create sweeping convection currents which may sweep aloft seeds, insects, etc. which can be distributed over wide distances and deposited as a "fallout." Some claim that the ordinary weather of high mountains, such as those of the Hawaiian Islands, features fierce updrafts leading

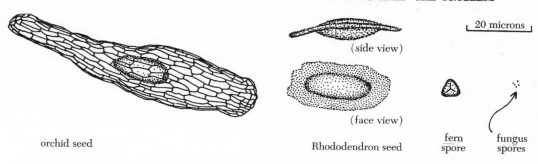

(side view)

(face view)

20 microns

orchid seed

Rhododendron seed

fern spore

fungus spores

2–8. Best adapted for wind-dispersal among plants are minute seeds and spores. Here the seeds and spores are enlarged to the extent that a typewriter letter would cover this page. The empty cells of the orchid seed make it very light; the wing of the rhododendron seed make it ideal for air flotation. Spores of ferns are dust-like, can be carried for long distances by wind currents; fungus spores are even smaller and can travel for weeks in air without falling.

to the upper air, providing a means of long-distance dispersal. An interesting possibility in this connection is the tendency for spores, seeds, etc. to become centers of condensation when they are carried into moist weather. This would be expected to happen when these items arrive in the vicinity of a high island. Surrounded by a film of water, such light disseminules become much heavier and fall, perhaps in a suitable location.

In earlier days, biologists noted such "freak" occurrences as the birds and butterflies swept out to sea during hurricanes, the violent effects of which are difficult to overestimate. Among many appealing examples is a gale of February 1881, which crossed the Scandinavian countries and transferred large quantities of plant debris, such as heather fruits and twigs, from Sweden to Denmark, a sea water distance of about seventy-five miles across the Kattegat strait. To be sure, there are records of sand from the Sahara falling on ships at sea four hundred miles from land. Spores of fungi, mosses, liverworts, and ferns are much lighter than many grains of sand carried into the air (2–8). Spores mostly vary between 10 and 100 microns (1/2500 to 1/250 of an inch) in diameter, and the most common sizes fall in the smaller size classes. Such sizes would permit transport virtually anywhere in the world by currents of the upper air. One fern common in the South Pacific, *Marattia*, can have enormous numbers of spores. A *Marattia* plant can form perhaps six large leaves a season. Each leaf has about fourteen pinnae (subdivisions), each bearing about forty-one pinnules (leaflets). Each leaflet has about two hundred groups of sporangia, and each group releases a total of forty-five thousand spores. The total number of spores produced by such a plant in one season thus totals 30,996,000,000. Do such spores arrive alive? Experiments involving trapping of fungus spores not only showed that large numbers and a wide variety of fungus spores could be picked up on sticky plates carried by airplanes at ten thousand feet or higher; many of these spores germinated when given proper conditions.

The parachute-like devices on the small fruits of members of the sunflower family (Compositae), such as dandelions, account for the exceptional efficiency of this family at dispersal, and its presence on remote islands. The *Olearia* illustrated here (2–9) has a prominent crown of fluffy "pappus," as this structure is called, which accounts for the fact that this genus has traveled far. Today, *Olearia* is primarily Australian (it probably had ancestors on another continent), but it has reached New Zealand and even faraway Rapa, in the Austral Islands, thus crossing a gap of about two thousand miles. Experimental evidence for the flight potential of fluff-like pappus is considerable. One observer of pappus-bearing fruits found that fruits of *Cirsium oleraceum,* a thistle, traveled ninety miles; *Senecio palustris,* a groundsel, sixty-three miles; while seeds of an orchid, *Goodyera repens,* spanned 130 miles.

Predictions that the upper air would be found to be important in transport of disseminules led the Hawaiian entomologist J. Linsey Gressitt to carry out extensive experiments in which insects were trapped in fine nets carried by ships at sea and by airplanes. Screening an estimated twenty-five cubic kilometers of air, Gressitt caught 1075 insects in this unlikely manner on transits

2–9. This aster-relative (*Olearia megalophylla*) owes its potential for transoceanic travel to the parachute-like structure which crowns its small fruits, shown enlarged, which can float for extended periods. The dandelion is a familiar member of the family to which *Olearia* belongs.

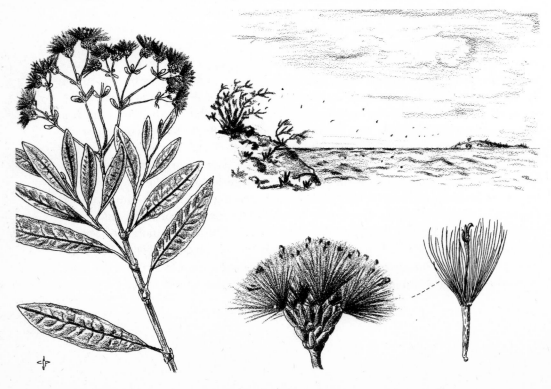

in the inhospitable seas between the United States and Antarctica. To be sure, some portions of these transits would be expected to be insect-poor, so the large numbers of insects which were in fact trapped, mostly at considerable distances from land, abundantly prove the activeness of insect dispersal. As Gressitt admits, it is safe to assume that most of the trapped insects were, in fact, dead. But if even a small proportion of these were alive and capable of reproducing upon arrival at an island, these experiments would account for the dispersal to islands which has, in fact, taken place. Moreover, the orders and families of insects and spiders caught in the nets correspond exactly with those which are the ones native on remote islands. They are insects with low weight or specific gravity and with less compact bodies, suitable for passive transport in air. This does not account for transport of larger insects, such as dragonflies, sphinx moths, and butterflies, which have reached islands such as the Hawaiian Islands. An occurrence such as Gressitt records of a live butterfly falling onto the deck of a ship at 71° S. Latitude off the coast of Antarctica indicates that a combination of passive transport and active flying can account even for larger insects.

The same is true for birds. In 1943 a flight of ducks reached Palmyra Island, one thousand miles south of the Hawaiian Islands. Some of them bore bands which had been attached in Utah. Wallace mentioned birds deviating from normal flights because of winds, etc.—stragglers—on the Azores. The list includes the kestrel, oriole, snow-bunting, hoopoe, and others. In these islands, which are at some distance from the mainland (3–21), "scarcely a storm occurs in spring or autumn without bringing one or more species foreign to the islands; and I have frequently been told that swallows, larks, grebes and other species not referred to here are not uncommonly seen at those seasons of the year."

The list of stray visitors to the Hawaiian Islands proves the magnitude of accidental visitation even in very remote islands:

pelagic cormorant	osprey
reef heron	black-bellied plover
white-faced glossy ibis	killdeer
lesser snow goose	Pacific godwit
American white-fronted goose	Wilson's snipe
emperor goose	short-tailed sandpiper
black brant	pectoral sandpiper
cackling goose	red phalarope
mallard duck	northern phalarope
green-winged teal	ring-billed gull
baldpate	glaucous gull
Gadwall duck	Bonaparte's gull
bufflehead	Pacific kittiwake
harlequin duck	Arctic tern
red-breasted merganser	black-naped tern
lesser scaup duck	belted kingfisher
greater scaup duck	marsh hawk

Many of these are not accustomed to long flights, nor was a barn owl which flew on board a whaling ship five hundred miles south of the Azores, reported by Wallace. In 1938, an owl flew aboard the *Duchess of Richmond* a thousand miles at sea in the Atlantic. Appreciable numbers of stragglers can be found in bird lists for various remote islands, such as New Zealand.

Do stragglers of this sort establish themselves and become part of the fauna of distant islands? Examples suggest that they do. The kingfishers in the above list were a pair. When first found in the Azores, the wheatear was thought to be a solitary straggler; later, a few were found breeding in the crater Corvo on Flores Island. On Tristan da Cunha in the South Atlantic, one of the most isolated islands in the world, purple gallinules were found. The American ornithologist Austin L. Rand says, "Almost surely the individuals of the species occurring in Tristan da Cunha represent strays from the Americas, amazing as it is. However, three individuals were recorded in 1951 and two in 1952. There is the possibility that a breeding colony has been established on the islands and these birds are the young of the year. If so, it would seem a very recent colonization from America. But either their regular occurrence as strays or their colonization helps us to realize how such 'weak-flying' birds as rails have colonized so many remote islands." A very convincing example of establishment of birds is that of Krakatau, where twenty-seven non-migrant species had become established between 1883 and 1919; but Krakatau is, of course, not a very remote island.

Transport by Birds. Dispersal of most island plants with large seeds cannot be explained by sea water flotation or by wind; even many small-seeded plants lack obvious adaptations of these two methods. The last best hope for such plants is transport by birds. This is, however, not the frail possibility it might at first seem. Birds can carry seeds either by eating them and depositing them upon arrival, or externally in feathers or in mud adhering to their feet. The first irony to which bird-transport skeptics will point, however, is that the birds which perform the widest migrations, such as the arctic tern, are not usually fruit-eating birds. On the other hand, fruit-eating birds, such as pigeons, do not undertake very extensive migrations. Those confronted with this paradox can still point to a middle ground: birds capable of some, occasionally long, migration which also eat fruits or seeds. The numerous species of ducks given in the list above of Hawaiian visitors would come in this category. External transportation of fruits or seeds is, however, a universal possibility for birds; even snail eggs or insects may be carried on feathers or in mud on feet. But in this case are there, in fact, birds with migratory routes which could serve for dispersal?

The facts are rather surprising. To cite only a few instances, the Pacific golden plover migrates from northern North America and Siberia southward to the Hawaiian Islands each year. Ducks, herons, and egrets often visit the Cocos (Keeling) Islands (presumably from the nearest island, Java) despite the lack of fresh water on Cocos Island. Regular visitors to Bermuda include the North American kingfisher, the ricebird, and a moorhen (gallinule). Two cuckoos leave New Zealand in winter: *Chalcites lucidus lucidus* for the Solomon Islands, *Eudynamis taitensis* for Polynesia and the Central Pacific, as far east as Mangareva. We have no way of knowing how migration routes of birds in past eras may have contributed to dispersal patterns.

Actual observations of small animals carried in feathers have been made. The Hawaiian entomologist Zimmerman picked a living bark beetle from the feathers of an owl knocked down in flight in the highlands of Fiji, and mentions a mallard duck shot down in the Sahara which bore snail eggs on its feet. He also lists an instance in which a living achatinellid snail was found on a Hawaiian bird. The extreme minuteness of many land snails and their eggs makes transport in this fashion not as improbable as it might at first seem.

Sticky, barbed, bur-like and other types of adhesive fruits are ideal for transport in feathers of birds, and are limited only by the distance to which a bird will fly. Fruits of *Pisonia aculeata* (2–10) will adhere to anything they contact.

2–10. Surrounded by plants with small adhesive fruits, this booby bird is a likely ticket for their transport to another island. Sticky discs permit fruits of the *Pisonia* to adhere to bird feathers. The needle-like tips on fruits of *Bidens* have backward-pointing barbs which act like fishhooks in fastening the fruits to feathers. Both of these plants have become widespread because of these efficient mechanisms.

Pisonia aculeata   *Bidens pilosa*

2–11. If the frigate bird nesting near this marsh migrates with muddy feet, seeds embedded in the mud can secure a ride to a distant location. Sedges of the sort illustrated may have reached a marsh on Easter Island in this way.

This probably accounts for the very great distribution of species of *Pisonia* across the Pacific, including many very small islands. In the Cocos Islands, *Pisonia* fruits have been seen carried on feathers of migratory birds.

The wide distribution of various species of the sunflower relative *Bidens* (2–10; 3–1) on many islands of the Pacific is a tribute to a dispersal mechanism, miniature barbed appendages on the fruits which catch in feathers. Tiny hooks on the calyx of a mint, *Hyptis,* enclosing the seeds of this plant account for its appearance on Krakatau during the revegetation there. The hooked, bur-like seeds of a strawberry relative, *Acaena,* have been found in the down of petrels on the Juan Fernandez Islands, west of Chile. Curiously, seeds of another *Acaena* have been found on petrels in New Zealand. This might account for the fact that *Acaena* jumps the enormous gap of water between these islands. Banding has identified petrels as performers of a seven thousand-mile transit across the subantarctic regions between South America and Western Australia. Some migrating petrels still bear some juvenile down excellent for adhesion of seeds of this sort, and before they fly they live in intimate contact with vegetation around their nests. Nests incorporate virtually all of the plant species native where these petrels live. When literally clouds of birds of this sort migrate annually, with reasonable certainty of reaching land, the potential for seed dispersal becomes formidable.

Transoceanic seed transport is probably often accomplished within the mud

2–12. Pigeons are fond of fruits and may carry seeds internally. The ancestors of this New Zealand fruit pigeon (*Hemiphaga novoseelandiae*) may have brought to New Zealand the fruit on which it is feeding (*Fuchsia excorticata*).

adherent to feathers, beaks, and feet of birds. In one study, twenty-one species of plant seeds were taken from mud on various parts of birds caught on Christmas Island, near Java. Most of these plants proved to be associated with ponds where birds would drink and which, in the process, become muddy. Wide distribution of sedges and other marsh and pond plants to islands has probably taken place in just this manner (2–11). One aquatic plant, the milfoil *Myriophyllum elatinoides,* grows in New Zealand and South America, and in between on subantarctic Macquarie Island. The Macquarie plants, however, no longer reproduce by flowers and seeds. Having lost this form of reproduction, they can only proliferate vegetatively, and thus stems, impossible as long-distance disseminules, are the only means of reproduction. Thus seeds must at one time have arrived either from South America or New Zealand, perhaps carried by petrels.

One curious observation concerns an albatross which had seeds of *Stilbocarpa* "glued" on its feet by means of an oily substance, supposedly formed by regurgitation. This oily substance was impervious to sea water and not easily rubbed off; thus it would form a waterproof casing for transportation of these seeds. Although successful attempts to remove seed-bearing mud from birds and germinate such seeds have been made, much more observation and experiment is necessary. Seeds of plants other than marsh plants might be carried in this fashion, and biogeographers might be surprised at the findings.

Internal transport of seeds depends on birds which will eat fruits and seeds and then migrate (2–12). Ducks, geese, and other large migratory birds have been examined and shown to contain many seeds and fruits, although these are chiefly marsh plants found where the birds last fed. Records of stomach contents, files of which are kept by many concerned with wildlife studies, are too numerous to mention. The form of many fruits of species native on oceanic islands suggests that other birds are often involved, however. Such islands abound in brightly colored fleshy fruits, either single-seeded (drupes) or many-seeded (berries). Such fruits, which are mostly purple, red, pink, blue, orange, or white, exert an undeniable attraction upon fruit-eating birds, as numerous studies on habits of such birds indicates. Mere ingestion of such seeds does not insure their safe arrival on a distant island, however. Skeptics protest that eating destroys seeds, that the fruits eaten are passed too quickly, that flights are too slow to account for arrival on many islands, that fruit-eating birds are non-migratory, and that birds habitually fly on an empty stomach. Taken collectively, these factors might seem to negate bird-dispersal of fruit seeds, but actually, they only lessen the probabilities. Indeed, if dispersal were excellent, as I have already said, island floras would be good copies of continental floras, which they are not.

Eating does not destroy seeds. Instead, passage through the digestive system of birds often enhances germination ability, and much experimental work in feeding fruits and seeds to birds and other animals abundantly proves this. One recent experiment—not with birds—was performed with the giant Galápagos tortoise. Seeds of the tomato native to the Galápagos Islands germinated much better after passing through the intestines of the tortoise than before.

Experiments with birds indicate that passage of fruits eaten by birds is fairly rapid; the longest time discovered in one series of experiments was 7½ hours. Only a few experiments have been done, however, and perhaps they are not representative. A famous example of dispersal often cited is the record of pigeons shot in Albany, New York; they were found to contain green rice seeds which "must have been growing 700 or 800 miles away . . . a few hours before." At the very least, this observation would negate the supposition that birds fly on empty stomachs, and other observations prove many exceptions do exist. Moreover, there is always the possibility that although most seeds eaten are passed soon, a few remain in gizzards of birds for longer periods of time. Also, if birds fly with almost empty stomachs, perhaps the smaller contents remain longer than the contents of a full stomach. Moreover, we do not know the digestive habits of birds subjected to violent winds which would cause them to be transported beyond their normal flight patterns and occasionally to islands. Indeed, we know nothing about the digestive habits of most birds.

Rapidity of flight, where records have been kept, indicate birds are capable of speeds varying from rather slow to two hundred miles an hour, and perhaps many are above fifty miles an hour. Winds, of which birds often take advantage, would raise normal flight speeds considerably, of course.

Migratory habits of some fruit-eating birds may be greater than suspected.

2–13. On the high crests of Tahiti, one can find a species of *Fuchsia* (*F. cyrtandroides*), the ancestors of which may have come to this volcanic island by means of long-distance transport by birds.

For example, Ridley found that "Hornbills and pigeons, in the tropics especially, travel across far-stretching areas of forest, often crossing arms of the sea, coming down to feed when attracted by the sight of a fruiting tree, and moving on when the fruit is cleared away." Some biologists have relied upon the abilities of pigeons, even supposing that pigeons once migrated much more frequently than at present. Even without the help of hypothetical vanished pigeons, we can note that on many islands of the world there are more than one species of pigeon. For example, six species (including doves) inhabit Samoa. On the numerous flights which must have been necessary for the establishment of these and other pigeons, seeds may well have been carried. *Fuchsia* is primarily a plant of Central and South America, but it has gained two other footholds: Tahiti (2–13) and New Zealand (2–12). *Fuchsia* probably owes these stations to bird transport, for *Fuchsia* berries are attractive to birds and contain numerous small seeds. The four species of *Fuchsia* from New Zealand and *F. cyrtandroides* from Tahiti are closely interrelated.

Of course, many birds other than pigeons and doves subsist on a fruit diet. Fruits unattractive, obnoxious, or even poisonous to humans are in fact good fare for birds. A case in point is poison ivy, the white berries of which are preferred by them. Fruits of *Scaevola* may be bitter, those of *Freycinetia* acrid (2–14), but actions do speak louder than words. Not only can birds be seen eagerly consuming such fruits, but a distribution map of species of *Scaevola* or *Frey-*

cinetia on Pacific islands would give mute testimony to feeding habits of birds. No other explanation is really satisfactory—but no other is really needed.

Although birds often feed on fleshy fruits attractive to them, there are records of their feeding on other fruits, such as fluff-bearing dry fruits of Compositae (sunflower family). Such fruits may become attached externally and transported on feathers, but if birds feed on them internal transport is also a possibility. On the North Sea island Helgoland, the scarlet grosbeak always feeds on one of these fruits, that of the sow thistle (*Sonchus oleraceus*). Portions of plants other than seeds can be food. A few ptarmigans killed on the island of Spitzbergen contained in their stomachs no fewer than one-fourth of the plant species native there, including small bulbs capable of growth.

Even bats are alleged to be agents in fruit distribution. Fruit bats are widely distributed in the Pacific, so this comes as no surprise. Those who have observed the feeding habits of fruit bats testify that bats are both voracious and messy eaters of fruits.

ESTABLISHMENT

Arrival is not enough. Long-distance dispersal dumps its victims in a crude and wasteful fashion, usually in the wrong places for their survival—if, in fact, they are in a condition to survive. Assuming that this not inconsiderable hurdle is overcome and that seeds, eggs, or individuals are deposited intact, what is necessary to produce the actual thriving populations which have perpetuated themselves on islands down to the present day?

The easiest situation is faced by plants reproduced by spores or seeds. With the exception of a few flowering plants in which plants are either male or female,

2–14. The mountain Scaevolas of Pacific islands, such as Kauai's *S. procera*, left, have probably island-hopped by means of birds which consume their purple fleshy fruits. The bright orange fruits of a Samoan *Freycinetia*, right, are eagerly sought by fruit-eating birds which may inadvertently transport their seeds to new localities.

a single seed or spore suffices to establish a population in plants. Animals are presented with the necessity of at least a mating pair, or at least a female bearing eggs or young. Animals would seem to suffer a disadvantage in this requirement, but immigrating plants have a disadvantage all their own: whereas animals can, at least to some extent, seek a suitable environment on arrival, plants must grow wherever their seeds or spores are deposited.

In the case of either a plant or an animal, arrival must be timed so as to coincide with a period in the island's history when it is, so to speak, ready to receive the immigrant. A forest species may successfully reach an island which has not yet developed a forest—and thereby it becomes a casualty. A good example of such a fate comes from the equatorial mid-Pacific. Zimmerman reports that on the tropical coral island Canton, "because of the variation in rainfall, the island's vegetation ranges from desert-like to lush. During and following a period of dry years when the island was in 'desert condition' only an occasional straggling, travel-worn *Hypolimnas bolina* butterfly was seen. After a period of rains which brought up a lush growth of plants from dormant seeds and roots, the butterfly became established from overseas immigrants. Single specimens of the monarch butterfly arrive, but this species had not succeeded in establishing itself up to 1941 (because of a lack of a suitable host?). Also, after a period of rainfall which left some persistent ponds, two species of dragonflies became established from immigrant parents. No dragonflies were seen on the island during the previous year. A return to arid conditions would result in the local extermination of the butterfly and the dragonflies. . . . The fact that the present establishment of the three discussed is recent suggests that conditions of food and water favorable for their maintenance are only temporary; that establishment and local extinction succeed each other as favorable and unfavorable conditions alternate, and that the present colonies of these particular species will in turn die out when severe drought recurs."

A subtle but effective barrier to establishment of plants may be the requirement of a particular pollinating agent, such as certain insects. How much of a barrier this may be is difficult to determine, but it must have operated.

And yet, even with prerequisites like these, establishment can be rapid. In the years between 1883 and 1908, thirteen non-migrant birds became established on Krakatau; by 1921, the total had risen to twenty-seven. The rapid upswing of plants established at Krakatau (2–2) is really quite surprising.

Plants reaching volcanic islands such as the Hawaiian Islands would have done well to be preadapted to bare lava, because the islands were barren for long periods of time. The present vegetation reflects this. Recent lava flows are covered rapidly by at least a few species. Surprisingly, one of the native ferns (*Sadleria*), the chief forest tree of the islands (*Metrosideros*), and a shrubby native tarweed (*Dubautia*) are among the first colonists on bare lava (2–15; 5–3, 5–4). Species which do not figure in the catalogue of lava-flow invaders may need the shade of a forest. In the Hawaiian Islands, development of soil is not a great necessity for a forest. On the Kona coast of Hawaii, the magnificent, tall *Metrosideros* forest, with all its varied botanical contents, grows on what is virtually soilless lava rubble.

Preadaptation for lava by some species is also illustrated by a pair of islands in the harbor of Auckland, New Zealand, the islands Rangitoto and Motutapu. Rangitoto is a recent volcanic cone, still predominantly bare lava, whereas Motutapu is much older geologically and has mature, silty soils. The two islands are interconnected by a short sand isthmus, so that there is hardly any barrier to dispersal from Motutapu to Rangitoto. And yet if one crosses from Rangitoto to Motutapu, one finds a number of plants which cannot be found on Rangitoto's lavas. Interestingly, the plants which do grow on Rangitoto include many genera which also occur on the Hawaiian Islands, or on Tahiti: *Metrosideros, Myrsine, Astelia*, for example. This seems to hint that floras of the volcanic islands in the Pacific may contain many plants which, at least at one time, were pioneering plants, suited to growth on bare areas. Indeed, weedy species accustomed to and requiring disturbed habitats would make the best immigrants, for not only could they survive difficult conditions prevalent on many islands, they could adapt rapidly to new situations that might arise. Plants of stable habitats, like continental forest trees, might be insufficiently plastic either to survive or to adapt to new situations.

HOW MUCH DISPERSAL IS ENOUGH?

Many of the examples of long-range dispersal mentioned above have a freakish quality, unlikely and haphazard. So do horseraces. Just as few who bet win at a race, so few dispersal units succeed in arriving. Of those which arrive, few will become established; but of course, very few people win the "daily double" at a racetrack either. Analogies such as these led the paleontologist George Gaylord Simpson to dub long-distance dispersal, "sweepstakes" dispersal. This emphasizes the irrational quality of dispersal, a quality which is annoying and almost unbelievable to some biologists. Many biologists who enjoy the study of orderly processes such as embryology feel uneasy with a process ruled by staggering chance, and feel safer by imagining solid, dry (but imaginary!) land bridges leading to islands. And yet oceanic islands, like the Hawaiian chain, have been populated by just such capricious chances of dispersal. Unlikely? Infrequent? Certainly, but the chances of maintaining a sizable island completely free from successful chance immigrants for five million years seem infinitely more unlikely. In fact, nothing at all like that has happened. If chance dispersal is inadequate, we should expect at least a few barren or almost barren islands, but virtually none except those which are extremely small, low, or in areas of poor rainfall suit that description.

The major islands of the Hawaiian group may be as much as five million years old, or even older if we include the islands which stretch westward to Midway.

2–15. Hints about how barren new islands were occupied are given by plants which colonize new lava flows. The Hawaiian fern *Sadleria*, left, can grow on completely bare lava. The flowering tree at right, New Zealand's pohutakawa (*Metrosideros tomentosa*), grows on new lava of Rangitoto Island in Auckland Harbor. Closely related species of *Metrosideros*, such as the Hawaiian ohia lehua, grow on lava flows of other Pacific islands.

Is five million years enough to account for the curious flora and fauna there? The original immigrants to those islands have altered, speciated into many different types in some cases, so that to account for the species now present, we need only estimate the number of basic forms upon which variations have taken place since their arrival (data from Zimmerman and collaborators):

Group of organisms	No. of species & varieties native to Hawaiian Is.	Estimated no. of original immigrants
Insects	3722	233 to 254
Land molluscs (snails)	1064	22 to 24
Birds (land & shore birds only)	70	15
Flowering plants	1729	272
Ferns & other pteridophytes	168	135

If we divide the number of original immigrants of a group of organisms into the estimated age of the Hawaiian Islands, we find that one successful establishment must take place every twenty thousand years, on the average. For land molluscs, the interval between successful colonizations would average more than two hundred thousand years; for birds, three hundred thousand. As we will see

(3–11; 3–12), there might have been now-vanished islands stretching eastward across the Pacific to the Hawaiian chain which could have served as way-stations (but not as a solid land bridge) for dispersing groups. Taking these facts and estimates into account, along with the information on observed and experimental evidence on dispersal in this chapter (evidence gathered only in the last hundred years), is it difficult to believe that long-distance dispersal alone provided the ancestors for the present-day life native to the Hawaiian Islands? All evidence points to this conclusion, and one can only agree with Zimmerman's justifiable satire, based upon the fact that Hawaiian plants and animals show affinity not to one, but many regions of the Pacific Basin, including the Americas: "If we resort to land bridges or (now-vanished) continents to account for the presence of the Hawaiian flora, then we may well have to build them in all directions."

If the reader now believes long-range dispersal sufficient for populating the Hawaiian Islands (or other volcanic islands, such as the Galápagos, or Tristan da Cunha), he may now wonder why, in fact, the successful establishments have been so few. Undoubtedly there is a tapering-off in the rate of successful colonization. There probably is a limit (3–9) to the number of species any given area can support, and as species either immigrate or evolve on an island, the number of new successful colonizations doubtless diminishes. There may be many other reasons for this, as the next chapter attempts to show. In addition to a decrease in successful colonization as an island's flora and fauna "mature," the beginning stages in colonization may be slow. Insects, land molluscs, and birds could not succeed without suitable host plants. Earlier elements in a food chain must make successful colonizations before later elements can establish themselves.

RELATIVE DISPERSAL ABILITY

In the above discussion, differences in dispersal ability (insects are better than mammals, for example) have been implied. The equation is not a simple one, however. To differences among groups with respect to size, resistance to sea water, wingedness or winglessness, we must add relative abundance (density, number of dispersal units) and relatively subtle features such as adaptability to inhospitable new environments. Do conifers such as pines and araucarias seem poor at dispersal because they have large seeds, because they produce relatively few seeds per plant, because they are adjusted to specialized and stable forest areas, because there are only a small number of conifers anyway, or (more likely) because of a combination of these and perhaps other factors? What makes for good dispersal in one group may be entirely different from that in another.

As a criterion of success in dispersal, we may use the widest gaps of ocean which have been crossed by particular groups. Although this may represent extreme, not typical, ability, it has been adopted below. The groups are listed in order from poor to good, animals separately from plants. Any given member of a group might deserve a higher or lower rating than the entirety of the group.

ANIMALS
  Primary-division fresh water fish (gaps of salt water only a few miles wide
    can be crossed)
  Terrestrial mammals
    Large mammals (perhaps a maximum gap of 25 miles, with the possible
      exception of a semi-aquatic hippopotamus on Madagascar)
    Small mammals other than rodents (possibly 200 miles crossed in the case
      of Madagascar civets or insectivores)
    Rodents (500 miles or more, as in the Galápagos Islands)
  Amphibians (perhaps 500 miles to Seychelles, perhaps 1000 miles to New Zea-
    land. See 2–16 for comparison of some amphibian families.)
  Reptiles
    Fresh water turtles (possibly 200 miles: Madagascar)
    Land tortoises (500 miles or more: Galápagos Islands)
    Snakes (500 miles or more: Galápagos Islands)
    Lizards (1000 miles to New Zealand for the lizard-like tuatara; perhaps
      more than 1000 miles for geckos. See comparison of some lizard families
      in 2–16.)
  Bats (2000 miles: North America to Hawaii)
  Land birds (2000 miles or more: North America to Hawaii; South America to
    Tristan da Cunha)
  Land molluscs (more than 2000 miles: Polynesia to Juan Fernandez Islands)
  Insects and spiders (more than 2000 miles)
PLANTS
  Conifers
    Pines, redwoods, araucarias (very short distances; pines are best, have
      crossed at least 200 miles, to Guadalupe Island from Mexico)
    Podocarps (perhaps 500 miles: Fiji to Samoa or Tonga, perhaps more for
      New Zealand podocarps)
    Junipers (perhaps 900 miles: North America to Bermuda or Europe to
      Azores)
  Flowering plants: because seed size and other factors vary tremendously
    within certain families, consistent taxonomic groups cannot be cited, only
    particular examples:

      Poor: oaks, prunes, walnuts, mangoes, other large-seeded forest trees
      Fair: fleshy non-floating fruits with moderate-sized seeds, such as
        Myrsine, Araliaceae, Rubiaceae, etc. Distributed by birds.
      Good: fleshy non-floating fruits with very small seeds eaten by birds:
        Vaccinium (huckleberry), *Fuchsia*, Hawaiian lobeliads
      Very good: aquatic plants with seeds which can be carried in mud on
        birds' feet, such as sedges, rushes, etc.

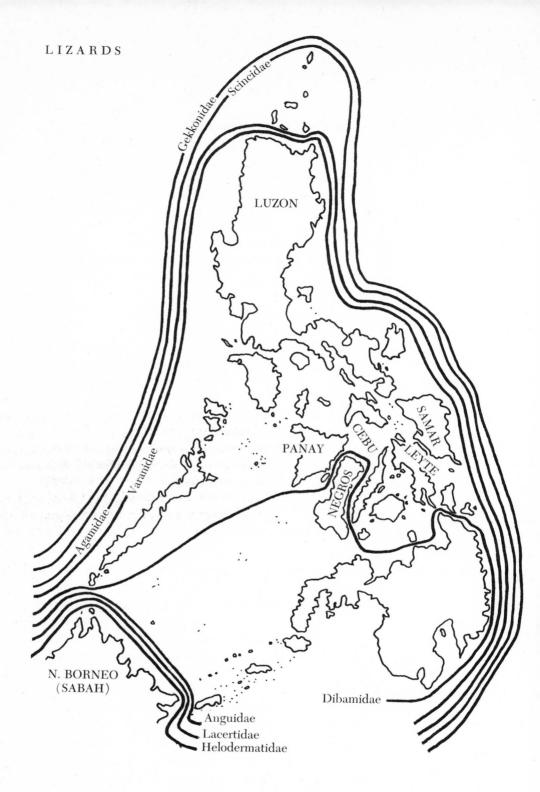

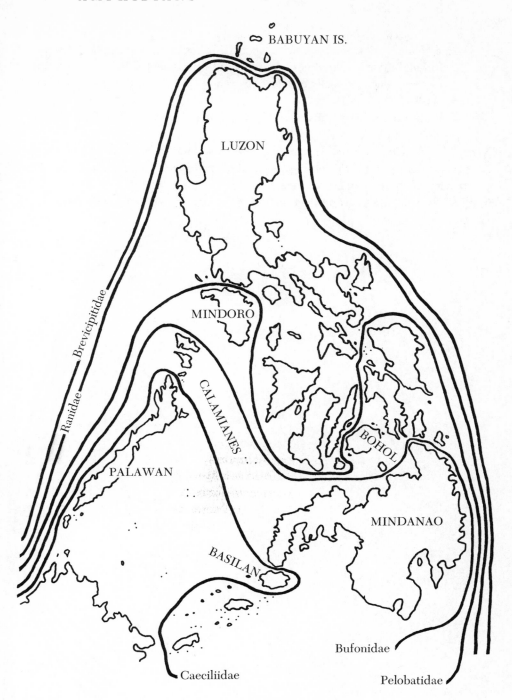

AMPHIBIANS

BAYAN IS.

BABUYAN IS.

LUZON

MINDORO

Brevicipitidae

Ranidae

CALAMIANES

PALAWAN

BOHOL

MINDANAO

BASILAN

Bufonidae

Caeciliidae

Pelobatidae

2–16. Invading the Philippine archipelago from the older shores of Borneo to the south, differences in dispersal ability among families of amphibians and reptiles become evident in their different distribution patterns. Suitable habitats are probably present on all the larger northern islands, so absence probably denotes poor dispersal ability. Among amphibians, frogs are much better dispersers than caecilians. Geckos and skinks exceed other lizards, although monitors (Varanidae) are nearly as good. The families which have reached the northern Philippines are also those most widely distributed on islands all over the world.

Excellent: fruits or seeds with special adhesive mechanisms (*Pisonia, Bidens, Acaena, Boerhaavia*); parachute-like mechanism: Compositae (asters, senecios, lettuces, etc.); extremely small windborne seeds: orchids

Unlimited: sea-water distributed (most beach plants: certain legumes, morning-glories, etc.)

Ferns, Mosses, Club-mosses, Horsetails, *Psilotum:* ability for dispersal of these bryophytes and pteridophytes is related primarily to size and specific gravity of spores: wind-dispersed

Fungi, terrestrial algae: somewhat better than the above because spores are generally smaller

3   Disharmony, Filters, Lines and Such

DISPERSAL acts upon whatever is available to be dispersed. Migrations to islands of all kinds occur, and the kind of island may dictate in no small degree how many plants and animals will become its occupants, what kind they will be, what shapes their evolution will take after arrival. The nature and history of each island or island group underlies, guides, and stamps with its own personality the many picturesque patterns of life destined to develop.

Darwin and Wallace divided islands into two sorts, oceanic and continental, a distinction which has proved generally agreeable to biologists. Oceanic islands arise from the ocean floor, never connected to any continent. Continental islands are portions of mainlands separated by the sinking of an intervening isthmus. This definition is a geological one, and although we may expect plants and animals to conform to an oceanic island pattern on the one hand or a continental island pattern on the other, there are factors which can alter, shift, or disturb the picture.

An island swept clean of its plants and animals by Ice Age glaciation, like the Kerguelens of the far-south Indian Ocean, has a biological history dating from recession of the ice, just as though it had at that point arisen from the ocean floor. A volcanic island which arises close to a continent, like Mexico's Guadalupe Island, may gain immigrants not greatly different from those of a continental island in the same position. A continental island separated from mainland for a very long period of time will retain few original inhabitants. Many of its organisms will have arrived later by overwater dispersal. To the extent that long-distance dispersal has provided immigrants, the flora and fauna will look like those of an oceanic island.

Some islands are oceanic but not volcanic, or only in part volcanic. For example, the Seychelles Islands in the Indian Ocean have rocks such as granite, slate, and hornfels which one could call "continental" rocks because they can be thought of as like those on continents. But presence of such "continental rocks" is best explained by presence of a larger, higher area of land which could have produced such rocks by pressure. This does not necessarily mean that a land area containing these rocks was in fact ever tied to a mainland area by dry land. The Seychelles, for example, do not seem to have an assemblage of plants and animals one would expect on a continental island, although they may well be old islands. The line delimiting the presence of a

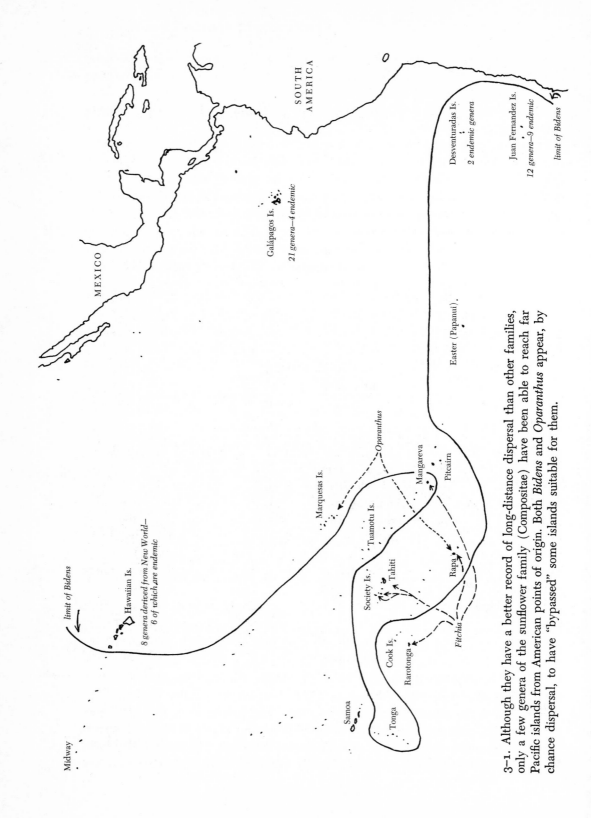

MEXICO

SOUTH AMERICA

Galápagos Is.
21 genera—4 endemic

Desventuradas Is.
2 endemic genera

Juan Fernandez Is.
12 genera—9 endemic

limit of Bidens

Easter (Papanui)

Oparanthus

Marquesas Is.

Mangareva

Pitcairn

Tuamotu Is.

Society Is.

Tahiti

Rapa

Fitchia

Cook Is.

Rarotonga

Samoa

Tonga

Midway

limit of Bidens

Hawaiian Is.
8 genera derived from New World—
6 of which are endemic

3-1. Although they have a better record of long-distance dispersal than other families, only a few genera of the sunflower family (Compositae) have been able to reach far Pacific islands from American points of origin. Both *Bidens* and *Oparanthus* appear, by chance dispersal, to have "bypassed" some islands suitable for them.

"continental" rocks, andesite, on Pacific islands (3–3) suggests that more land may have been present where these islands now occur. The andesite-bearing islands may be vestiges of formerly large islands, but this is no reason to believe that they were at one time part of a huge continent—in fact, they probably never were.

Traces of an island's history are threaded through its plants and animals, a history biologists can unravel if they can understand "what it is trying to tell us." Not surprisingly, disagreements do arise among biologists when they interpret history via the composition of floras and faunas. The pictures presented here are those which appeal to me as the most likely, but other points of view, as my hints will indicate, do exist.

DISHARMONY

When factors such as closeness or remoteness from mainland areas are taken into account, there are not two types of islands but many. We could go on subdividing islands into large and small, dry and wet, old and new, tropical, temperate, or frigid until there are almost as many categories as islands, and categorization substitutes complication for explanation. Instead, we can view islands as seen from the viewpoint of their immigrants.

If we imagine a group of animals standing on a shore awaiting dispersal, some will be able to travel—some far, some only a short distance—and some not at all. The fact that some cannot migrate means that they will be absent on oceanic islands, an absence we note with the term "disharmonic." A disharmonic flora or fauna lacks some groups because of their poor dispersal capacity, groups one would expect to be on an island because they are on a mainland area similar in climate. Despite the fact that we cannot always be sure why a particular species is missing in a particular place, the presence on an island of an assemblage of plants and animals which includes poor dispersers as well as good, and which spans much the same groups as on a nearby continental area, is a good example of a harmonic condition, and thereby a continental island. For example, Ceylon's broad range of animals and plants differs only slightly from that of adjacent India.

As we can see in 3–1 and 3–3, there are limits beyond which certain groups have not been able to progress. Among conifers, the heavy-seeded araucarias and kauris (*Agathis*) have not been able to penetrate very far into the Pacific from their "base" in the old lands of the southwestern Pacific. They have been unable to reach beyond Fiji and New Caledonia. Another genus of conifers, *Podocarpus*, has penetrated farther, probably because its smaller seeds are enclosed in a fleshy structure attractive to birds. The presence on Fiji of lizards, snakes, frogs, conifers, and many genera of flowering plants correspond to the eastward terminus there of the andesite rocks. Although Fiji itself lacks many kinds of plants and animals (mammals, for example) and is thus disharmonic compared with, say, New Guinea, Fiji is a threshold for many groups. Islands farther east, such as Samoa, are even more strongly disharmonic. Samoa seems eminently habitable by species from Fiji, so disharmony here is best interpreted as poverty of species due to the difficulties of long-distance dispersal. Although climate, soils, etc. may differ from one island to another and provide some basis for difference in numbers and kinds of inhabitants, spaces of sea water between islands are usually the primary explanation of disharmony.

The best dispersers among New World flowering plants include members of the sunflower family, Compositae (3–1). They have, by means of long-distance dispersal, reached farther into the Pacific in relatively recent geological time than have other plants from the Americas. And yet they, too, have their limits. In viewing the map (3–1) we notice several anomalies. *Bidens,* the best disperser of the genera shown, has followed a circuitous path, bypassing Samoa, Rarotonga, and other likely islands. *Oparanthus* is present on the Marquesas and on Rapa Island, but is completely absent on the Society Islands, which would offer even better fields for occupation.

Another distribution map (3–2) shows patterns which might seem difficult to explain. A New Zealand araliad (ivy family), *Kirkophytum lyallii,* occurs on Stewart Island and other nearby islands, including Larger Solander Island. The Solander Islands are two recent volcanic islands near Stewart Island. Despite the fact that only a mile separates Larger from Smaller Solander, a different species, *K. robustum,* occurs on Smaller Solander—and then again on The Snares, far to the south. The distribution of *Kirkophytum robustum* on these islands is exactly the same as that of Buller's albatross (*Diomedea bulleri*), which may account for this curious distribution pattern, since the seeds could well have been carried by this bird.

Another New Zealand plant, *Metrosideros parkinsonii* (3–2), grows in woodlands of South Island, skips North Island completely, but favors a site on Little Barrier Island. This distribution matches that of a petrel (*Procellaria parkinsonii*) which nests on the knolls and hilltops where the *Metrosideros* grows.

Thus the "chance" which seems to govern distributions may have a simple and logical explanation. Chance of this sort, however, results in disharmonic distributions.

An island can contain both a harmonic and a disharmonic flora or fauna. This seeming paradox can be explained by history. New Caledonia is an example: the "old" elements of the flora—conifers, many primitive flowering plants—probably represent a good picture of what might be expected on land in that general latitude many millions of years ago, perhaps as long ago as the Cretaceous. These plants can be said to be harmonic, in keeping with the floras of southern continents in those remote ages. In contrast, there are "new" plants in the New Caledonian flora which are markedly disharmonic. Compositae, notoriously good at dispersal, are almost absent. The most conspicuous one present is an everlast-

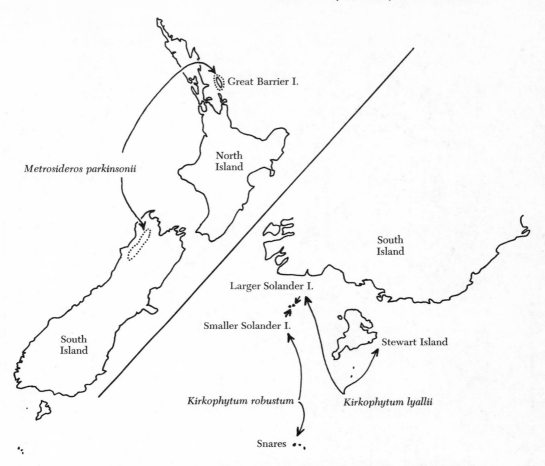

3-2. Two New Zealand plants which show peculiar distributions: *Metrosideros parkinsonii* skips from South Island to Great Barrier Island, but misses North Island. Two species of *Kirkophytum* occur on islands near South Island—but not in a way one would expect. For a possible explanation, see text.

ing-flower, *Helichrysum*, which proves identical to a species on Australia and is probably a relatively recent immigrant from there. The explanation for a harmonic "old" flora together with a disharmonic "new" flora on New Caledonia is that in ancient time, immigration was once much easier, probably at a time when more land was present. Either New Caledonia was larger, other land masses existed nearby, or both, so that access by immigrants was greatly facilitated. More recently, New Caledonia has become more isolated, so that plants with good dispersal can enter from Australia and other nearby lands, but most

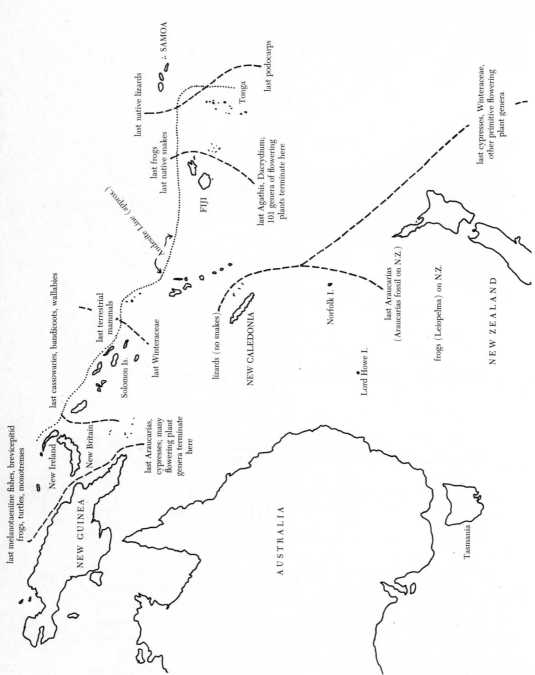

3-3. Spaces of sea water have proved barriers to migration for plants and animals according to their dispersal ability. As one follows their distribution eastward from their source areas, they "drop out." The lines on this map indicate the farthest-east limits for animals listed at the top of each line and the plants at the bottom of each line.

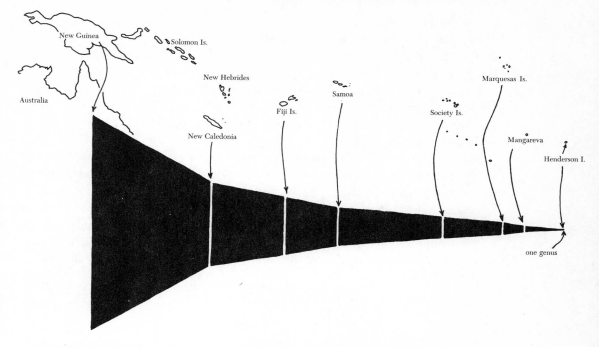

3–4. A "filter-bridge" is formed by a family of weevils, Cryptorhynchidae; the number of genera in this family progressively decreases on islands farther from the source area (New Guinea). Tapering of this "filter" is probably caused not only by distance, but also by the fact that farther islands are also, as it happens, smaller ones.

cannot manage to cross the long water gap. Perhaps also, the well-established old flora permits few footholds for newer immigrants.

FILTERS

If, instead of viewing the flora or fauna of an island as a whole, we look at particular groups in it, and compare their representation to that on other islands, we find a tendency for representatives of a group to be progressively fewer at stations farther and farther from a source. For example, the number of genera in a weevil family dwindle as we follow their penetration from the western into the eastern Pacific (3–4). This has been called a "filter" or "filter bridge." If distance is the only criterion, and if islands along a path of ocean are all about equally habitable, one might expect diminution because greater total distance means greater difficulty in long-distance dispersal. Although demonstrated by the weevils of 3–4, a similar tapering-off occurs in group after group, both in the area shown in 3–4 and in other parts of the world. Some will note that in

3–4, decrease in number of genera is also linked to progressively smaller size of islands, and that the less hospitable features of smaller islands participate in the "tapering." This is true: the two factors probably operate together in this particular case. Factors rarely operate singly in biological problems.

The taper of the funnel in 3–4 depends upon the ability of dispersal of these weevils. A group poorer at dispersal would show a much more abruptly tapered funnel. A group excellent at dispersal, such as ferns, would form a "funnel" with nearly parallel sides.

Filter bridges could be demonstrated by numbers of species, but perhaps better by the number of genera within a family or by families themselves which manage to reach an island. The Hawaiian Islands are comparatively "poor" in families, although the total number of species is sizable. Total number of species, therefore, is not a way to show a filter bridge situation, because although the original number of immigrants may be small, as it was in Hawaii, they may diversify into a large number of species following arrival—the "filter in reverse" of the next chapter.

LINES

A "break" between floras of two adjacent regions—for example, a harmonic flora on one island, a disharmonic one on the next—has an unalienable attraction for plant geographers. Faunal breaks are often even more pronounced and yield corresponding excitement for zoogeographers. Wallace, in his book *The Malay Archipelago,* noticed perhaps the most striking of these invisible barriers and celebrated it by drawing a line (3–5). Wallace's Line is famous not only because it represents a sharp limit in distribution of some mammals, but also because it follows a course one would not expect from looking at a map. It traverses some rather narrow straits, as between Bali and Lombok, which one might not have predicted to be effective barriers. Starting between this pair of islands, it separates Borneo from Celebes and (as corrected by T. H. Huxley) divides the Philippines so that Palawan and the adjacent Calamian Islands to the north fall on the western side, and finally leaves Taiwan west of the line. Wallace noted that this line corresponds to the shelf of shallow seas, shaded in 3–5, "so shallow that ships can anchor in any part of it." He suggested that the islands westward of the line were all one continent at a former time, but that the prominent volcanic activity in that region had resulted in subsidence of this land mass, leaving the mountaintops as islands. During the Pleistocene, large quantities of rain water, instead of reaching the ocean, were withdrawn in the form of huge polar ice caps. The seas thus experienced a net loss of water and were proportionately lower. Lowered levels of oceans during the Pleistocene seem the better explanation today for why dry land connected the islands west of Wallace's Line.

As for the effect on the animals, Wallace says, "when we examine the zoology of these countries . . . . we find what we most require . . . . evidence of a very striking character that these great islands must have once formed a part of the continent, and could only have been separated at a very recent geological epoch."

Mammals present on or near the westward side of Wallace's Line but which do not transgress the line are listed below. *None* of the families or genera listed are represented on the east side of the line unless "some species" or "most species" indicates that a portion of the species in a genus is barred, but part cross the line:

INSECTIVORA
Erinaceidae (hedgehogs, etc.)
Soricidae: *Crossogale, Nycteromys,* and some species of other genera
MENOTYPHLA
Tupaiidae (tupaias)
DERMOPTERA
Galeopithecidae: *Galeopterus* and *Galeopithecus* (flying lemurs)
PRIMATES
Lorisidae: *Nycticebus* (lorises): some species
Cercopithecidae: *Nasalis, Simias,* and most species of *Macacus* (macaques) and *Presbytis*
Hylobatidae: *Hylobates, Symphalangus*
Pongidae: *Pongo* (orang-utan)
EDENTATA
Manidae: *Manis* (pangolins)
LAGOMORPHA
Leporidae (hares)
RODENTIA
Sciuridae (squirrels): 12 genera containing 87 species; some species in other genera do not cross
Spalacidae (bamboo rats): 2 species
Hystricidae (hystrichomorphs): 4 genera containing 11 species (1 species reaches Philippines)
CARNIVORA
Canidae (dogs): *Cyon javanicus*
Ursidae (bears)
Mustelidae (weasels): 8 genera
Viverridae (civets, mongooses, etc.): 6 genera and some species in 4 other genera
Hyaenidae (hyenas): (a fossil species is known from Java)
Felidae (cats): *Felis* (most species)
PROBOSCIDEA
Elephantidae (elephants): *Elephas;* also *Mastodon* and *Stegodon* as fossils

3-5. "Wallace's Line" commemorates Wallace's discovery that two great provinces, the Oriental and the Australian-New Guinean, have rather sharp boundaries as far as mammals are concerned despite a seemingly continuous chain of islands. The line Wallace drew is unexpected until we notice that islands west of the line are surrounded by shallow water and were once connected with Asia. Huxley added a correction to the northern end of Wallace's Line. The modified Weber's Line shows a barrier for Australian mammals like Wallace's for Oriental ones, whereas the original Weber's Line shows the zone in which the two faunas meet in about equal proportions.

PERISSODACTYLA
  Tapiridae (tapirs)
  Rhinocerotidae (rhinoceroses)
ARTIODACTYLA
  Suidae (pigs): *Sus* (some species)
  Hippopotamidae (hippopotami): (a fossil species is known from Java)
  Tragulidae (chevrotains): *Tragulus* (most species)
  Cervidae (deer): *Muntiacus* (muntjaks); some species of *Cervus*
  Bovidae (cattle, antelopes): *Capra, Capricornis, Nemorrhaedus; Bison* (fossil); some species *Bos* (cattle)
  Giraffidae (giraffes): 3 species in 2 genera known as Pleistocene fossils

The above list is indeed an amazing one, for it includes virtually all sizable mammals. The famous embryologist Haeckel even stated that crossing the strait between Bali and Lombok is like leaving a present-day fauna to meet a Mesozoic one, referring to the fact that instead of mammals, reptiles seem to predominate. However, this distinction is accentuated by the fact that the Lesser Sunda Islands to the east of Bali are rather dry, and some biologists believe that increasing dryness eastward accounts for the termination of certain groups.

Some animals other than mammals show a relatively high degree of "respect" for Wallace's Line. Borneo has 420 species of breeding birds, Celebes only 220; whereas Java has 340, Lombok has a mere 120; but these facts might also reflect poorer climate and smaller island size east of the line. Another possible explanation is that the number of species in the Australian-New Guinean region is smaller, so that decrease across transitional areas is to be expected. Primary-division fresh water fishes are stopped by Wallace's Line. One family, Cyprinidae (carps), is represented by 162 species on Borneo, none on Celebes; 55 species on Java, one on Lombok. One family of birds (Capitonidae, the barbets) has never crossed the line. Easily dispersed groups, such as many of the plants and insects, show no diminution as they cross Wallace's Line, except to the extent that ecology and island size dictates that fewer plant and insect species can secure a foothold.

One good line seems to invite another. The reader will realize that with the rich faunas and floras of Australia and New Guinea farther to the east, the number of species does not continually decrease into those areas. The Indo-Malaysian or Oriental elements do fade out eastward, but the Australian-New Guinean elements increase. The point where one could say that mammals characteristic of the two provinces are about equal in number, and that a balance point occurs, has been designated as Weber's Line. Max Weber was a biologist skeptical about the value of Wallace's Line. He chose instead to emphasize the point of balance between the two regions. Those who favor the idea of Weber's Line call the belt of transition it denotes "Wallacea," and emphasize that it is an unstable area of intermingling.

One could prefer another line in this region, and such a line (Mayr's modification) has been drawn to indicate the limit of the Australian-New Guinean fauna (3–5). This line forms an admirable counterpart to Wallace's Line, because it does delimit a similar area of shallow seas which has been called the Sahul Shelf. Just as many animals do not cross Wallace's Line, an impressive list of animals do not extend beyond the limits of the Sahul Shelf. Animals so restricted include monotremes, kangaroos, wallabies, and birds of paradise. Of the marsupials, which are famed for being characteristic of the Australian-New Guinean region, none of the larger forms have crossed the modified Weber's Line. A few smaller marsupials have managed to escape beyond the limits of the Sahul Shelf: a phalanger does reach Celebes, Ceram, Timor, and the Moluccas, and a bandicoot (*Rhynchomeles*) reaches Ceram. Rafting might account for these cases.

Other regions are suitable for drawing of biogeographic lines, although none are, or are likely to become, so famous as those of the southwestern Pacific. Some lines which have been designated in the northwestern Pacific can be seen in 3–6.

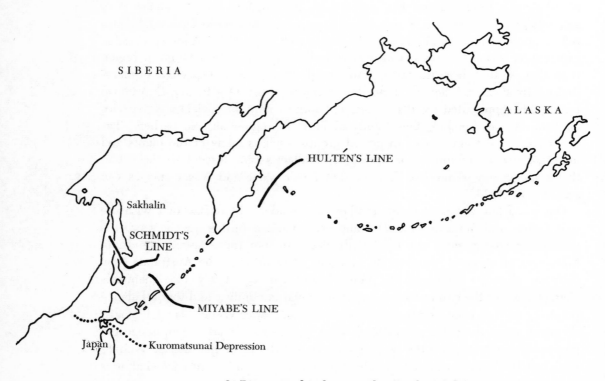

3–6. Biogeographic lines in the North Pacific.

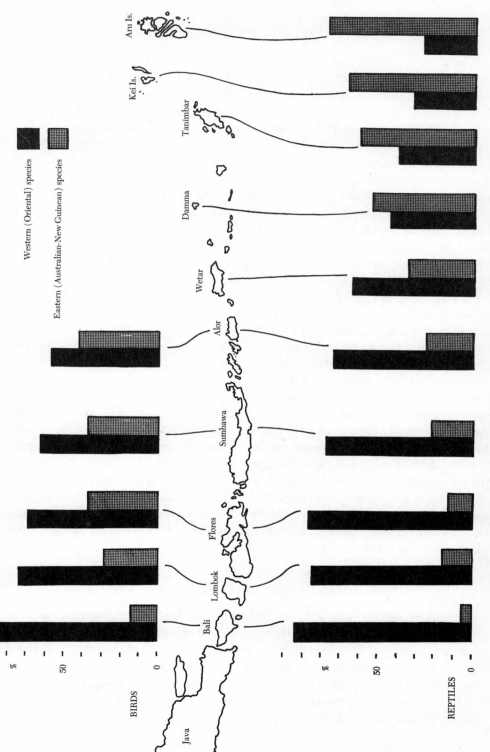

3–7. Mammals "obey" Wallace's Line between Bali and Lombok, but for animals with better dispersal ability, such as birds, reptiles, and butterflies, there is no "boundary" but a "filter," like that of 3–4. Because both Oriental and Australian species are involved, the Lesser Sunda Islands shown here serve as a "two-way filter bridge": percentages of eastern species decrease westward, western species decrease eastward.

TWO-WAY FILTER BRIDGES

What is an absolute barrier for a mammal may be only a moderate deterrent to migration for a bird or reptile. The distribution of better-dispersing groups will show not absolute breaks, but a series of thresholds, or diminutions, each of which could be, if one were line-minded, named as another line. A magnificent example of this occurs in the Wallace's Line area (3–7). Ernst Mayr, who knows the birds of the southwestern Pacific so well, has drawn on information not available to Wallace. When the number of Oriental birds and the number of Australian-New Guinean birds is computed for each of the Lesser Sunda Islands, we can see how effective each of the straits between these islands is in "filtering out" birds from west to east or from east to west. As 3–7 shows, the Lesser Sundas are a two-way filter bridge, with a steady decrease in both directions. This is shown not only by birds, but also by reptiles and other groups. The decrease in either direction is steady, but the break at the Bali-Lombok strait is slightly greater for birds, less for reptiles and amphibians. Examples of birds which find the Bali-Lombok strait impossible to cross include the Australian genera *Meliphaga* and *Philemon* (honeyeaters) and *Cacatua* (cockatoo), which extend westward to Lombok but do not occur on Bali.

A similar two-way filter bridge—with a slight difference—is formed by the Aleutian Islands (3–8). Species of plants in this region can be divided into western (Asiatic), eastern (American) and holarctic (which means present around the northern regions of the world). The progressive decrease of western species eastward and eastern species westward across this island chain is evident, despite the strong overlay of holarctic species. Evidently many holarctic species have good dispersal mechanisms, for they form a large and nearly constant proportion of the floras of each of the Aleutian Islands. A study on a group with poorer dispersal, the carabid beetles (Carabidae), shows that the western species have not come farther east than Attu, whereas the eastern (American) species are present (to be sure, in diminished numbers) all the way to the Commander Islands, nearest to Siberia. In carabid beetles, as in flowering plants, there are holarctic species.

ISLAND SIZE AND ECOLOGY

The above effects are ones of distance and sea water barriers, and to organisms they mean difficulties of dispersal and arrival. Difficulties of establishment are controlled by island habitat. Habitats are often dictated in a general way by size of an island. A larger island tends to be higher, higher regions tend to be wetter, so a greater variety of habitats which can support a greater number of species is present. This can be shown by the four islands in the Gulf of Guinea and their flora:

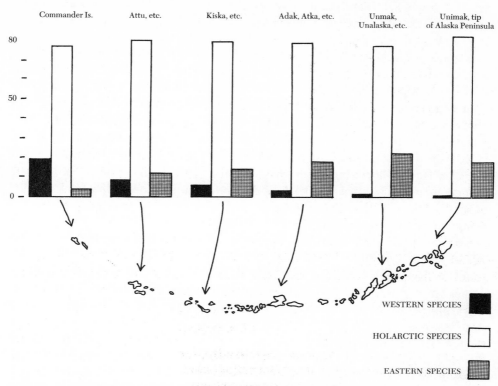

3–8. Although many flowering plants occur throughout the Arctic region and are thus called holarctic, others are characteristically Alaskan or Siberian. For these latter two groups, the Aleutian Islands serve as a "two-way filter bridge" like the one in the Lesser Sunda Islands in 3–7.

Island	Maximum elevation, meters	No. of native plant species	Ratio, species /meter
Annobon	655	115	.175
Principe	948	276	.291
S. Tomé	2024	556	.274
Fernando Po	2850	826	.290

The important role of altitude is revealed in the very nearly uniform ratio between altitude and number of species, except for Annobon, which has fewer species than might be expected, perhaps because it is not only small but the most distant from the African mainland. These four islands do have areas corresponding to the altitudes they reach, and both altitude and area may play a part in floral richness. A large flat island, however, would seem to have little advantage over a small flat island other than being a larger target for disseminules to hit. Over a long period of time about the same species would tend to reach a small flat island as a large flat island. Even tiny islands can support an assemblage of species. For instance, small and isolated Marotiri (Bass Isles) in the Austral Islands possesses several species of plants, several insects, and two species of land snails. To avoid extinction, there must be a certain minimum area on which a certain number of individuals can live. Very small islands cannot, probably, support larger animals unless they are migratory.

In many regions, such as on most Pacific Islands, moist forest can exist only above a certain elevation (about 2000–2500 feet in the Hawaiian Islands). Wet forest is often much richer in species than lowland scrub or lowland dry forest.

Extreme cold decreases number of species sharply, as in Antarctica. Only three species of flowering plants have been reported from Antarctica, and although interesting insects do live on the Antarctic continent, the total number is small. The fact that two species of penguins have become adapted to this continent is truly remarkable by any standards.

Extreme dryness is a limitation, but not as severe as one might imagine. Easter Island has a very limited flora and fauna on this account, perhaps also on account of its great remoteness and relative newness. But the Galápagos Islands, which are mostly rather arid, have about 615 species and varieties of ferns and flowering plants. If the Galápagos Islands were in a climatic zone like that of the Hawaiian Islands, they would doubtless support many more species. Although the Hawaiian Islands are larger and higher, and thus do have the ecological advantage, they are far more remote from a source area than the Galápagos Islands. Nevertheless, about two thousand species of ferns and flowering plants are native to the Hawaiian chain, showing the floristic richness permitted by moister climate.

AGE AND SATURATION

Any island probably has a saturation point based upon the size and climate offered to its plant and animal inhabitants. This saturation would be expressed both as the total number of organisms, or within particular groups—the maximum number of birds, reptiles, etc. The tendency for saturation to be achieved is shown in a graph for birds on islands of the southwestern Pacific, 3–9. If islands are near a source area and have a climate similar to that of the source area, they would all tend to reach a point of saturation soon. Smaller islands would support fewer species than larger islands, so saturation levels depend upon island size.

Remoteness, smallness, or dryness of islands are all factors which make their faunas or floras drop far below the level one would expect for saturation (3–10). Another possible factor is newness of islands, but all the remote islands included in 3–10 are certainly not new.

If an island is reasonably old, surely a large number of immigrants will have been able to reach it. But immigration continually occurs and with it another

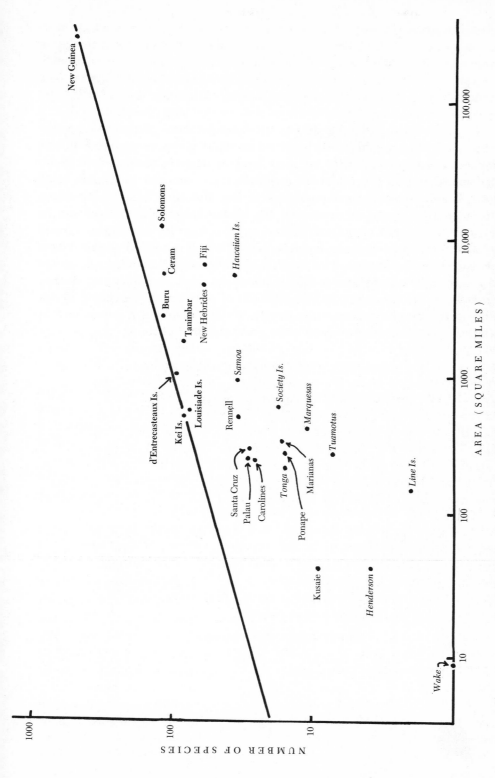

3-10. Saturation is not suggested by all of the islands on this graph, which was made with the same methods as 3–9. Islands which come closest to saturation (bold face) are close to a source area (New Guinea) and have a favorable climate. Islands somewhat farther from the source area (regular printing) fall short of the saturation level for birds. Islands far below the saturation level (italics) are islands which are either very far from a source area or poor ecologically (low, dry).

This table shows the small, but appreciable percentage of plants which have made the jump from the Americas to the Hawaiian Islands. The percentage of pantropic species is higher for ferns because ferns have better dispersal. Similar figures can be developed for Hawaiian animals. A large group like insects is a good indicator: 95 per cent of insects are considered to have "Pacific" affinities, 5 per cent "American."

If we view a map of the Pacific (3–19), however, we find that the nearest high islands (which would be the only effective source of immigrants) to the Hawaiian chain are as far, or farther than, America: the Marquesas, Fiji, Samoa, the Solomons. How, then, can these relatively small and distant sources have outdone America in supplying organisms to the Hawaiian Islands? The best hint is offered by geological studies of the Pacific Ocean and its underwater contours (3–11). South and west of Hawaii, the floor of the Pacific reveals numerous flat-topped mountains, or sunken atolls, which are called guyots. These guyots represent the last stage in the disappearance of an island. Volcanic islands are thought to originate as craters above the ocean surface. Darwin hypothesized that erosion gradually forms a shelf of soil around the shores of the island, and on this shelf, coral reefs develop, forming a broad ring around the island (see 4–3). The central mountain gradually disappears, so that a ring-shaped atoll lacking a central peak is all that eventually remains. These atolls are only a few feet above sea level, and relatively slight geological changes will result in their sinking below the ocean surface where, as guyots, they are invisible to all but the techniques of modern oceanography. The life cycle of an island is relatively rapid, taking perhaps only a million years. Thus, many chains of high islands were perhaps present not long ago, and have since disappeared (3–12). The effect that these island chains, now present as vestigial guyots, may have had is difficult to estimate, but they must have had some function in furthering distribution patterns. Moreover, the lowering of the sea in the Pleistocene exposed much more land surface which could have been active in dispersal in the Pacific.

The Hawaiian chain itself has changed. Within this chain, there is a clear sequence from west to east with regard to age (5–2). The eastern islands are younger, the western older. Even today, the eastern most island, Hawaii, is very active volcanically. This sequence is seen even on each island: the westernmost mountain on Maui, Puu Kukui, is old and eroded, whereas Haleakala, a mountain to the east, is not greatly eroded and still has some barren lava flows. Thus, the many tiny islands and reefs which stretch westward between Kauai and Midway may once have been high islands capable of receiving immigrants and dispersing their descendants long before the major islands of today had grown in size.

The question of how much land, now vanished beneath the sea, was once available as a route for migration will plague biogeographers for many decades to come. The route across Beringia (Siberia to Alaska) is generally agreed to have existed; Australia may have been partly or wholly bridged with Asia in a

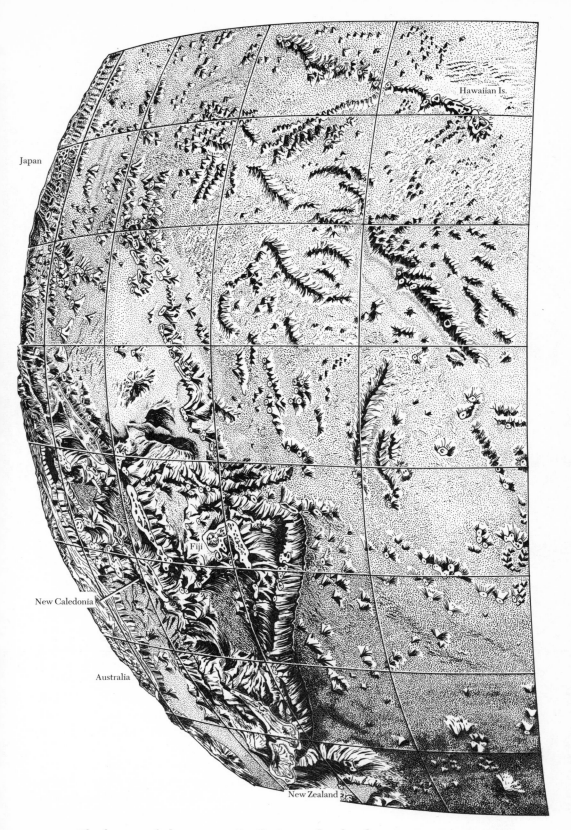

Japan

Hawaiian Is.

Fiji

New Caledonia

Australia

New Zealand

3–11. The bottom of the western Pacific is not flat, but has many mountain ranges, some of which reach above the surface. Submerged mountains indicate, at least in some cases, former archipelagos or large islands which have served as stepping-stones for migration to distant archipelagos, such as the Hawaiian Islands.

59

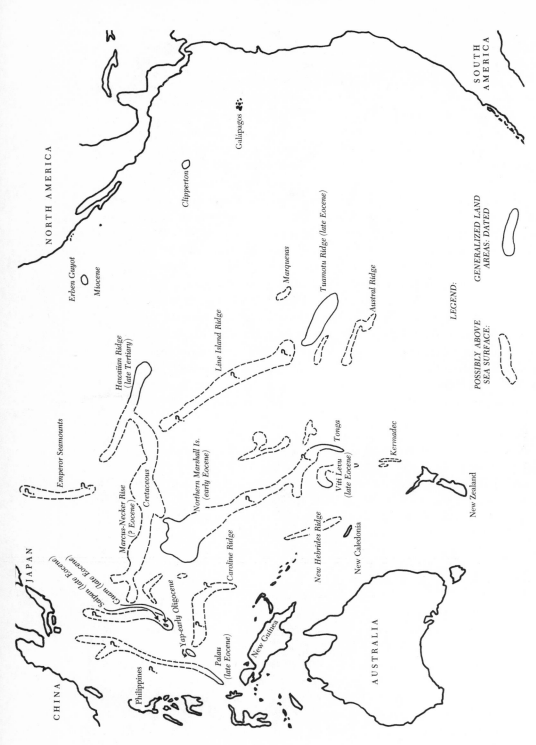

3–12. Former areas of dry land in the Pacific Ocean are suggested by fossils in dredges or surface samples examined by geologists. Probable land areas in Tertiary time are indicated by solid lines, possible ones by broken lines. Such land areas may have aided "island-hopping" by plants and animals in past eras.

very antique past; but few such land bridges probably existed. Although one can safely say that more land was present in some areas than now exists, the relative constancy of continents and oceans and their position within recent geological eras seems secure. It is within these recent eras that the greatest populating of islands has occurred. If major changes in the composition of lands and oceans have occurred, they were far too ancient to have mattered to more than a fraction of today's island inhabitants.

Has Antarctica, as some contend, formerly served as a migration route across the South Pacific, feeding migrants to New Zealand, or, in the other direction, to South America? Fossils tell us that Antarctica was certainly once warmer, and the plants present there formerly must have required some sort of connections with South America, New Zealand, and Australia. The presence of araucarias both in South America and Australia and nearby islands attests to this route, because araucarias are so very poor at dispersal; indeed, fossil araucaria wood has been discovered in Antarctica. Also, species which are now restricted to warmer (northerly) parts of the Southern Hemisphere may once have extended well down to Antarctica, if not on that continent itself. With a greater southern range of this sort, species with good dispersal might easily have been in striking range of Southern Hemisphere lands now remote from them. With only a relatively small amount of additional land, plants and animals in the far south might have been afforded a nearly dry path from South America to Australia or New Zealand, or vice versa. Antarctica may have been a pathway, but it was probably never a burgeoning center of primary origin and evolution, as some claim.

Migration Routes

Few species, surely, could have taken identical routes of migration. Consequently, the maps one often sees which have arrows pointing to the Hawaiian Islands or other islands in an attempt to show how species arrive, are generalizations and thus conceal more information than they reveal. Analyses of where each genus in a particular island or island-group has its closest relatives are the most useful, if bulky, way of presenting this information. This has been done by Wallace for the Azores and Bermuda, and for the Hawaiian Islands by Zimmerman.

Biological Provinces

A favorite sport of biogeographers is to carve up an ocean, usually the Pacific, into provinces, regions, subregions, etc. At first glance, this might seem to be a good idea. However, although differences are emphasized, the reason for each division is a different one. Some divisions are based on the fact that their islands have a poorer assemblage of species than those of the neighboring region, some that the floras and faunas are older, some that marsupials are present, etc. Worse, no two maps of this sort agree, because no two biologists will emphasize the same features. If you enjoy or are curious about these exercises in boundary-drawing, you will have to look beyond the covers of this book.

ARCHIPELAGO EFFECTS

Theoretically, an archipelago should offer a richer biological assemblage and different evolutionary products from those of a single island. Isolation, that primary desideratum for active evolution, is offered in a multiple and particularly favorable form. Taking advantage of the numerous pockets within an archipelago, a single immigrant can diversify into a large number of intricately interrelated species, even genera.

Invasion and Reinvasion. One phase of what happens in an archipelago can be described in terms of successive entries made into its environments. During these migrations, evolution not only takes place, but is probably spurred along and, in turn, encourages further migrations. A diagram of a hypothetical archipelago, 3–13, shows how this might have happened. The four species A, B, C, D, are on both islands in this diagram, with the exception of A, present on only one island. One can ask if anything has, in fact, happened which would not have occurred on a single island. First, the presence of more numerous islands in a limited area multiplies the probable number of species which can be formed. Interisland isolation is more effective in creating several distinct populations than barriers (such as valleys, ridges, etc.) within a single island. Second, there is in the course of evolution a tendency for a new group to overtake the parental stock, which is thus extinguished. If this were consistently true, we could draw a map of conditions years later; the larger island in 3–13 would retain species B and D, the smaller C and D, and A would be extinct. Also, not shown, even if a species is common to both islands, it can take different directions: B could produce another species, X, on one island, but it could give rise to Y on the other.

3–13. A hypothetical history of an animal or plant immigrant (A) that evolves into a hill species, (B), which invades the eastern island, then forms a mountain species, (C), which migrates to mountains on the western island, and finally from this stock a marsh species is developed. Invasion, change, and reinvasion on islands of an archipelago promote evolution of new species.

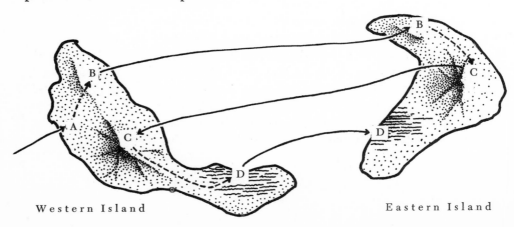

Western Island   Eastern Island

Does such a process, however, really happen in an archipelago? The curious patterns of the Galápagos finches (described further in Chapter 15) suggest just this. As the map, 3–14, shows, the larger central islands have more numerous species per island. This would be expected because they are larger and more ecologically diverse—both dry lowlands and moist uplands. What might not be expected is that *endemic* subspecies are present only on the *outer* islands, as the figures in parentheses indicate. There is only one species endemic to a single island (*Camarhynchus pauper* on Charles Island), but perhaps seventeen endemic subspecies on the various outer islands. How can this be explained? According to one theory (3–15), the various species arose on the smaller islands on the periphery of the archipelago, then dispersed to the central islands. In the central islands, which are higher, ecological conditions are more varied and can thus support more species. These species can become versatile, developing various ecological specializations. These "invigorated" species can then reinvade

3–14. The Galápagos Islands are famous as the locale of Darwin's finches (see 15–18). The number of finch species follows the island name; the number in parentheses indicates the number endemic to that island. The central islands support more species but have fewer endemics than the outer islands.

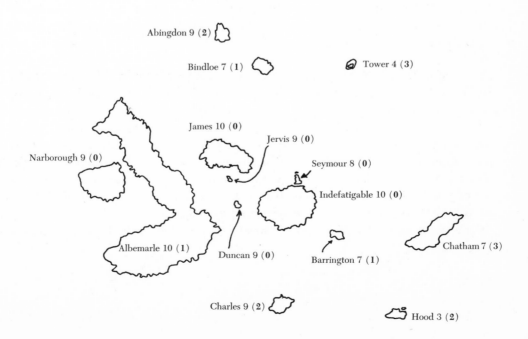

Culpepper 4 (2)

Wenman 5 (1)

Abingdon 9 (2)

Bindloe 7 (1)   Tower 4 (3)

James 10 (0)
Jervis 9 (0)
Narborough 9 (0)   Seymour 8 (0)

Indefatigable 10 (0)

Albemarle 10 (1)   Duncan 9 (0)   Barrington 7 (1)   Chatham 7 (3)

Charles 9 (2)   Hood 3 (2)

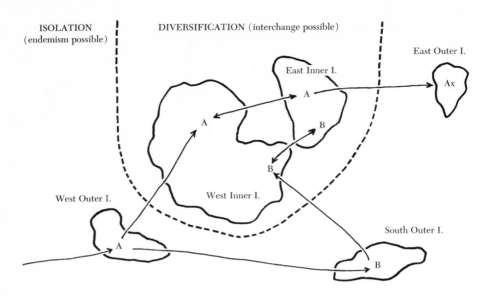

ISOLATION
(endemism possible)

DIVERSIFICATION (interchange possible)

East Outer I.

Ax

East Inner I.

A

A

B

West Outer I.

West Inner I.

B

B

South Outer I.

A

B

3–15. The situation in 3–14 might have happened in this way: inner islands are ecologically rich and can support more species and permit adjustment to a wide variety of environments. The isolation necessary to formation of new species, however, is best offered by outer islands.

the peripheral islands. Such immigrants to the outer islands experience more isolation and develop into endemic subspecies. Without this isolation, the diversification begun in the central islands could not result in endemic subspecies. Any changes would be "swamped out" and the original conditions favored in the populations which remain on the central islands. These processes are summarized in a diagram, 3–13. From the original immigrant, species A and B are formed. These both disperse to the central islands, where no new subspecies form, but ecological races can develop. From species A, an endemic subspecies, Ax, is formed on one of the outer islands.

Reacting to Dispersal. The islands of an archipelago may yield different patterns when exploited by groups with good and poor dispersal, respectively. In 3–16, one genus with five species (A–E) has poor dispersal, another with five species (F–J) has good dispersal. Of A–E, four out of five succeed in reaching Inner Island; only two reach Outer Island. As time passes, C and D become extinct on the mainland, leaving these as relicts on the islands. Of these, C is on both islands, D only on Inner Island. A group with poor dispersal acts differently. Of F–J, all five have established on Inner Island, four reached Outer Island. Extinction of G and H on the mainland has occurred, and G is also now extinct on Inner Island. So in contrast with the poor-dispersing group, the easily dispersing species

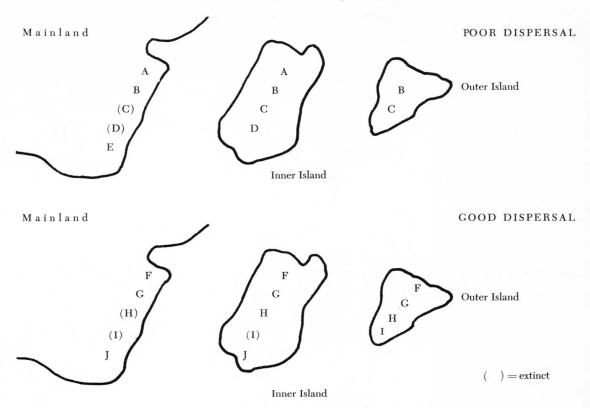

3–16. In the natural course of events, dispersal occurs and is eventually followed by extinction of the immigrants. A group of species with good dispersal ability (F–J) will be better represented on Outer Island. Relicts (species extinguished on the mainland) are more frequent on Inner Island among the group with poor dispersal (A–E), but more frequent on Outer Island among those with good dispersal.

yield (a) more species on Outer Island; (b) relict species on Outer Island instead of Inner Island.

Similarly, we can discriminate between immigrant and relict patterns by means of species distribution in an archipelago (3–17). If dispersal is recent, a pattern like a filter bridge is formed, the number of species tapering with distance. If dispersal took place long ago and all species have had an opportunity to reach all of the islands, a relict pattern is developed: species which survive are preserved rather at random on the islands of an archipelago.

Archipelago Factors Considered Together. Isolation, island size, ecology of islands, age of islands, and dispersibility are factors which operate jointly, not individually. Which are the most important, which less so? The abundance of

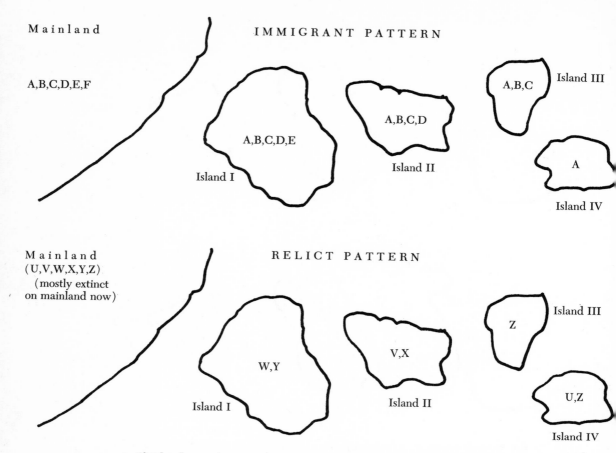

Mainland

A,B,C,D,E,F

IMMIGRANT PATTERN

A,B,C,D,E
Island I

A,B,C,D
Island II

A,B,C
Island III

A
Island IV

Mainland
(U,V,W,X,Y,Z)
(mostly extinct
on mainland now)

RELICT PATTERN

W,Y
Island I

V,X
Island II

Z
Island III

U,Z
Island IV

3–17. If islands receive recent immigrants, the number fades out progressively with distance from the mainland source, like the filter of 3–4. If islands preserve relicts, the species (which presumably have had sufficient time to reach all of the islands) are preserved randomly.

species offers a convenient phenomenon for analysis, because the numbers of species on certain islands are well known, and these actual numbers can be compared to predictions of how many should occur using mathematical equations. The Galápagos Islands are good for this purpose, because a prediction must suit not a few, but seventeen islands. The islands are all about equally distant from the mainland of South and Central America, so the mainland does not affect one much more than another. Is area, as has been claimed, of primary importance in determining numbers of species on islands? By converting actual observations to mathematical formulas, variable, unknown, and uncertain facts cannot be expressed. Biological phenomena, unlike those of physics, rarely fol-

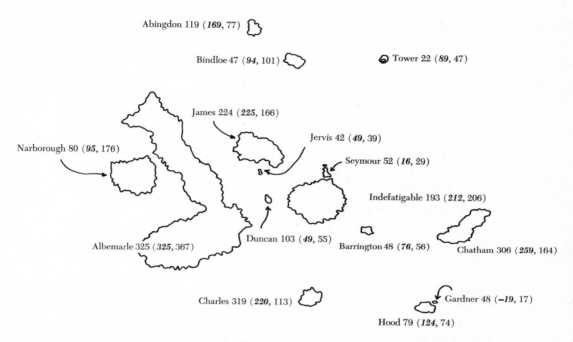

Culpepper 7 (*−24*, 28)

Wenman 14 (*14*, 35)

Abingdon 119 (*169*, 77)

Bindloe 47 (*94*, 101)   Tower 22 (*89*, 47)

James 224 (*225*, 166)

Jervis 42 (*49*, 39)

Narborough 80 (*95*, 176)

Seymour 52 (*16*, 29)

Indefatigable 193 (*212*, 206)

Albemarle 325 (*325*, 367)   Duncan 103 (*49*, 55)   Barrington 48 (*76*, 56)   Chatham 306 (*259*, 164)

Charles 319 (*220*, 113)   Gardner 48 (*−19*, 17)

Hood 79 (*124*, 74)

3–18. The number of plant species which each island of the Galápagos Islands supports is indicated after each island name; biologists seek factors to explain the relative richness or poverty of these islands. Mathematical calculations have been used to predict the number of species one would expect (in parentheses). The first of these (bold-face italics) is a prediction based on many factors, the second a prediction based merely on area. The latter is more accurate for small islands but the former suits larger islands better (figures from Hamilton, et al.).

low precisely the specifications of a mathematical equation. Nevertheless, we may learn much about whether area, or altitude, or other factors are important in governing richness of species by an attempt to predict by mathematical means how many species would be expected on particular islands. One notable study which uses sophisticated mathematics, summarized in 3–18, shows that area alone does not control the number of species. For larger islands, a complex equation incorporating for each island maximum altitude, isolation (distance from nearest island; distance from center of archipelago), area of the island, and area of the adjacent island, produces a more accurate prediction. This, the authors of those predictions say, shows that for larger islands, the number of factors controlling species number is greater. For smaller islands, area is the predominant factor, for a simple equation they use, based upon area of the island, predicts the number on smaller islands more closely. For the larger islands, the factors controlling species abundance are, in order of their importance: maximum elevation; area of adjacent island; distance from the nearest island; distance from the center of the archipelago; area of island. If we assume that the equation based on area alone is more accurate for islands twenty square miles or less, and the equation based on all factors is more accurate for islands forty-five square miles or more in area, we find that the predictions can be subdivided into the following categories (in parentheses is the number of species by which the prediction was in excess or was deficient):

Smaller islands (prediction based only on area):

Nearly correct: Jervis, Barrington, Hood
Too many predicted: Culpepper (21), Wenman (21), Tower (25)
Too few predicted: Gardner (31), Seymour (23), Abingdon (92)

Larger islands (prediction based on many factors):

Nearly correct: Albemarle, James
Too many predicted: Bindloe (47), Narborough (15), Indefatigable (19)
Too few predicted: Charles (99), Chatham (47)

Perhaps, as the authors of these predictions say, these deviations can be accounted for by "vagaries of interisland dispersal." Can they be accounted for by any reasons more definite than this? If we examine the listing above, we find that too many species are predicted for Culpepper, Wenman, and Tower. This is probably because in addition to small area, these islands are very low; in addition, the first two are very remote from the rest of the archipelago. Distance is probably also responsible for the fact that too few species are predicted for Gardner and Seymour. Gardner is separated from Hood by a very narrow strait, as Seymour is from Indefatigable. Between the two in each pair, migration is virtually unrestricted, and has probably increased species abundance beyond what area alone would dictate. Too few species are predicted for Abingdon, perhaps because the elevation of the island (2500 feet) permits a very much greater number of species than on other small islands. That this is true is suggested by the fact that the multiple factor equation overpredicts by fifty, not underpredicts, for Abingdon.

Using the complex equation, too few species have been predicted for Bindloe, Narborough, and Indefatigable. Either some factor or factors have been left out of the equation, or perhaps certain factors are more or less important than indicated in the equation. Narborough is certainly one of the most recent islands and is largely bare lava, and this probably helps account for the small number of species which have reached it or developed on it; a rain shadow cast by Albemarle may explain its poverty also. Even prediction according to area alone suggests it ought to have more than the ninety-six species it does. Recentness may also account for the underpredictions for Bindloe and Indefatigable. The reverse is probably true for Charles and Chatham. In the case of Charles particularly, a marked underprediction has occurred. Both of these islands are, according to geological evidence, older than the others; they are also moister; these two factors have produced more soils, and this would help explain why they are richer than predicted.

Thus, factors listed by the prediction authors do operate, but we must add others, such as geological age and climate. But more importantly, the relative significance of factors may vary from island to island, both in the Galápagos and elsewhere. A factor of overriding importance to the richness of one island may be negligible to another, and mathematical modes cannot be expected to predict the many interesting variations in the populations of islands.

ISLANDS OF THE WORLD

What are the special characteristics of the world's islands which destine them for certain plant and animal peculiarities? The following brief summaries may help to answer that question. If the brevity of these descriptions tantalizes or annoys the reader who wants to supplement these pictures of island-life phenomena with accounts of the islands themselves, there is a wealth of information available, although sometimes in unlikely places. In this book, two island groups are reconstructed in detail: the Galápagos Islands (Chapter 15) and Madagascar (Chapter 16). There is no substitute for an extended work on an island or island group which discusses geological history, or gives a summary of the flora, or a synopsis of the fauna, or all three. Unfortunately, few works manage all three, because few biologists can bridge the gap among these fields and synthesize information concerning islands. The age which has produced works like Wallace's *Island Life* has unfortunately faded. The books and articles mentioned below and elsewhere in the preceding and following chapters do not form a complete list, but the works cited at the end of this book, and in the important references by Darlington and by Blake and Atwood will lead one to nearly all the important papers and books.

PACIFIC OCEAN (3–19)

To those who might protest that this book concerns Pacific Islands to an inordinate extent, I can only apologize and reply that most islands occur in the Pacific, and thereby they show a much broader gamut of organisms and processes than do islands of other oceans. Representing the excitement generated in the natural sciences by problems in this region are the Pacific Science Congresses, ten of which have, to date, been held. The *Proceedings* of these Congresses contain many papers of interest.

Aleutians. Although the Bering Strait was continuous land in the Pleistocene and Tertiary, the Aleutian Islands are oceanic (volcanic) and have flora and fauna

SKA

Guadalupe .

Hawaiian Is.

Revillagigedo Is.

Clipperton .

Cocos .

Line Is.

Malpelo .

Galápagos Is.

SOUTH
AMERICA

Is.

Marquesas Is.

Society Is.

Tuamotu Is.

Tahiti

nga

Gambier Is.

Mangareva

Sala y Gomez

Desventuradas Is. :

Ducie

Austral Is.

Rapa

Henderson

Easter

Morotiri

Pitcairn

Juan Fernandez Is.

Chiloe

Tierra del Fuego

3–19. Islands of the Pacific Ocean

derived from both east and west, as described in an interesting symposium in the Bishop Museum publication *Pacific Basin Biogeography.*

Kuriles. These islands stretch between the Kamchatka Peninsula of Siberia and the northernmost island of Japan, Hokkaido. They are oceanic and show a biota much like that of Kamchatka, with a depauperated representation of Japanese flora and fauna.

Japan and Sakhalin. Although volcanism has added to the extent of these islands, they are continental islands, connected with the Asiatic mainland as recently as the Pleistocene. The presence of primary-division fresh water fish, large mammals such as bears, conifers and relict flowering plants demonstrates the continental nature of the islands. Numerous groups of plants were pushed southward all over the Northern Hemisphere during periods of cooling, and extinguished in far northern areas. Thus some relatives of Japan's flora are found in distant pockets, such as western North America and the Appalachian Mountains, but lacking in intervening areas. Japan's Mount Fuji reaches 12,388 feet, and much of the Japan Alps is over eight thousand feet, so that a full range of temperate climates is present.

Ryukyu Islands; Bonin Islands; Volcano Islands. These are chains of volcanic islands south of Japan, some still active volcanically. They have a relatively poor flora and fauna compared to the Japanese islands, which have influenced the biota on these island chains.

Taiwan. Connected with mainland China in the Tertiary and Pleistocene, Taiwan is a classical example of a continental island. Like Japan, Taiwan possesses large (although mostly medium or small) mammals; conifers and relict flowering plants are present. Mountains of Taiwan reach to over thirteen thousand feet, providing alpine climates; southern Taiwan is nearly tropical. Hainan, off the south China coast is, like Taiwan, a continental island, but with more tropical aspects.

Philippines. The Philippines combine continental island features with oceanic islands populated by means of filter bridge action. As mentioned above in connection with Wallace's Line, Palawan and a few small islands north of it were connected with Borneo, and thus the entire Sunda Shelf at one time, probably as recently as the Pleistocene. Connections of this Shelf to at least some of the other islands seem likely. Primary-division fresh water fishes (mostly cyprinids) occur on Mindanao and Mindoro, and large mammals have managed to migrate to some larger islands other than Palawan. The Philippines have a varied tropical climate, also cool uplands where pines and rhododendrons are native. Many interesting maps, such as that of 2–16, can and have been drawn to show the gradual depauperation of the Borneo fauna as it extends into the Philippines. For these reasons, the Philippines have been called a "fringing archipelago." Those interested in reviewing this situation would do well to read the lucid book of Dickerson, as well as the accounts of Inger, Merrill, and Taylor (see References).

Borneo, Sumatra, Java, Bali. These are the Greater Sunda Islands, continental islands west of Wallace's Line. Although they differ among themselves, they are rich by virtue of their moist, tropical climate, which has served as a suitable habitat for the Indo-Malayan fauna and flora. Some plants and animals such as the orang-utan, now extinct on mainland Asia, persist in these islands. Not generally appreciated is the fact that Java, Sumatra, and Borneo all have mountains exceeding twelve thousand feet, and thereby support an alpine flora and fauna. Wallace's book *The Malay Archipelago* is a delightful classic dealing with the life of this region, and the fact that it is a classic should not dissuade one from reading it.

Celebes, Moluccas, Lesser Sunda Islands, Aru Islands. East of Wallace's Line, these islands have an unstable geological history. Although they are not part of the Sunda Shelf, some connections may have occurred. For example, a few primary-division fresh water fishes do not stop at Wallace's Line, but extend to Lombok and Sumbawa. Most of the islands may be oceanic islands, but their close association both with the Greater Sunda Islands and the Australian-New Guinean region has produced the two-way filter bridge situation commemorated as "Wallacea." Celebes has many peculiar forms, both recent and fossil.

Australia. Some will say Australia is not an island, it is a continent. But certainly it is possible to view Australia as the world's largest island, although those who do so are likely to be reminded that South America could be regarded with almost equal justification as an island which happens to be connected via Panama to North America at present. Australia is a better example of an island than South America because it is smaller, its isolation has been more nearly complete, like that of an oceanic island, and many of its immigrants are very antique ones or products of long-distance dispersal. Geologists admit no land connection with Asia in any recent period, but a very brief connection in the Cretaceous has recently been proposed for several reasons.

The very pronounced isolation of Australia has resulted in the development of many peculiar groups, such as the marsupials, into a broad spectrum of forms (Chapter 6). Relict groups, such as the monotremes, have persisted there from Triassic or Jurassic time. Examples from Australia are considered in several chapters which follow because Australia's biota show island-life characteristics in a heightened form. Western Australia has experienced isolation from eastern Australia, and the plants of the west are rather different, although they have related counterparts in the east in most cases. The Nullarbor Plain, one of the world's most desolate regions, has maintained this isolation which was once enforced by invasion of the sea. Despite the low proportion of high land, Australia has a wide range of climates from tropical to cold temperate, ideal for producing evolutionary diversification in the flora and fauna.

Tasmania. Because Tasmania has had Tertiary and Pleistocene connections with the Australian mainland, it may be regarded as a continental island. Tasmania has served as a refuge for some plants and animals wiped out on the mainland. A good recent account of Australian biogeography likely to escape notice is the book by Keast, Crocker, and Christian. In addition, handbooks such as those by Blackall, Keast, McKeown, McPhee, Marlow, Troughton, and Whitley are steadily making the natural wonders of Australia and Tasmania accessible to the public.

New Guinea. A land connection between Australia and New Guinea occurred in the Tertiary and, to a greater extent, in the Pleistocene, when the Sahul Shelf was above water. New Guinea's extent today is probably greater than previously, except for times when it was connected with Australia. For most of its history, New Guinea has been a series of small islands, and this may help to explain why there are no families of plants, and few genera, endemic to the island.

New Guinea can be regarded as a tropical refuge for plants and animals from the Australian mainland, just as Tasmania is for cool-temperate groups. Many plants and animals present in Queensland, Australia, continue north into New Guinea, and the barrier is not a sharp one. New Guinea has remarkable alpine regions matched only by the high peaks of Borneo and the Philippines. Among the interesting groups which have developed in New Guinea are the birds of paradise (Chapter 11). Although New Guinea has long been a focus of bio-geographers interested in primitive plants and varied groups of animals, no good or comprehensive study of this fascinating island has yet appeared. Perhaps it is still too poorly known and too complex to inspire such a volume as yet.

Melanesian Arc. This term can be used for New Britain, New Ireland, the Solomon Islands, the New Hebrides, and lesser islands which stretch eastward from New Guinea. They appear to be oceanic islands which, by virtue of their proximity to New Guinea and their similar climate, have inherited portions of New Guinea's lowland and mountain (but not alpine) biota. The fact that they form a sort of filter bridge is evident in 3–4. Fiji, which terminates the arc, must be old because it has some antique plant groups, and some "continental" rocks, such as granite, quartz diorite, quartzite, schist, arkose, andesite and rhyolite.

New Caledonia. To the botanist, New Caledonia is one of the world's marvels on account of its remarkable collection of ancient conifers and flowering plants. The zoologist is unimpressed: New Caledonia lacks mammals and even snakes, and has a relatively poor fauna although there are a few unusual birds. The contrast between these two pictures must somehow be resolved. One possibility is that more land was present, perhaps in the Cretaceous, and plant immigrants crossed to the island from nearby land, either over dry ground or a short water span. Mammals may never have arrived because they were not present when some of the antique plant forms were able to reach New Caledonia. The presence of heavy-seeded conifers suggests that relatively moderate gaps of water at most separated New Caledonia from other conifer-bearing areas. In any case, New Caledonia is an ancient island with a complex geological history. Some of its plant and animal curiosities are discussed in Chapters 12 and 13. Although there are cool mountains above three thousand feet and good rain forest, New Caledonia was once much higher, as "continental" rocks suggest. It may have emerged as a major island in the Oligocene. The disparity between the picture presented by plants and that by animals is not unique: Fiji and New Zealand offer similar difficulties.

New Zealand. New Zealand consists of three major islands: North, South, and Stewart (3–2). Many lesser islands extend south to Antarctica. New Zealand is undoubtedly very old, as is indicated by the presence of many conifers; a primitive frog, *Leiopelma;* a curious relict reptile, the tuatara (Chapter 12); and some flightless birds, such as the kiwi and moa, whose flightlessness was not recently acquired (Chapter 9). There is no reason, from the animal side, to believe that New Zealand was ever connected with other major islands, and certainly not with Australia. Plants such as the kauri suggest short water gaps set New Zealand off once, but the gaps have widened considerably, for most of New Zealand's flora seems the product of long-distance dispersal—*Fuchsia,* for example. Additional land and more moderate climate may have aided the spread of plants to New Zealand in the far-south Pacific. New Zealand has, as might be expected, many "continental" rocks. This is also true of islands off New Zealand, such as the Auckland Islands (granite, olivine, gabbro, schist, gneiss, andesite), Bounty Islands (granite), Campbell Island (mica schist, quartz conglomerate, sandstone, chert), Chatham Islands (mica, schist, micaceous andesite) and the Kermadec Islands (hornblende granite). These rocks suggest a much greater extent for these islands in former times. New Zealand's high mountains and moist lowlands provide favorable niches for temperate groups, and extreme climates characterize the islands closer to Antarctica. Many good books, cited in other chapters, cover the natural history of New Zealand. *The Subantarctic Islands of New Zealand,* edited by Chilton, is a classic natural history work for the far-southern islands.

Polynesia. Samoa, the Cook Islands, the Austral Islands, the Gambier Islands, the Marquesas, and the Hawaiian Islands are mostly "high" (mountainous) islands of wholly volcanic origin. Their plants and animals reflect this clearly. Tahiti and Hawaii are high enough to have acquired alpine elements in addition to tropical lowland and montane elements. Conifers, snakes, lizards, and mammals have been unable to reach any of these islands except for Tonga, which has probably been able to secure lizards and one podocarp by virtue of nearness to Fiji. Many lower islands, such as Easter, the Tuamotus, and the Line Islands, are present within the area delimited as Polynesia, but their depauperate biota consists mostly of elements scattered across the entire Pacific—"pantropical." Among the higher islands, elements are mostly from Indo-Malaysia, but an appreciable number with American affinities occur here also (3–1). All of the islands are relatively recent, and probably none of them were populated much before Pliocene times. Most publications dealing with this region have been published by the Bishop Museum in Honolulu. This museum's dedication to the natural history of this region deserves the highest praise. Chapter 5 is concerned mostly with Hawaiian plants and animals.

Lord Howe and Norfolk Islands. These are old oceanic islands east of Australia. They contain relict groups, such as the *Araucaria* on Norfolk Island, which are not easily dispersed. Greater land masses might have aided such dispersal. The problems of these islands are well discussed in some interesting articles by Paramonov.

Micronesia. This broad area of the Pacific consists of relatively low islands. Some of them, such as the Palau Islands and Ponape, have some small mountains, but many larger groups, such as the Tokelau, Gilbert, Caroline, Marshall, and Mariana Islands consist almost wholly of atolls or low platform-like islands. Micronesia is thus biologically defined by the depauperate biota—pantropical species with good ability at long-distance dispersal are most common. Some elements are Oriental, conforming to the relative closeness of some Micronesian islands to the Oriental region. The terms "Micronesia," "Melanesia," and "Polynesia" are, of course, based primarily upon races of people who inhabit these areas, but these patterns do not conform completely to the picture of plant and animal distribution. Some would argue that the Tokelau Islands, near Samoa, are Polynesian, but their depauperate biota allies them more closely with the Ellice Islands. Good descriptions of Micronesia's geography and natural history have been furnished in volumes by Fosberg and by Gressitt.

Juan Fernandez and Desventuradas Islands. These islands lie off Chile, are oceanic, and have affinities with adjacent South America. The Desventuradas Islands are drier; moist rain-forest conditions on the Juan Fernandez have permitted a relatively rich flora. The islands must be of at least moderate age, because of relicts like *Lactoris* and *Thyrsopteris* (Chapter 13). The fauna is less striking. Although most of the biota is America, a lone fragment of the Indo-Malayan fauna is present in the genus of land snails *Fernandezia,* probably a product of long-distance dispersal. Juan Fernandez plants are discussed in Chapter 8. A remarkable three-volume work, *The Natural History of Juan Fernandez and Easter Island,* covers all aspects of these islands in a splendid way.

Galápagos Islands. An entire chapter is devoted to this group of oceanic islands of moderate age (Chapter 15). They lie off the coast of Ecuador. Cocos Island, between the Galápagos and Costa Rica, is a moist oceanic island, probably of about the same age as the Galápagos; the Darwin's finches are represented on Cocos by an endemic genus, *Pinaroloxias.* Clipperton, about halfway between the Galápagos and the Revillagigedo Islands, is a low, dry, tropical island. The vast bulk of studies on the Galápagos, Cocos, and Clipperton have been published by the California Academy of Sciences, although contributions are now appearing all over the world.

Revillagigedo Islands. These are oceanic islands near Mexico, probably relatively recent, with close affinities to the Mexican flora and fauna, but with one Pacific element: *Tornatellides* (12–3). Some examples of their fauna can be seen in 14–1. Scientific papers published by the California Academy of Sciences cover biological aspects of these islands.

WEST INDIES (3–20)

Formerly thought to be continental islands, the larger islands (Greater Antilles) are now confidently viewed as oceanic. Cuba, Hispaniola, Jamaica, and Puerto Rico are at once the largest and the oldest of the islands. They are composed of complex volcanic rocks and marine limestone and might, to some extent, have been interconnected in the past. Although they are close to Yucatan, Florida, and Honduras, there has evidently been no connection with these lands, at least when the islands were being populated by plants and animals living there today. The Greater Antilles demonstrate their oceanic nature in the random way in which establishments have been made. The relict insectivore *Solenodon* (12–11) is on Cuba and Hispaniola, but not on the other two. A fossil monkey and an octodont rodent are on Jamaica. On Cuba exclusively are an atelopodid frog, a xantusiid lizard, and an amphisbaenid reptile, *Cadea*, as well as a relict plant, the cycad *Microcycas*. Puerto Rico has an endemic rodent genus. Thus, there has been no single port of entry into the West Indies, and chance has operated, as it must on oceanic islands. With the exception of Trinidad, which was once connected with adjacent Venezuela, the Lesser Antilles are oceanic. Both North American and South American elements have mixed in the West Indies, and although there is an endemic family of birds, Todidae, there are no indications of truly great antiquity for the West Indies. Interesting giant birds from Cuba are discussed in Chapter 9. The kinds of vertebrates represented in the West Indies are present in proportion to their ability to travel, as are the plants. A well-documented work on the zoogeography of this area was offered by Barbour, another by Simpson. Most of the work on animals of the West Indies has been done at, and is published by, the Museum of Comparative Zoology at Harvard University and The American Museum of Natural History in New York.

MEDITERRANEAN

The Mediterranean has had a varied geological history. Although there are some oceanic volcanic islands, such as Pantelleria and the Lipari (Aeolian) Islands, most Mediterranean islands are continental. The Balearic Islands were connected with the Iberian Peninsula as recently as the Pliocene, and Corsica, Sardinia, and Italy were interconnected in the Pleistocene. Because of the recentness of most islands, they contain few relicts. An exception is the syncarid shrimp *Parabathynella fagei* on the Balearic Islands. An appreciable number of endemic plant species and subspecies have developed on Mediterranean islands. The development of distinct species and races on these islands and on islets near them has provided a number of interesting studies, such as those on the wall lizard *Lacerta* (Chapter 7) or on land shells (*Helix, Helicella,* etc.). Admirable summaries of Mediterranean island life have been provided by Colom for the Balearics and by Allorge and collaborators for Corsica.

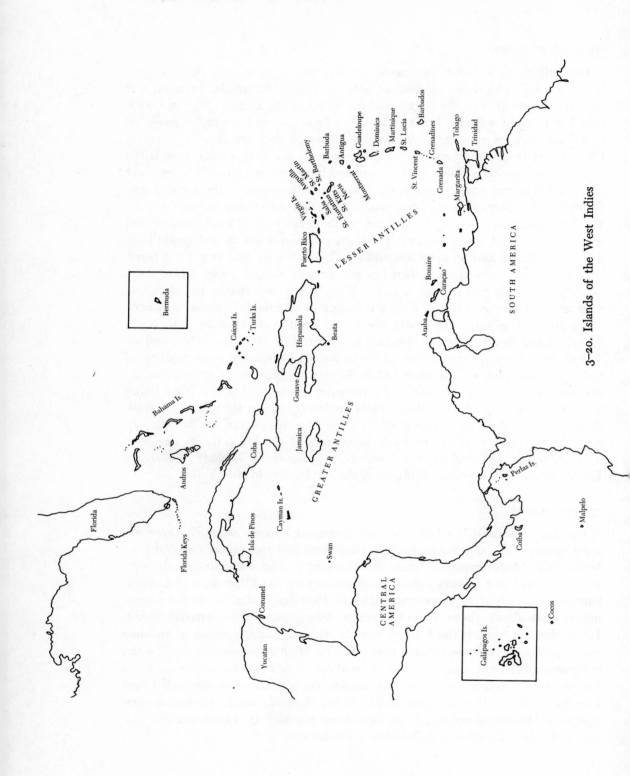

Florida

Florida Keys

Bahama Is.

Andros

Cuba

Isla de Pinos

Cayman Is.

Swan

Yucatan

Cozumel

CENTRAL
AMERICA

Coiba

Cocos

Malpelo

Perlas Is.

GREATER ANTILLES

Jamaica

Gonave

Hispaniola

Beata

Caicos Is.

Turks Is.

Bermuda

Puerto Rico

Virgin Is.

Anguilla

St. Martin

St. Barthelemy

Saba

St. Eustatius

St. Kitts

Nevis

Montserrat

LESSER ANTILLES

Barbuda

Antigua

Guadeloupe

Dominica

Martinique

St. Lucia

Barbados

St. Vincent

Grenadines

Grenada

Margarita

Bonaire

Curaçao

Aruba

SOUTH AMERICA

Tobago

Trinidad

Galápagos Is.

3–20. Islands of the West Indies

ATLANTIC OCEAN (3–21)

Newfoundland, Greenland, and Iceland. The biological patterns of these islands are very much affected by the fact that they were almost completely glaciated in the Pleistocene, erasing their life. Large mammals rather than small are present, probably because they were able to walk over solid ice connections from arctic North America. No strictly fresh water fishes are present on these islands, nor are reptiles or amphibians. Birds and plants are relatively recent immigrants via long-distance dispersal.

British Isles. The British Isles are located on a continental shelf, less than one hundred fathoms below sea level. During the Pleistocene, much or all of this was above water. The very low level of endemism in the British Isles, the presence of primary-division fresh water fishes, large continental mammals, and conifers testify to the fact that the British Isles are recent and continental. Great Britain was separated from the mainland only about seven thousand years ago, Ireland somewhat earlier. The British Isles, therefore, offer few island characteristics.

Bermuda. A truly oceanic island, but formerly of slightly greater extent. As might be expected, mammals, frogs and snakes are absent, but one lizard is present. Among plants, only a juniper represents the conifers, but actually junipers are unlike other conifers in having berry-like cones which can be bird-distributed.

Azores, Cape Verde Islands, Canary Islands. These are oceanic islands, still rather active volcanically in some cases. "Continental" rocks have been reported from the Azores (granite, gneiss, Miocene limestone, rhyolite), the Cape Verde Islands (syenite, quartzite, granite, diorite, andesite, Jurassic and Cretaceous vertically dipping limestones), and the Canary Islands (diorite, schist, rhyolite, syenite, gabbro, and Cretaceous limestone). The level of endemism is rather low except on the Canaries, which have a richer flora perhaps because of their proximity to the mainland. The palm and the pine on the Canaries probably arrived by overwater dispersal, just as did a palm and a pine on oceanic Guadalupe Island in the Pacific Ocean. The flora of the Canary Islands and the presence of a tortoise there in the Pleistocene suggest somewhat greater age than that of the other island groups, but proximity to the mainland is inextricably involved. Some interesting Canary plants, *Aeonium* and *Sonchus,* are discussed in Chapter 8. Geography, geology, zoology and botany of the Cape Verde, Azores, Madeira, and Canary Islands have been described in an interesting collection of papers by Allorge and collaborators.

St. Helena. This remote island is oceanic and volcanic, but its interesting flora suggests time has been available. Some of the curious tree-composites are discussed in Chapter 8. A fine account of the natural history of the island was offered by Melliss in a book difficult to find but worth the trouble.

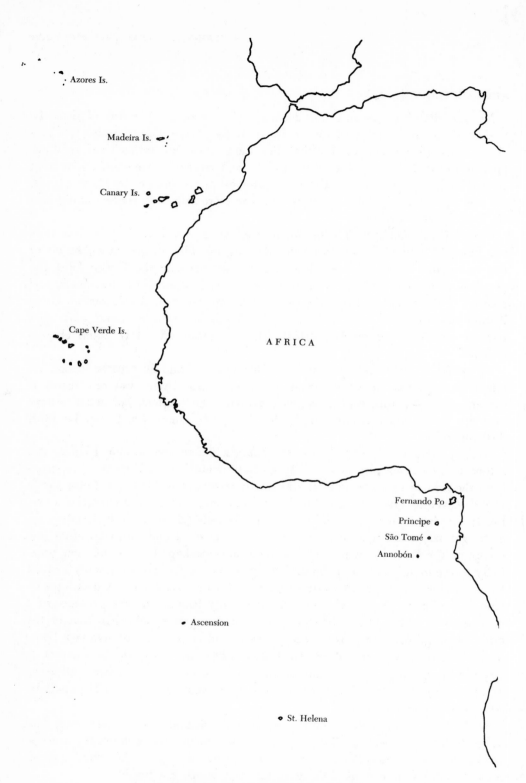

3–21. Islands of the Atlantic Ocean

Gulf of Guinea islands. These oceanic volcanic islands (Fernando Po, S. Tomé Annobon, Principe) offer few surprises on account of their proximity to the African mainland. Much interesting information, however, has been offered by Exell and by Amadon.

Ascension Island, Gough Island, and the Tristan da Cunha group. These are small oceanic volcanic islands of the South Atlantic; their plants and animals do not suggest great age. However, "continental" rocks on Tristan da Cunha include augite andesite and hornblende andesite; on Ascension, granite, gabbro, syenite, and granite-jasper conglomerate have been found. Animals from these islands are discussed in Chapter 9. The Norwegian Expedition to Tristan da Cunha, 1937–38, resulted in many papers on the natural history of those islands, and Gough Island was examined by a Norwegian Antarctic Expedition.

Tierra del Fuego and the Falkland Islands. Large animals, such as a llama and a fox, suggest continental nature for Tierra del Fuego, although primary-division fresh water fishes are absent there. The Falkland Islands lie on the continental shelf of South America, and the presence of an endemic fox in the Falklands suggests continental origin, but why should only a fox and no other larger mammals have crossed to the Falklands? The plant life of Tierra del Fuego and the Falklands suggests nothing which would not be expected for oceanic islands in this latitude.

ANTARCTICA AND ADJACENT ISLANDS (3–22)

Antarctica may deserve to be called a continent on the basis of size, but its flora and fauna are merely those of a very cold island. Biogeographers note the presence of coal, the *Glossopteris* flora of the Permian, and the presence of more recent plant and animal fossils, and have often speculated on whether or to what degree Antarctica was a major bridge leading to New Zealand, Australia, or South Africa. There is, at present, no unanimity of opinion on this point, but the extent of Antarctica must have been greater than it is now. One can safely say that floras and faunas now pushed farther north once existed here, and thus they must have to some extent aided dispersal. This also applies to Macquarie, the Kerguelens, Amsterdam, and St. Paul, which have suffered glaciation. That these islands were formerly of greater extent is indicated by "continental" rocks on South Georgia (quartz-diorite, granite, gabbro, peridotite, schist, quartzite, slates, Mesozoic shales, tuffs), the South Orkneys (graywacke, slate, quartzite, arkosic conglomerate, altered diabase, spelite), the South Shetlands (schists, gneiss, andesites, diorites, phyllites), the Crozet Islands (granite, mica-schist, trachyandesite, crystalline limestone), the Kerguelens (rhyolite, syenite, monzonite, diorite, aplite), St. Paul (rhyolite, rhyolite tuff), and Macquarie (granite, hornfels, sandstone and marble, the latter possibly transported there by ice sheets). The interesting plant forms of these islands (see Chapter 8), discussed in Hooker's *Flora Antarctica,* indicate that whatever their preglacial history may have been, these islands now bear the flora of oceanic islands. Penguins form a conspicuous element on these islands, and are discussed in Chapter 9. Interest in Antarctica

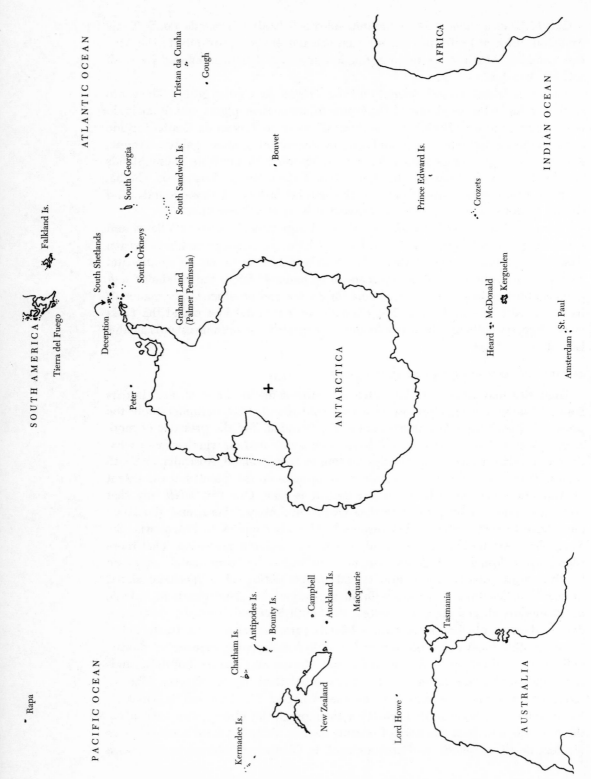

3-22. Islands of the Antarctic region

3–23. Islands of the Indian Ocean

and adjacent areas has increased in recent years, virtually every major nation has sent one or more expeditions there in past decades, and the accounts of antarctic natural history are scattered through many volumes.

INDIAN OCEAN (3–23)

Ceylon. Ceylon is clearly a continental island, connected to the Indian mainland until late in the Pleistocene. As might be expected, it has primary-division fresh water fishes and many large mammals, but a few which might be expected are absent. Jackals, chevrotains, sloth-bears, leopards, and elephants are present, but wolves, wild dogs, tigers, certain bovids, and rhinoceroses are absent. Known from Ceylon in fossil form are giraffes, rhinoceroses, a hippopotamus, lions, and elephants, so one may assume that these species died out because the large areas in which they succeed best were not present after Ceylon became separated. Ceylon's flora contains few surprises compared with that of mainland India, and apparently Ceylon has not functioned as a relict area for plants or animals to any appreciable extent.

Cocos (Keeling) and Christmas Islands. These are two small oceanic islands with depauperate floras and faunas. A good natural history of Christmas Island, edited by Andrews, was published by the British Museum.

Seychelles Islands; Aldabra; Socotra; Maldives. The Seychelles seem to be oceanic, but a formerly greater extent is suggested by the fact that they have "continental" rocks, such as granite, syenite, slate, and hornfels. Perhaps smaller gaps of water once separated them from the mainland. The flora is unusually rich in palms, including the famous coco-de-mer *Lodoicea* (Chapter 9). An endemic family, Medusagynaceae, might be related to the rose family (Chapter 13). Primary-division fresh water fishes and conifers are lacking. However, among amphibians, such poor dispersers as caecilians and frogs are present. An extinct tortoise is known from the Seychelles, and lizards and snakes occur, but mammals are absent. Endemism among birds is high. Aldabra is famous for its giant tortoise (Chapter 7), while Socotra features the remarkable plant *Dendrosicyos socotrana* (8–14).

Mascarene Islands. The three small islands, Mauritius, Reunion (Bourbon) and Rodriguez are volcanic oceanic islands, favored by a moist climate. The presence of a "continental" rock, clay-slate, on Mauritius suggests a greater surface and height earlier in the history of this island. The fauna of these islands includes recently extinct tortoises, two endemic genera of snakes (Mauritius only), geckos, and—significantly—curious birds, including many flightless ones (Chapter 9).

Madagascar and the Comoro Islands. Near Madagascar, the Comoro Islands have inherited some Madagascar plants and animals, and offer such similarity that they may be considered part of Madagascar's biotic province. The Comoro Islands have "continental" rocks such as schist, granite, grano-diorite, monzonite, and andesite. Madagascar is perhaps the most interesting single island in the world, and deserves a chapter all by itself—Chapter 16.

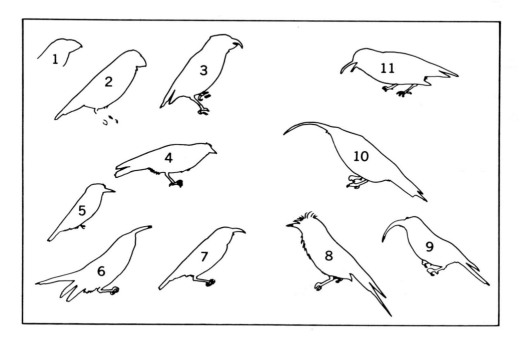

PLATE I   The Hawaiian honeycreepers, Drepanididae, have diversified both in appearance and food sources:

1. ou
Psittacirostra cantans (head only) with puncture weed (*Tribulus*) fruit

2. ou
Psittacirostra kona on flowering *Myoporum sandwichense*

3. koa finch
Pseudonestor xanthophrys with beetle on koa twig

4. ual-ai-hawane
Ciridops anna with fruits of *Pritchardia* palm

5. apapane
Himatione sanguinea

6. iiwi
Vestiaria coccinea with flowers of ohia (*Metrosideros polymorpha*)

7. amakihi
Loxops virens

8. crested honeyeater
Palmeria dolei

9. mamo
Drepanidis funerea with *Clermontia* flowers

10. akialoa
Hemignathus procerus with tubular flowers

11. nukupuu
Hemignathus wilsoni using bill to find insects on bark

Charles S. Papo
1962

PLATE II   A selection of New Guinea's birds of paradise reveals the bewildering way in which every part of the body is converted to an arresting display for the purpose of attracting females. All birds shown here are males. Female birds of paradise tend to resemble the males in size and form, but are dull brown, buff, or black, and lack spectacular plumes.

1. MacGregor's bird of paradise
Macgregoria pulchra

2. lesser superb bird of paradise
Lophorina superba minor

3. six-plumed bird of paradise
Parotia lawesii

4. greater sickle-bill
Epimachus fastuosus

5. ribbon-tailed bird of paradise
Astrapia mayeri

6. twelve-wired bird of paradise
Seleucidis melanoleucus

7. magnificent bird of paradise
Diphyllodes magnificus

8. king bird of paradise
Cicinnurus regius

9. greater bird of paradise
Paradisea apoda

10. enameled bird
Pteridophora alberti

PLATE III Darwin's Finches (Fringillidae, subfamily Geospizinae) have become classi-cal examples in the lexicon of evolutionary processes. They illustrate a variety of phenom-ena: adaptive radiation, formation of races and species, variability within species, endem-ism, change in ecological preference. Shown here are all the species, together with some of their food sources (males only, except for *Geospiza magnirostris*).

1. tool-using finch
Cactospiza pallida

2. mangrove finch
Cactospiza heliobates

3. vegetarian tree finch
Platyspiza crassirostris

4. large cactus ground finch
Geospiza conirostris

5. cactus ground finch
Geospiza scandens

insecpivtorous tree finches:
6. small:
Camarhynchus parvulus
7. medium:
Camarhynchus pauper
8. large:
Camarhynchus psittacula

9, 10. large ground finch
Geospiza magnirostris (9, 10)

11. medium ground finch
Geospiza fortis

12. small ground finch
Geospiza fuliginosa

13. sharp-beaked ground finch
Geospiza difficilis

14. warbler finch
Certhidea olivacea

15. Cocos Island finch
Pinaroloxias inornata

Charles S. Papp
1962

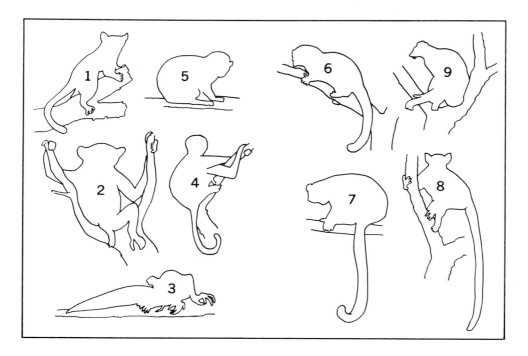

PLATE IV   Spread over several continents in past ages, lemurs are now restricted to Madagascar. Their structure and habits are those of primitive primates, well down the evolutionary tree which leads to the anthropoids.

1. mouse lemur
Microcebus murinus

2. woolly avahi
Avahi laniger

3. aye-aye
Daubentonia madagascariensis

4. sifaka
Propithecus verreauxi

5. mongoose lemur
Lemur mungoz

6. dwarf lemur
Cheirogaleus major

7. ruffed lemur
Lemur variegata

8. ring-tailed lemur
Lemur catta

9. indri
Indri indri

Charles S. Papp, 1962.

PLATE V   To the roster of flightless island birds Madagascar contributes *Mesoenas benschi*, a member of the endemic family of rail-relatives Mesoenatidae. (From Milne-Edwards and Grandidier.)

PLATE VI   Wattles around the eyes help identify these birds as *Philepitta schlegeli* of the endemic Madagascar bird family Philepittidae. (From Milne-Edwards and Grandidier.)

PLATE VII   Although its classification was in doubt for many years, sickle-billed *Neo-drepanis coruscans* now seems to be a member of Philepittidae. (From Milne-Edwards and Grandidier.)

4 A Filter in Reverse

DISPERSAL to an oceanic island is like a filter, narrowing down to a handful of species those which arrive and establish. Somehow, this process must be reversed in order to achieve the diverse and novel biological productions living today on remote islands. The mechanism is, of course, evolution. The remainder of this book is, with my apologies, a rather curious book on evolution. Curious because only island patterns have been selected for presentation, although references to continents do inevitably creep in. Islands, it is true, do present a sort of microcosm of the entire picture of evolution in many ways, and the basic genetic processes are the same despite the fact that results often quite different from those on continents do occur. To the reader who wishes to obtain a more complete picture of evolution as a whole, I can only recommend a comprehensive book, such as Simpson's *The Major Features of Evolution* or Grant's *The Origin of Adaptations*.

The starting point for the origin of island species and then, ultimately, genera, is a varied population of interbreeding individuals. Natural populations are just as varied as human populations. There is a certain irony in this: if an island population begins with a single immigrant, how can it foster a varied group of offspring? One answer, which neatly skirts this question, is that island populations don't always begin with a single immigrant. A pair capable of mating would be the minimum for all but a few animals. In the process of dispersal, odds would be that arrival of a pair would be rare—a single individual or a small flock would be more likely. Thus, a small flock might be the initial colony. A female carrying several eggs or young (gravid female) is often mentioned as a quite acceptable substitute for a pair capable of mating, although the chances for arrival of a potential mother in safe condition are admittedly somewhat limited.

If only a single immigrant begins a population, deriving a highly varied population might seem difficult. A single fern spore or a single plant seed can initiate a colony, and one might think that a uniform progeny might result. Not so, says genetics, for reasons which are apparent if we remember that an individual has not one, but two sets of chromosomes, and thus two sets of genes which are likely to differ in many features. When these are scattered by chance through the offspring, even though a single plant is self-fertilized, differing individuals will result. A classical example from Mendel of a self-pollinated pink-flowered pea yielding both white-flowered and red-flowered offspring will suffice to show this. Nevertheless, the variability within a single individual without augmentation is probably not sufficient. But as generations produce more individuals, each has a certain chance of producing mutations and collectively, the fund of mutations can become quite large. No organism is free from mutation for very long. Although most mutations are unfavorable, only a small number of favorable mutations may permit a species to enter new areas or survive as an old area changes. If two island species can hybridize with each other now and then, they will both become more variable, and, because of this variability, better able to adapt and survive. This appears to have happened repeatedly in forest plants of New Zealand.

As Darwin noted, a wild species is anything but uniform. The fact that so many breeds of cats or kinds of chrysanthemums can be extracted from a single species (admittedly with the aid of hybridization in some cases) testifies to this. Island species are no exception. This can be easily seen in a land snail from the Pacific, *Partula*. This Polynesian genus, famous among biologists for its examples of variability and evolution, can be collected in large numbers within a limited region, so a good idea of the variability of a species can be gained at a glance. Such a collection of a Samoan *Partula* has a range from white to dark brown (4–1). This species, *P. actor,* has chalky flecks on the shell. Some shells have a greater number or density of flecks than others, but variation in this respect is not as pronounced as the grades from translucent white to deep chocolate. Other examples of gradation can be seen in species of *Partula* from the Society Islands (4–2). *Partula rosea,* from Huahine, can vary from white to brownish-purple. Intermediates show a white spiral, varying from wide to narrow. *Partula lutea,* from Bora-Bora, consists of both yellowish and brown shells—showing that in some species there are relatively sharp differences among individuals. Sharp differences usually result from a very small number of genes which differ within a species, whereas grades indicate that a large number of genes control inheritance in these features. The *Partula taeniata* population from Moorea in 4–3 shows that several characteristics can vary independently. The shells of this population grade from white to dark brown, and also differ from one another in presence and degree of striping (spiral), striations (fine vertical lines), and size.

A clue to the variability of island species and why, despite the limited number of immigrants, species can become quite diverse and give rise to new species, is suggested by the "weedy" nature of many immigrants. "Weedy" plants or animals—those which mutate and change rapidly in an evolutionary sense—also seem often to have the best dispersal mechanisms. Certainly an immigrant unable to change would not adapt rapidly to a new environment, and such a species might be extinguished in only a few generations after arrival. The butterflies on Canton Island mentioned in Chapter 2 probably became extinct, but they might have been able to survive if they could have adapted rapidly to plants which grow well on Canton even in dry years. Thus, organisms with a high mutation rate would be favored on islands, and might be said to be favored by natural selection. Also, plants and animals which do not have specific preferences

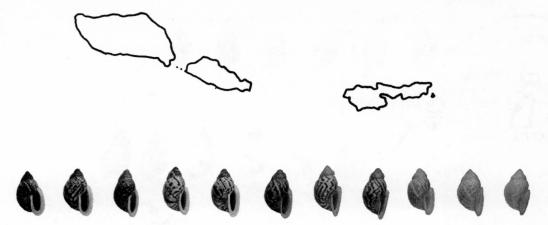

4-1. Individuals of the Samoan land snail *Partula actor* are of various shades from white to dark brown. Indicated above are the Samoan islands Savaii, Upolu, Tutuila.

regardless of how variable they are would be better as island pioneers than those which are accustomed only to a rather precise set of conditions. In other words, crabgrass or dandelions would be better immigrants than lilies or edelweiss.

The many grades, sorts, and variants to be found within a species, such as one of the Partulas, serve as the raw material for evolution. From Moorea's *Partula taeniata,* a striped-shelled species, a white-shelled species, and a brown-shelled species might be developed out of the various sorts which now coexist and interbreed. Small-shelled and large-shelled species might also be derived from such an assemblage. The Darwinian explanation, by which natural selection sorts out minor changes until the end products differ markedly from the beginnings, does play the major role, but where small populations occur—as they often do on islands—another phenomenon may perform remarkable alterations. This phenomenon—often called "drift"—is the tendency for one of two expressions of a feature which coexist in a population to increase in frequency merely by chance, finally shutting out the second feature, which is thus lost. This "all-or-nothing-at-all" process works best in small populations because if a large number of individuals composed a population, wiping out one of the alternative expressions would be difficult (unless one were better adapted, in which case natural selection would be operating). If brown-shelled and white-shelled Partulas were present in equal numbers in a large population, brown might, by chance, increase over white, but white would keep turning up repeatedly, generation after generation. In a small population of, say, twenty-five snails, brown might "shut out" white "accidentally."

Moreover, the immigrants which reach an island usually do not contain all the features which can be found within their species. The nature of these

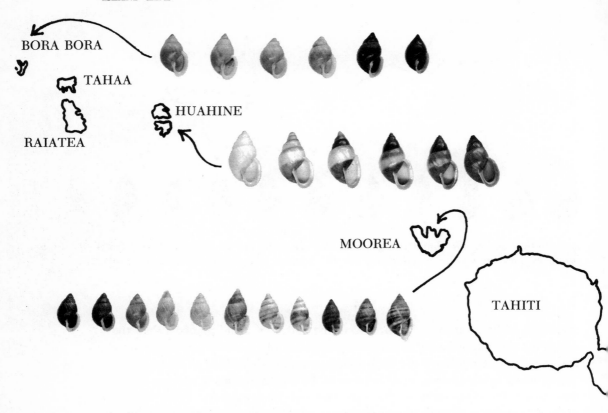

4–2. Species of *Partula* from the Society Islands not only differ from each other, they each contain grades in color, pattern, size, and shape. Shown here are *Partula lutea* from Bora Bora, *P. rosea* from Huahine, and *P. taeniata* from Moorea.

individuals and the ways in which they differ from individuals left behind on the mainland, combined with the action of drift, will determine the nature of an island population. Studies on mice accidentally introduced onto islands in various parts of the world (Block Island, near Rhode Island; Skokholm, near Wales) show how these factors operate.

"Drift" may explain an interesting feature seen in another species of *Partula*, *P. suturalis* (4–4), which occupies the valleys of the richly sculptured island of Moorea (4–3). Two subspecies of *P. suturalis* exist. The eastern subspecies, *strigosa*, has remained the same for many years, but the western, *vexillum*, changed considerably in the years between two observations (1907 and 1919)— an unusual occurrence in such a short space of time. *Partula suturalis vexillum* formerly consisted of colonies containing both dextral and sinistral shells, as well as some colonies of dextral shells only. In the process of extending its range,

4–3. The elaborately sculptured landscape and favorable climate of Moorea have provided a fertile field for evolution of the land snail *Partula*. Bora Bora, below, offers less opportunity; a single mountain, it lacks the ridges and valleys which provide isolation, the key to species-making.

some colonies which are pure sinistral have been formed. Left-handed and right-handed shells are probably about equal in survival value, so the tendency for sinistral shells to develop exclusive colonies is probably due to "drift." The same is true of the formation of pure dextral colonies from ancestors which consisted of a mixture of the two types. Some *Partula* species other than those under consideration are entirely dextral, some entirely sinistral, and "drift" may have played a part in the development of these.

This same species (4–4) is interesting because the western subspecies has increased its range, while the eastern has remained within the same confines to which it had been limited earlier. We will probably never know why this particular situation has happened, but observational and experimental evidence in other species in other groups of plants and animals suggests how such cases have, in general, happened. The explanation is a combination of mutations and natural selection. Mutations have occurred in both subspecies, but evidently *vexillum* has mutations favored by natural selection which permit it to migrate into, and compete within, valleys formerly occupied only by other species of *Partula*.

Thus "drift" may stabilize changes when new populations are small and isolated, but as individuals become numerous, natural selection is the major factor. Darwin hypothesized that only minor changes—like the grades of *Partula actor* in 4–1—were always the raw material of evolution. Today, evolutionists

4–4. *Partula suturalis*, endemic to Moorea, has shown change within historical time. When reported by Garratt in 1884, the two subspecies were confined within the areas on the south part of the island. Crampton's 1932 study shows that the subspecies *strigosa* had stayed the same, but *vexillum* had spread. Although originally composed of mixed dextral (D, right-handed spiral) and sinistral (S, left-handed spiral) colonies or all-dextral shells and colonies of all-sinistral shells have developed during the spread of *vexillum*.

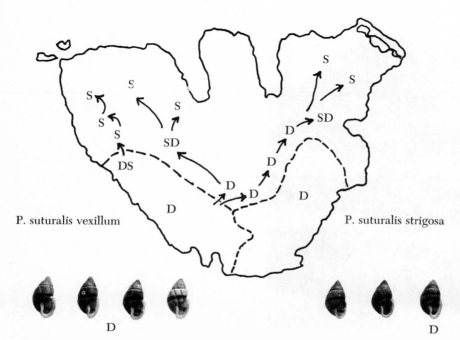

P. suturalis vexillum

P. suturalis strigosa

S

D

D

believe that both minor changes, such as color and pattern of fur, and major changes, such as the switch from a carnivorous to a herbivorous diet, may be favored by natural selection, although only an extremely small number of changes can pass through the scrupulous screening which natural selection always provides. Most biologists believe that most genes have some selective value, some prominently so, and very few genes are "neutral." In other words, some changes are strongly favored by natural selection, some strongly and quickly rejected, some only slightly favored, some slightly rejected, and a few go unchallenged by natural selection. If a gene is only slightly advantageous, it will not change in frequency very much in a population of a hundred individuals which have it because of natural selection, but drift may shift the frequency. In a population of many individuals, the effect of natural selection on such a gene may be marked over a number of generations.

Not all genes have a single effect. A gene which controls the color of a shell might also control whether the pattern is striped or solid. Thus, establishment of a particular gene in a population might bring with it several changes.

We can see changes in color, pattern, shape, and size in the *Partula* shells, but we cannot see that physiology may also differ from individual to individual. Ability to use new species of plants for food, ability to live in drier or wetter conditions, ability to reproduce in a shorter period of time, ability to withstand dry periods better are among the many features which might be expected to vary the same way as visible differences do.

Admitting that a population can become "preadapted" to a new environment, how can it change and become different from the population it left? The paleontologist G. G. Simpson tells us that a species can occupy an "adaptive peak" and that it also, when it is capable of doing so by virtue of mutations, can cross a "valley" to a new and different "peak." Perhaps the changes of *P. suturalis vexillum* within historical time might represent just such attempts to reach new "adaptive peaks." A *Partula* might, hypothetically, change from one food plant to another, with intermediate stages in which the species fed on both.

But a species will always stay just a single, though diverse, species unless by means of some process, the part of the population which has been pushed into a new environment becomes cut off from individuals which remain in the old environment. Isolation is thus all-important, and biologists believe that evolution of new species without isolation is virtually impossible. For example, although Moorea, Tahiti, Raiatea, Tahaa, and Huahine (4–2) each have several or many species of *Partula, P. lutea* is the only one which lives on Bora-Bora. Bora-Bora (4–3) is a small island, and perhaps *P. lutea* could never split into two distinct species because populations could never become permanently isolated from each other on such a small island where topography provides no strong barriers.

Fortunately, there are many sorts of isolation. The island itself is the ideal model of isolation. Groups of islands, such as the Society Islands, combine isolation of each island with the possibilities for infrequent dispersal to neighboring islands. This explains why almost none of the species of *Partula* on the Society Islands occurs on more than one island. Not as drastic a barrier as sea water but still remarkably effective is the contrast in topography and climate between deep moist valleys and high, exposed ridges. That these valleys are isolated pockets is shown by *Partula*, where each species occupies a certain valley or group of valleys, but very few species occupy all the valleys on an island. Geographical isolation has played a major role on islands, and may help to explain why so many new species have developed on pieces of ground which, though small compared with the world's bigger islands, have sufficient barriers, such as ridges, rivers, and valleys, to promote effective separation of neighboring populations.

There are other sorts of isolation, and a list may suggest how effective isolation really can be. For example, in plants isolation is provided by adaptation to certain soil types, for different soil types are often "islands." On volcanic islands, a lava flow which forks, leaving islands of untouched vegetation, has created isolation for plants unable to grow on new lava. The continuous lava flows involved in building of the Hawaiian Islands may have created isolation time and time again, and may help to explain the thousands of species which have originated on those islands. On an island where so many and such violent geological events have provided a succession of isolation-producing happenings, especially rapid evolution is likely to result. Indeed, the large number of species which have been produced on volcanic islands may well owe their origin, ironical as it seems, to volcanic devastation.

Highly significant is reproductive isolation: the inability of individuals from two species or incipient species to interbreed. A recent study of *Partula taeniata* on Moorea has shown that reproductive isolation is involved in the origin of distinctive populations. If a population is invading a valley, it would be most successful as a new group if individuals did not interbreed with populations already resident in that valley. Development of barriers to interbreeding may well have had considerable significance in the origin of the many species and races of *Partula*.

In plants, different pollinating agents can keep two species from mingling. A hybrid often cannot be pollinated by an insect which easily negotiates flowers of one of the parent plants. Thus, the hybrid does not form seed, and hybrids vanish without leaving offspring. In animals, strong territorial instincts—the instinct to occupy particular plots and fend off intruders—promotes isolation. The list of types of isolation could be extended much more.

Aiding isolation is a certain amount of extinction. The organism which moves from one "adaptive peak". to a new "adaptive peak" often suffers extinction of forms in the "valley." Conditions of the "valley" may change, so that it can no longer live there. If a *Partula* were evolving from scrubby woodland near the shore up through moist forest to alpine grassland, burning of the forest would extinguish individuals and isolate those on the alpine grasslands from those near the shore.

Once a population becomes isolated, not only will it continue to change, but its parent population will also, in most cases, continue to change. Just as two cars each traveling at the rate of fifty miles per hour in opposite directions are actually leaving each other at the rate of one hundred miles per hour, so species, on the whole, tend to diverge from each other (see 15–19 for a clear example).

The species of *Partula* may not seem to comprise a very amazing example of evolution. They are of interest not for their end-products, but because they show the opening stages of evolution. *Partula* attracted biologists because in the sheltered environments of islands results of evolutionary experiments can be observed better than in mainland areas, where situations are often much more complex and confusing. To show later stages in evolution, island plants are also superior to those on continents, and the next two chapters show examples which have proceeded far beyond the stages *Partula* has achieved.

5 The Adaptive Approach

WHEN the descendants of an island immigrant fan out into new ways of life—some occupying moist forests, some bare lava—they are undergoing a process called adaptive radiation. Radiation into new habitats is progressive, and although the beginnings may be almost imperceptible, the gradual accumulation of small changes can yield many distinctive products. Good examples are shown by the tarweeds, a group belonging to the sunflower family (Compositae). Tarweeds, named for their resinous hairs, occur in western North America (mostly within California) and in the Hawaiian Islands—a good example of long-distance dispersal. Tarweeds may have achieved this leap by virtue of the fact that each tiny fruit at the periphery of a flower head is enfolded by a sticky leaf-like structure (bract), which may become attached to the feathers of birds.

Of these tarweeds, there is a group of species, forming the section called *Fruticosae* of the genus *Hemizonia,* which are shrubs almost entirely restricted to islands off California and Mexico (5–1). Perhaps the mainland relatives have mostly become extinct, for now *Hemizonia minthornii* is the only one which now occurs there, and it is restricted to a small area around Santa Susanna Pass. *Hemizonia greeneana* has been collected once on the coast of Baja California—perhaps a chance occurrence, or a vestige.

Because of their perennial habit, the shrubby Hemizonias are ideally suited to living on islands. Most mainland tarweeds are annuals, drying up in late summer after they flower; their annual cycle is closely adjusted to more sharply marked seasons. On the islands, however, the growing season is longer; temperatures are more even throughout the year—cooler in summer, warmer in winter than on the mainland. Island tarweeds can be found in flower in any month of the year. The shrubby habit is ideal, because a few flowers can be formed at any time, taking advantage of the long growing season. Early in the evolution of Hemizonias, there was probably adaptive radiation into various environments, and today's island Hemizonias represent one arm of that radiation. Taking the shrubby Hemizonias by themselves, however, we can see that from a basic form, they have begun to evolve separately on each island, adapting to particular island environments.

The one left on the mainland, *H. minthornii,* has the smallest leaves. Its tiny needle-like leaves, covered with resin, are ideally suited for enduring the hot, dry mainland summers. The smaller surface, varnished with resin, minimizes loss of water from the plant. That the leaves of *H. minthornii* have adapted

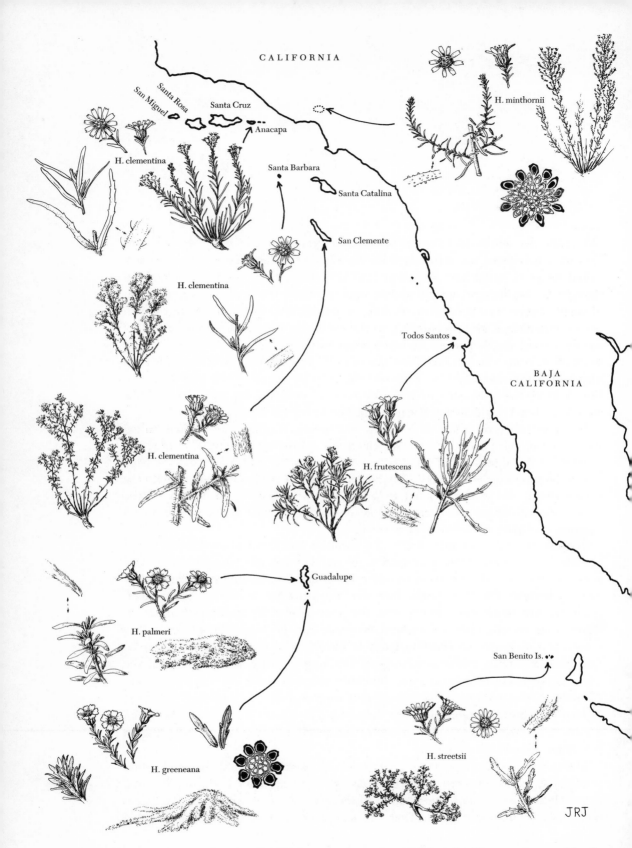

5–1. A genus of tarweeds, *Hemizonia*, is represented by shrubby species on islands off California and adjacent Mexico. Although not markedly in contrast with each other, the species show many interesting distinctions which mark the beginnings of adaptive divergence. For each population illustrated, habit, leaves, and a head of flowers is shown.

116

to California's mainland conditions seems certain, but the flower heads (seen in section, below, in the group of drawings of this species) still retain a primitive structure. The southern island species—*H. frutescens, H. streetsii, H. greeneana,* and *H. palmeri*—have a much more specialized flower head structure (section among drawings of *H. greeneana*). *Hemizonia clementina* has heads which are intermediate between these two conditions.

Hemizonia clementina seems an unstable species which may be reaching for new forms. Plants of this species from three islands (illustrated in 5–1) differ from one another in certain ways. The Anacapa Island plant has long toothed leaves with both long and short hairs; the Santa Barbara Island plant has medium-sized leaves with very short hairs only; the San Clemente Island plant's leaves are shorter and covered with numerous felty hairs.

Hemizonia clementina has a habit suited to the climate of the northern islands: a woody rootstock, which gives rise to slender stems. These stems can last for a season, die back to the subterranean rootstocks when dry weather forces cessation of growth, but new stems can form whenever the return of moister conditions permit. On these northern islands, spring fogs may offer an opportunity for flowering denied to mainland tarweeds.

The Guadalupe Island species, *H. palmeri* and *H. greeneana,* are very unusual among tarweeds in their growth form. *Hemizonia palmeri* scrambles among lava boulders, forming a small shrub. Its leaves are covered with a thick silvery felt. This cover both reflects light and shades the leaf surface, preventing drying-up of the leaves. *Hemizonia greeneana* is an unusually shaped plant by any standards. It grows on gravelly volcanic cinder cones, and instead of having a spiky upright shape like most tarweeds, the branches bend downward, so that the plant has a mound-like or even cone-like appearance. Although the leaves are not green, not silvery or even hairy, they do have a "condensed" form by virtue of the fact that margins curl around to the lower surface. Leaves are coated by the resinous secretions of the plant. Thus, *H. greeneana* has adaptations for desiccation-resistance different from those of *H. palmeri,* but probably equal in effectiveness. The difference in habit between *H. clementina* and the Guadalupe Island species may be adaptations to the soils on the northern islands versus the loose lava and cinders of Guadalupe Island. The Guadalupe Island species are also distinctive in that the heads of flowers bear relatively few of the tongue-like ray flowers.

Hemizonia frutescens is a perennial, but a small perennial with slender branches quite unlike the thick branches of the Guadalupe Island species. Leaves of *H. frutescens* are very long, narrow, and hairy. The leaf shape of this species may be yet another adaptation for desiccation-resistance, for their form is very condensed. The various adaptations in leaves of Hemizonias look almost as though the island species were "casting about" for ways of avoiding the summer-crisped leaves of their mainland relatives. Flowers of *H. frutescens* are rather inconspicuous.

Hemizonia streetsii, on the San Benito Islands, has short, hairy, toothed leaves. This species forms the smallest plants among these island tarweeds—some are like annuals, flowering the first season, perhaps surviving to a second year, perhaps not. Thus, *H. streetsii* is adapted to dry conditions by growing as a perennial as long as water permits, or completing its life cycle in a short time if necessary. Rainfall is very irregular in the area off Baja California where the San Benito Islands are located.

Given longer periods of time, *Hemizonia clementina* might develop into different species on the islands where it occurs. With distance spacing these islands apart, isolation could aid this. However, even if this were to happen, the species might not look markedly different from one another because these islands have similar climates, and if adaptive radiation is occurring, highly distinctive end-products are probably impossible.

TARWEEDS GO HAWAIIAN

The island Hemizonias represent the beginnings of adaptive radiation, or they represent a case of adaptive radiation where, although distinctive species have resulted, their progress is limited by the distinctiveness of their habitats. All of the island Hemizonias grow not very far above sea level, all grow in relatively dry and open situations. If a group such as these island tarweeds were presented with a full range of habitats from very wet to very dry, sea level to alpine, bare lava to deep soil, what would happen? The Hawaiian tarweeds (5–3 to 5–6) have just that answer.

Also very important to the Hawaiian tarweeds is the fact that the number of other plants which "seek" to occupy the various habitats on these islands is not very great compared with the vast assemblage of continental plants, any of which might undergo similar adaptive radiation. Lacking competitors, the Hawaiian tarweeds have been able to "fulfill their destinies," to exhibit all their evolutionary "talent" virtually unopposed. Thus, there could be alpine tarweeds, forest tarweeds, etc., and this, in fact, has happened. The considerable size and topographical diversity offered by the six major islands of the Hawaiian chain (5–2) have provided an ideal site for this evolution.

From the immigrant of many centuries ago, an assemblage of species divided into three genera has developed: *Dubautia, Argyroxiphium,* and *Wilkesia.* The most widespread of these is *Dubautia,* which grows on all of the major islands. Some of these are small shrubs, growing in open situations like the tarweeds of the islands off California and Mexico. *Dubautia menziesii* (5–3) is one of the few plants which can withstand life on the bare cinders at the summit of Haleakala, Maui. Stiff black stems resist the tearing of winds. Leaves are few, stubby, and succulent; their small surface minimizes the drying effects of the alpine air, their thickness retains water. Only a small leaf surface needs to be exposed to the brilliant alpine sunshine, and the tight clusters of leaves suffice. Snow in

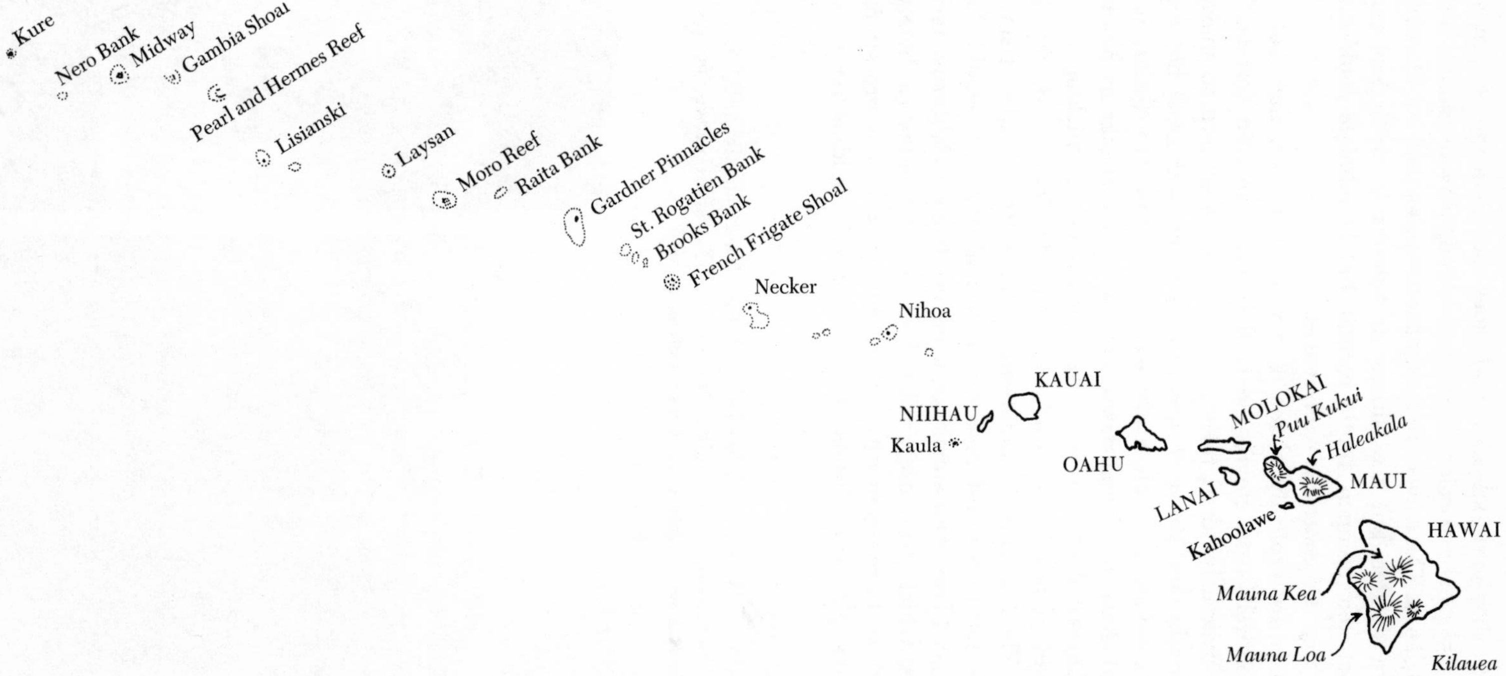

HAWAI

MAUI

MOLOKAI
Puu Kukui
Haleakala

Kahoolawe

Mauna Kea
Mauna Loa
Kilauea

LANAI

KAUAI

OAHU

NIIHAU
Kaula

Nihoa

Necker

French Frigate Shoal
Brooks Bank
St. Rogatien Bank
Gardner Pinnacles

Raita Bank

Moro Reef

Laysan

Lisianski

Pearl and Hermes Reef
Gambia Shoal

Lisianski

Midway
Nero Bank
Kure

5-2. The long Hawaiian chain is an exercise in vulcanism. As islands have been added to the eastern end of the chain in times past, many new situations have been opened for occupation by plants and animals.

winter at this ten thousand-foot elevation does not damage *D. menziesii*. *Dubautia ciliolata* (5–4) is a species of another island, Hawaii, where it favors bare lava around Kilauea. The leaves are not as succulent as those of *D. menziesii*, the stems are more slender, but the climate at Kilauea is much less extreme. The small leaves betoken the open, bright habitat, but *D. ciliolata* could not survive in the snows that *D. menziesii* experiences.

Although tarweeds are typically plants of dry, open places, they have been able to enter an entirely new environment: the Hawaiian rain forests. These forests, soaked by over a hundred inches of rain each year, are so moist that mosses coat tree trunks, and many shrubs can take root and grow not only on soil, but on tree branches. In such shady environs, a few Dubautias, such as *D. knudsenii* (5–4), form true small trees, and may have trunks as much as a foot in diameter. Leaves of these species are much larger, mimicking the large, often leathery leaves of other rain-forest trees. Broader leaves suit the diffuse light of the forest. The leaves of *D. knudsenii*, being leathery rather than membranous, suit the Kauai rain forest because occasional dry days would damage more delicate foliage. Forest Dubautias are a far cry from a California tarweed.

The silverswords, which are closely related to the Dubautias (a hybrid has been reported), belong to the genus *Argyroxiphium* (5–5). They are among the world's most unusual plants, evolutionary products one could never have pre-

5–3. On the high alpine slopes of Haleakala in the Hawaiian Islands, few plants can withstand the dryness, sun, and cold. One of the Hawaiian tarweeds, *Dubautia menziesii,* has succeeded in adapting to these extremes.

dicted by looking at their tarweed ancestors in California. Looking like a fantastic silvery yucca on the vermilion and purplish cinder cones of high Maui, the Mt. Haleakala silversword, *A. sandwichense,* is one of the few plants which can withstand the rigors of this inhospitable crater. Within the crater, bare lava or cinders are seared by alpine sunshine; the rainfall which drenches lower elevations is shut out by the crater walls; and at altitudes of nine thousand feet, extremes from heat to snow make for a punishing alpine regime. The Haleakala silversword has found ingenious answers to these problems.

Leaves of the silversword are covered with a mat of fiber glass-like hairs which, microscopically, are so formed that they act as mirrors, reflecting the excessive alpine sunshine. The name of the ancient Hawaiians for the silversword was *ahinahina,* the word for gray repeated twice—"extremely gray" (glass, mirrors, and silver were unknown to the ancient Hawaiians). In addition to the hairs, the leaves show other adaptations. They are thick and extremely condensed in form; if a leaf is broken open, a sort of jelly can be squeezed out. This substance, also found in the leaves of many Californian tarweeds, serves to retain water, a mechanism useful in the face of alpine aridity. The flowers of this plant are a deep maroon color, and the flower stalk has a stocky covering like the tarry secretions of the Californian tarweeds.

Curiously, the species most closely related to the Haleakala silversword is *Argyroxiphium caliginii,* which grows under diametrically opposite conditions. Atop Puu Kukui, the westernmost mountain on Maui (5–2), may be found the rosettes of *A. caliginii,* swathed in almost perpetual clouds and rain, seated in a bog. Puu Kukui is lower (5788 feet) than Haleakala (10,032 feet), and thus receives much more rainfall, because in the Hawaiian Islands clouds drop most of their moisture between 3000 and 6000 feet. The upper reaches of Puu Kukui

5–4. Extremes in leaf shape are illustrated by two species of *Dubautia.* At left is *D. ciliolata,* narrow-leaved shrubby inhabitant of dry lava fields. *Dubautia knudsenii,* right, is a broad-leaved tree found in rain forests.

5–5. The spectacular Hawaiian silverswords are rosette-forming tarweeds. The Haleakala silversword *Argyroxiphium sandwichense* (above right) is one of the wonders of the Hawaiian flora. On Maui's other mountain, Puu Kukui, grows the bog-loving silversword *A. caliginii* (left). Middle, the closely related greenswords: *A. grayanum* from Puu Kukui and *A. virescens* (bottom) from Haleakala.

5–6. Unique in appearance but related to the silverswords is *Wilkesia gymnoxiphium*, the iliau of Kauai. The massive cone of flower heads is resinous, as befits a tarweed.

may receive three hundred or more inches of rain per year, and the mountaintop is one large quaking bog. Unlike the Haleakala silversword, which dies after flowering, the Puu Kukui species can produce new rosettes as shoots from the old plant; these reproduce the plant by rooting in the mud of the bog. Leaves of the Puu Kukui silversword are nearly as silvery as those of the Haleakala plant, but they have a mechanism for jettisoning excess water (hydathodes, vein tips along the leaf margins) lacking in the Haleakala species. Flowers of *A. caliginii* are tawny in color, unlike the conspicuous maroon of *A. sandwichense*. The silvery leaf-habit seems to have been retained by the Puu Kukui species even though this feature is not as advantageous there as it is on Haleakala.

Less conspicuous than the silverswords, but equally curious, are the greenswords of Maui, which also belong to the genus *Argyroxiphium*. The Haleakala greensword, *A. virescens*, is a plant of dry mid-altitudes on Mt. Haleakala. Its heads of reddish-brown flowers, its moderately hairy green leaves, its sticky flowering stalks make it not unlike a gigantic perennial version of some of the annual rosette-tarweeds of California. In contrast, the Puu Kukui greensword, *A. grayanum*, is a low branching shrub. Its dense green rosettes can be seen tufted among the shrubbery of the Puu Kukui bogs. The flowers are inconspicuous and yellow, but not greatly unlike those of the Haleakala greensword. The rosette-shrub habit is suited to the open bog conditions, since year-round growing conditions can be matched by indefinite length of stems. The leaves are flat, their breadth apt for dim cloudy conditions, whereas narrower leaves of *A. virescens* match the bright, dry habitats of Haleakala where that species grows.

Just as the silverswords and greenswords show adaptive radiation to the sharply different climates offered by Maui's mountains, a related genus, *Wilkesia* (5–6), shows equally curious adaptations to Kauai. In the dry semi-open places, especially on titanium-rich soils, of Kauai's canyons and cliffs may be seen the bizarre pole-like stems of *Wilkesia*. They bear a terminal rosette of narrow thin leaves, arranged not in spirals but in successive rings. Leaves are tough and fibrous, more like leaves of grass than those of other Hawaiian tarweeds. *Wilkesia* almost never branches, so that its awkward and straggling poles merely push upward until they are crowned, eventually, by a spectacular display of bright yellow flowers, borne in sticky resinous heads. The life of the plant, despite the five to ten years involved in formation of the gangling stems, is terminated by this flowering. The pole-like habit permits *Wilkesia* to reach out of the surrounding shrubbery into the light, a valuable asset because the regions where it grows are more densely wooded than areas where the Haleakala greensword grows. *Wilkesia* represents a most improbable form for a tarweed to have taken, but it can be understood as an ingenious adaptation to the island conditions where it grows.

THE VERSATILE HONEYCREEPERS

Where one large-scale example of adaptive radiation has occurred, one may expect to find more, and among animals, the family of Hawaiian birds known as honeycreepers or Drepanididae is a superb instance. Like the Hawaiian tarweeds, the drepanidids live everywhere from sea level to high mountain regions. Beginning with a warbler-like or tanager-like ancestor, the honeycreepers have managed to carve out many ways of life. As can be seen in Plate I, this family has a range of form, most conspicuous in beaks and plumage, which is greater than that of many other bird families. The beaks bear a direct relation to the diet and habits of the genera and species. They have evolved as built-in tools, varying from the thick, parrot-like bills of *Psittacirostra*, ideal for cracking large seeds, to the curved, delicate beaks of *Drepanis* and *Hemignathus*, sensitive instruments for probing flowers for nectar or for locating small insects. As one might imagine, the larger beaks of *Psittacirostra*, powerful as heavy pliers, are accompanied by a strong musculature, whereas the sickled-billed species, which remind one of gently grasping forceps, have much weaker bill muscles.

Sources of food for the honeycreepers (5–7, Plate I) include many insects, particularly beetles as well as their larval, pupal, and immature stages. *Pseudonestor* frequents the koa acacia, where it rips open twigs and branches to find such prey with its formidable beak. The longer upper half of Pseudonestor's beak can be

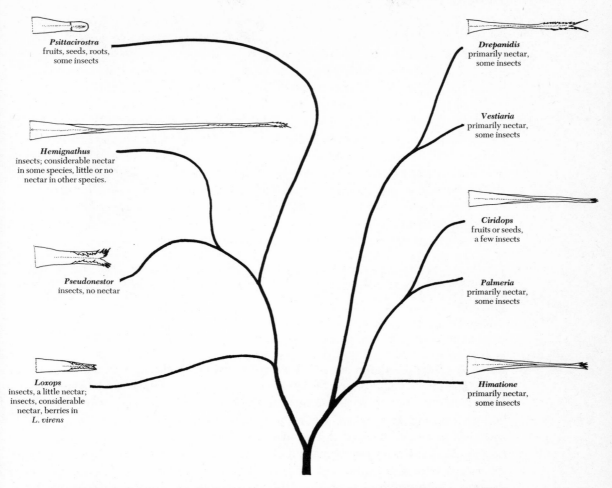

Psittacirostra
fruits, seeds, roots,
some insects

Drepanidis
primarily nectar,
some insects

Hemignathus
insects; considerable nectar
in some species, little or no
nectar in other species.

Vestiaria
primarily nectar,
some insects

Ciridops
fruits or seeds,
a few insects

Pseudonestor
insects, no nectar

Palmeria
primarily nectar,
some insects

Loxops
insects, a little nectar;
insects, considerable
nectar, berries in
L. virens

Himatione
primarily nectar,
some insects

5–7. An evolutionary tree of the Hawaiian honeycreepers (Drepanididae) according to Amadon. The development of the genera has featured divergences in food habits; the tongues shown correlate in size and shape with the diet of each genus.

used as a probe. Seeds and fruits favored by *Psittacirostra* include the large woody fruits of *Myoporum* (shown in flower behind *P. kona*), the fleshy fruits of *Freycinetia* (2–14), or the tough bean-like seeds of legumes, such as *Erythrina* or koa (2–5). On Laysan, a small, low island where such trees do not grow, the extinct *P. cantans* turned to fruits of the puncture-weed, *Tribulus,* and roots of *Boerhaavia.* Fruits of the Hawaiian palm, *Pritchardia,* were eaten by *Ciridops* (*Ciridops* is extinct now), which did not consume the hard seed, but only the fleshy part surrounding the seed. The long, curved beaks of *Drepanis* and *Hemignathus* may be suited for entry into the similarly curved tubular flowers of *Cyanea* (5–10) and *Clermontia* (5–11) to secure nectar, but they are also

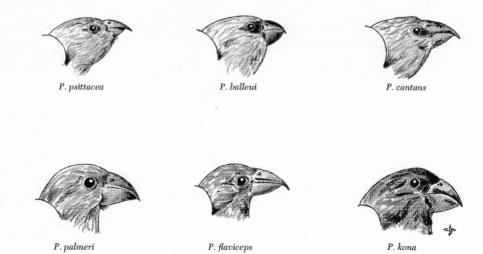

P. psittacea	P. balleui	P. cantans
P. palmeri	P. flaviceps	P. kona

5–8. The drepaniid genus *Psittacirostra* has species with divergent beak shapes and sizes. Although these distinctions are minor compared with the drepaniids as a whole, they may be related to differences among the species of *Psittacirostra* with respect to diet.

suited to sifting through moss, soft bark, rotting wood, and leaves in search of insects. The lower mandible of beaks of *Drepanis* and *Hemignathus* is somewhat shorter than the upper. *Hemignathus* can use the lower as a woodpecker does its bill, for opening up crevices, while the upper can probe for larvae. The bright and very attractive flowers of the ohia tree are sought by *Vestiaria, Palmeria, Loxops, Drepanis,* and *Himatione,* all of which are primarily nectar-feeders, with the exception of some species of *Loxops* which prefer insects. On Laysan, where the ohia (*Metrosideros*) is absent, *Himatione sanguinea freethii* seeks nectar in flowers of beach plants such as the morning-glory (2–4) and *Portulaca.* All of these birds supplement their diets with occasional insects, usually smaller ones or immature stages which can be handled by their smaller beaks.

In his excellent paper on the honeycreepers, Dean Amadon of The American Museum of Natural History has prepared a phylogenetic tree to the genera. This has been reproduced in 5–7, with the addition of a summary of diet and drawings of tongues. Tongues can be interpreted as suiting the diet very closely in most cases. The ancestral type was probably like that of *Loxops* or *Pseudonestor,* of moderate length, forked at the tip, fringed, and capable of inrolling the fringed margins. Inrolling permits the tongue to function as a tube, sucking up nectar. Exaggeration of such a tube has been accomplished by *Himatione* and *Hemignathus* (also by *Drepanis;* the margins in 5–7 are shown spread out rather than inrolled). The shorter and markedly fringed tongues of *Loxops* and *Pseudonestor* seem suited to insect consumption, whereas the short, rounded tongue of *Psit-*

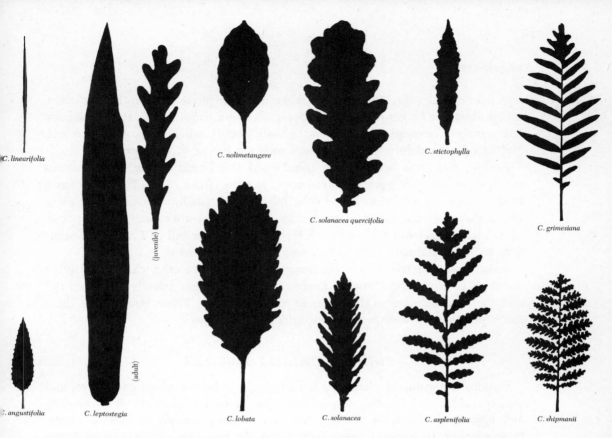

C. linearifolia

C. nolimetangere

C. stictophylla

(juvenile)

C. solanacea quercifolia

C. grimesiana

(adult)

C. angustifolia

C. leptostegia

C. lobata

C. solanacea

C. asplenifolia

C. shipmanii

5–9. Species of *Cyanea,* a Hawaiian genus of Lobeliaceae, differ widely in leaf size and shape, differences which may be correlated with their respective habitats and plant forms.

tacirostra grapples with tough seeds. Thus both the beak and tongue of *Psittacirostra* are not unlike those of a parrot, which it mimics in its diet.

Although we cannot predict the future of the honeycreepers (many of which are now rare or extinct), we can say that we have discovered them still active in adaptive radiation, still diversifying. The six species of *Psittacirostra* (5–8) differ from each other in beak size and shape: *P. psittacea* has a small bill, *P. kona* a very large one. The tendency for the upper mandible to be longer than the lower is shown by some Psittacirostras, not by others. This may be correlated with the feeding habits, for *P. psittacea* favors fleshy fruits, such as the *Freycinetia* (2–14), *Cyanea* (5–10), or *Clermontia* (5–11), as well as caterpillars, whereas *P. kona* eats the tough seeds of *Myoporum* when they are dry and hard. *Psittacirostra bailleui* consumes *Myoporum* seeds, but when they are green and softer, corresponding to its less powerful beak. *Psittacirostra palmeri* and *P. flaviceps* prefer the lentil-like seeds of the koa acacia. Thus, even though a cycle of adaptive radiation has led to the general type of beak shared by all species of *Psittacirostra,* radiation has by no means abated.

Psittacirostra cantans, which lives on treeless Laysan Island, has longer, stouter legs than do the other Psittarostras. This, too, is a phase of adaptive radiation, and presumably longer-legged individuals have been favored by natural selection in Laysan's environment, but not on the main islands, where trees provide roosts, and legs designed for running on bare rock are not at a premium.

Loxops, the small warbler-like member of the Drepanididae, also contains examples of continuing adaptive radiation. *Loxops virens* (Plate I), which has a longer, more curved beak than do the other species, habitually consumes more nectar than they do. The smallest species, *L. parva,* uses its small, straight beak to find insects in loose bark, whereas the longer, heavier bill of *L. virens* permits it to probe underneath bark and secure deep-seated insects.

Counterpointing the story of the honeycreepers are two other cases of adaptive radiation in birds: the Darwin's finches of the Galápagos Islands (Chapter 15) and the vanga-shrikes of Madagascar (Chapter 16). These three cases show many parallels, as well as many intriguing distinctions.

NEW MODES IN LOBELIADS

Curiously, a group of plants has been thought to have evolved parallel to, and perhaps influenced by, the drepanidids: the Hawaiian lobeliads. Both literally and figuratively far from the tiny-flowered lobelias familiar as garden plants, these gigantic Hawaiian representatives provide examples of adaptive radiation which ought to be, although they are not, as famous as the Drepanididae. To be sure, the lobelia family (Lobeliaceae) is not restricted to the Hawaiian Islands. It has, however, developed more curious forms on these islands than elsewhere. Of the lobeliad genera on the Hawaiian chain, only one, *Lobelia,* ranges beyond the islands—it is worldwide in distribution. Although the Hawaiian species of *Lobelia* are unusual in their growth forms and colors, the endemic genera are more striking: *Brighamia, Trematolobelia, Delissea, Rollandia, Cyanea,* and *Clermontia. Brighamia* (8–12) is one of the world's most curious plants, the outcome of a peculiar evolutionary direction. *Trematolobelia* has a dispersal mechanism which claims attention in Chapter 10. *Delissea* and *Rollandia* both offer fascinating examples of adaptive radiation.

Delissea has achieved a surprising degree of diversification in growth form, leaf shape, and other features, but the species of this genus appear to have lost their momentum, and may be fast disappearing in the Hawaiian Islands. Few recent collections of these species have been made and *Delissea* may be, as has been alleged, a "decadent genus." *Rollandia* has radiated entirely on one island, Oahu, with the exception of a single species. If you want to track down the details of these stories, the monograph by Joseph Rock is the place to look.

Time, space, and ecology have been more generous to *Cyanea,* permitting development of the most diverse species imaginable; two of these are shown in 5–10. They are difficult to fit within the conventional limits of tree, shrub, or herb. One would reluctantly dub *C. leptostegia* a tree, for it is a tall, single-stemmed palm-like plant, bearing a single dense rosette of leaves. Although it has wood, the wood is very soft, and this tree doubtless represents a rosette-herb which has succeeded in developing a gigantic form, as have other "overgrown plants" described in Chapter 8. *Cyanea leptostegia* trees may exceed thirty feet; leaves are up to a yard in length (5–10). Clustered among the leaves are groups of pink flowers, each with thread-like sepals and a curved floral tube, the petals of which roll back, exposing the narrow tube of stamens. Fruits are narrow, hollow, and purple. The drier rain forest of Kauai is the habitat of *C. leptostegia; C. atra* lives within Puu Kukui's dripping, mossy forest. A smaller succulent herb only about a yard tall, *C. atra* has only a few branches. Its leaves are large, but wide and rough, covered with tiny prickles. The flowers are rich purple outside, but the inside of the petals is white; sepals are short and rounded; fruits are oval, orangeish-purple.

Cyanea atra and *C. leptostegia* are only two of at least sixty species of *Cyanea* now known from the Hawaiian Islands; more are likely to be found in remote areas. Some are tall, like *C. leptostegia,* some no more than a foot high. *Cyanea* includes plants which are hairy, hairless, or even have thorns (10–15). Leaves also reveal a highly diverse display of form (5–9). Most Cyaneas are relatively low plants with leaves shaped like those of *C. angustifolia, C. nolimetangere,* or *C. lobata.* The extremely narrow leaf shape of *C. linearifolia* suggests adaptation to more sunny, open locations, because narrow leaves, inefficient at light-gathering and offering a minimal surface to desiccation by warm air, usually are found in bright locations. The long strap-like leaves of *C. leptostegia* are what one would expect of a single-stemmed, tall, palm-like plant, for a single crown of small leaves could hardly manufacture sufficient food for a large plant. The narrow leaf form in this species is related to the sunnier positions which the leaf-crown attains atop the long unbranched stem (5–10). One might well ask how such leaves would be appropriate for a young plant far short of the forest canopy. In fact, leaves of young plants are different. Juvenile leaves of *C. leptostegia,* as shown in 5–9, are broad and lobed, as if to spread their surface wider. Plants of shady locations, such as ferns, often have "open," "lobed," "subdivided," or "deeply cut" leaves, because thinner leaves, with the blade spread as widely as possible, are more efficient at light-gathering in dim situations. This type of leaf, as one might expect, characterizes those Cyaneas that never reach far above the forest floor, as the species on the right half of 5–9 show. All of the leaves illustrated there are those of adult plants. They have not all evolved the same patterns, but this is what one would expect: different answers to the same problem, evolved independently. The more elaborate forms, such as *C. solanacea, C. grimesiana, C. asplenifolia* (whose name commemorates a fern *Asplenium*), and *C. shipmanii* show that such patterns have evolved from ancestors which probably looked like *C. nolimetangere* or *C. lobata.* Most Cyaneas occur only in very limited areas on the islands, and few occur on more than a single island. On a mainland area, only a few of these evolutionary experiments would probably survive—if they

5–10. *Cyanea* has explored highly divergent modes of plant form, flower shape, and flower color. Above, the palm-like *C. leptostegia* of Kauai's drier forests, with dense clusters of pink flowers at right. Below, *C. atra* from the very wet forests of Puu Kukui, Maui, has short, succulent stems. Flowers, right, are purple outside, white inside; fruits turn orange at maturity.

would have occurred at all. But in the many isolated sites of the Hawaiian Islands, with opportunity for invention and a minimum of repressive competition, origin and maintenance of these species has been permitted. Each species represents a fragile essay, closely attuned to the environment it occupies.

Another genus of lobeliads, *Clermontia,* is relatively uniform in growth form. Some are tall, almost tree-like shrubs, some are small, sparsely branched, but the range of forms is not very great. They all have elliptical, leathery leaves, easy to recognize in the Hawaiian forest. *Clermontia* seems to have confined its evolutionary diversification mainly to flowers (5–11). The array of floral form, color, and size is greater than that in some families of flowering plants. Three of the species illustrated, *C. grandiflora, C. micrantha,* and *C. oblongifolia,* appear to have a double flower because the sepals are as long as, and the same color as, the petals. *Clermontia arborescens* differs from the other species in its short, crown-like formation of sepals as well as its thick, succulent petals. The flowers of *C. arborescens* and *C. oblongifolia* are four times or more the length of the tiny blossoms of *C. micrantha.* Of the two plants for which flowers are illustrated in *C. grandiflora* (5–11, middle), one has rose, moderately curved, wide flowers. The other has greenish flowers, narrow and curved almost into a circle. Within the genus *Clermontia* as a whole, flower color ranges from blackish purple to white, with green, pink, red, even bluish represented in various species. How can this remarkable diversity in flowers be explained?

Where great variety of floral types occurs in a single genus, the biologist usually suspects different pollinating mechanisms. Often one can guess the type of pollinator from the shape and color of flowers, using known preferences of insects or birds as a guide. If this were reliable, we would expect Clermontias—and Cyaneas—to be pollinated by birds, which are, as with hummingbirds, attracted by brightly colored (usually reddish or orangeish) tubular flowers. This plan is seemingly well satisfied by Clermontias, as well as other Lobeliaceae. Moreover, as the flower of these opens, a brush at the tip of the anthers becomes filled with pollen, forming a structure ideal for strewing pollen grains onto the feathers of a bird's head if the bird inserts its beak into the tube of the flower. *Cyanea* and *Clermontia* flowers do contain nectar, which would give birds a reason for visiting them. Moreover, insects would also be attracted by nectar, and birds visiting flowers might thus find not only nectar, but insect prey as well. This matches closely the diet of certain of the honeycreepers, such as *Vestiaria, Hemignathus, Loxops,* and *Drepanis.* We know from observations made when these birds were more abundant that they did, in fact, visit these flowers and perhaps, in the process, pollinate them. Did the lobeliads and the drepanidids influence each other's evolution? Some claim that they did, and that different floral types were evolved to attract pollinators. Those holding this view would say that lobeliads might also have influenced drepanidids; birds with long beaks would be favored if lobeliads with long-tubed flowers were abundant sources of food for birds. The size and degree of curvature of drepanidid beaks and lobeliad flowers often seem

5–11. *Clermontia*, a Hawaiian genus of lobeliads, shows amazing diversification with respect to floral form and color. Most are shrubs or small shrubby trees. Above, *C. micrantha;* shrub at left; flowers, right, are small and bright red. Center, two forms of *C. grandiflora* from Puu Kukui, Maui, differing in color and flower curvature. Below, left, the large green flowers of *C. oblongifolia* from Mt. Olympus, Oahu; at right, *C. arborescens* from Puu Kukui, Maui has thick succulent green petals but a short crown-like calyx.

to match well—if one picks certain birds, certain lobeliads—and make this interpretation tempting.

Detractors of this hypothesis ask why lobeliads still reproduce in regions where drepanidids are extinct or nearly so. Self-pollination is possible in lobeliad flowers, so a flower can form fruit even if a pollinator is not present. Skeptics might ask why the number of lobeliad species is so great, the number of honeycreeper species so few—how can only a few drepanidid species have triggered the explosion of *Clermontia* and *Cyanea* into the floral diversity we see today? This is not an easy question to answer. However, a variety of floral forms might have suited a given drepanidid, and several quite different types might compete quite well for the pollinating services of a single drepanidid species.

There must be some explanation, ultimately, for the mystery of the floral variety of the Hawaiian lobeliads; pollination does seem to be a key. Without a doubt, the lobeliads were cross-pollinated when they were actively evolving. They can continue, despite the loss of their pollinating agents, to maintain themselves, but if this is true, it does not augur well for the future of the lobeliads. In the long run, exclusive self-pollination decreases diversity, and is only a "delaying action" in maintaining the existence of species such as those of the Hawaiian Lobeliaceae. They may outlive their pollinating agents, but the evolutionary future is dim, and disappearance of a number of the lobeliads might be traced to this in part. The increasing inroads of man into the Hawaiian forests will, of course, take their toll in extinction of the Hawaiian tarweeds, drepanidids, and lobeliads, but the main reason for their disappearance will be that they are delicate products of evolutionary campaigns won without opposition. Plants and animals from the continents are forged in the furnaces of stiff competition, and thus lantana and guavas, mynah birds and sparrows, can outperform and displace the fragile inventions of adaptive radiation on islands.

A CATALOGUE OF ADAPTIVE RADIATORS

The most striking example of adaptive radiation on an isolated area is, without a doubt, that of the Australian marsupials, which occupy the next chapter. But many other examples should not go unforgotten, so a sort of appendix which follows will give an idea of some, by no means all, instances where this phenomenon occurs. For those willing to ferret out details, some of these would reward an inquisitive reader.

AUSTRALIA

Animals: marsupials (Chapter 6); bower birds (Chapter 11); parrots; kingfishers (kookaburra, etc.); skinks and geckos (Chapter 7)
Plants: Proteaceae (especially *Grevillea* and *Hakea*); *Eucalyptus; Melaleuca* (bottle brush); *Acacia* (especially the phyllodial acacias); porantheroid Euphorbiaceae (spurges); Stylidiaceae (triggerplants); Goodeniaceae (es-

pecially *Scaevola, Goodenia*); Loranthaceae (mistletoes); Rutaceae (*Boronia* and allies); Compositae; chloanthoid Verbenaceae; Xanthorrhoeaceae (grass trees); Pittosporaceae

NEW GUINEA

Animals: birds of paradise (Chapter 11)

NEW ZEALAND

Animals: Callaeidae (huia birds, etc.: Chapter 10); insects (wetas: Chapter 9; others)

Plants: Scrophulariaceae (*Hebe*—Chapter 8); Rubiaceae (*Coprosma*); Araliaceae (*Pseudopanax*, etc.: Chapter 8); Compositae (*Olearia; Senecio; Celmisia;* others); Podocarpaceae (especially *Podocarpus* and *Dacrydium*); Pittosporaceae

NEW CALEDONIA

Plants: Podocarpaceae (especially *Dacrydium* and *Podocarpus*); Araucarias; Euphorbiaceae (*Phyllanthus*); Araliaceae (*Tieghemopanax*)

HAWAIIAN ISLANDS

Animals: Insects (many remarkable groups, a few of which are discussed in Chapter 9; for others, see Zimmerman's *Insects of Hawaii*)

Plants: Gesneriaceae (*Cyrtandra*); Rutaceae (*Pelea*, etc.); Araliaceae (*Cheirodendron*, etc.); Compositae (*Lipochaeta, Bidens*); Rubiaceae

JUAN FERNANDEZ ISLANDS

Plants: Compositae (several genera: Chapter 8)

GALÁPAGOS ISLANDS (Chapter 15)

Animals: Darwin's finches; lizards (*Tropidurus;* iguanas)
Plants: Compositae (*Scalesia*); cacti (*Opuntia*)

PACIFIC (general)

Animals: molluscs (several families of land molluscs, including Achatinellidae, Tornatellidae)

CANARY ISLANDS

Plants: Crassulaceae (*Aeonium*—Chapter 8); Compositae (*Sonchus*—Chapter 8)

MADAGASCAR (Chapter 16)

Animals: lemurs; tenrecs; various reptiles, amphibians; vanga-shrikes
Plants: *Kalanchoe* (Crassulaceae); Sarcolaenaceae; Compositae

6   *The Magnificent Substitutes*

SEVENTY million years ago or more in the Cretaceous, the Australian continent, a land of cycads and conifers with millions of years to elapse before the coming of the great *Eucalyptus* forests, boasted only a few mammals: the monotremes. Monotremes, a peculiar formulation which combines reptile-like eggs with a crude mammary system, have, in fact, persisted to the present, a feat which Chapter 12 may explain. At this time, however, a mammal with a clever new reproductive device entered Australia. This animal, a marsupial, was no longer encumbered by the egg-laying and nesting procedures which monotremes must follow even at present. As the Latin word *marsupium* implies, marsupials have a pouch. The pouch is a sort of flap of skin, and protects young embryos, born tiny and bare. Within the pouch are nipples, providing nutrition during the long period when parent and infant must be joined as a single package, inseparable until weaning. Marsupial young seem extremely vulnerable, but actually they are tough as leeches and manage, although blind and worm-like, to crawl to the pouch and its nipples soon after they are born.

The marsupial way of life, though a bold innovation, was later to be given a comeuppance by the placentals. In placentals, young are born only when relatively mature, and they need not be constantly attached to the nipple. They can, in fact, be weaned much sooner than can marsupials. For months, the marsupial embryo must remain firmly attached to the nipple, a union as compulsory as the contact of capillaries by which the life of a placental embryo is threaded to that of its mother prior to birth.

So, unaware of the rampant ways in which the more efficient placentals were later to find their many answers to problems of existence, marsupials entered Australia. This isolated continent, which spans from desert to rain forest, from tropics to icy mountains, provided a remarkable spread of opportunities. Isolated within this continent, with no mammalian competitors except the antique and fading monotremes, the marsupials were given the option of almost any conceivable way of life. From a single immigrant stock perhaps seventy million years ago, the marsupials eked out their audacious venture, almost like participants in a biological experiment proving the breadths and lengths of possibilities achievable within the basic framework of the marsupial scheme. The evolutionary ability of the marsupials proved the equal of their continent, evolving in a world of their own, as if it were the only one which existed. Mostly invisible during the day, these nocturnal creatures make nights in Australia and New Guinea a universe teeming with furious activity from the tips of high trees to recesses of the ground.

In fact, the Australian-New Guinean marsupial fauna comprises the most important group of marsupials left on earth. There are only two other living groups, the true opossums (Didelphidae) and the South American marsupial rats (Caenolestidae). The true opossums are a curious paradox—they are the most primitively constructed marsupials, yet they are also feverishly successful, in the vanguard of mammals able to cope with man's ever-changing world. Opossums, which belong to fifty-eight species in eleven genera, have been able to invade new regions within historical time. They probably owe their success to a truly incredible ability to subsist on almost any conceivable food source, a definitive example of the omnivorous habit, as well as their ability to reproduce quickly and prolifically. In such ways, opossums have stood up to competition from placental mammals on continental areas. The South American marsupial rats, three species in three genera, are much less successful, but survive well in a few areas.

In terms of human history, the "new world" is not the Americas but Australia, and European explorers who encountered Australia's marsupials dubbed them with names of placental mammals: "cats," "mice," and "wolves." Scientific names of marsupials often are translations of these common names: the Tasmanian marsupial wolf is *Thylacinus cynocephalus,* which literally means "the wolf-faced pouched wolf." The use of names like "marsupial mouse" may seem ridiculous, if understandable, but it does tend to underline the way in which marsupials mimic, even in fine details like the nature of their teeth, placentals which have adapted to similar ways of life. On the other hand, some marsupials have evolved forms and ways of life entirely without counterpart among placentals. For these unique creations, our nomenclatural resources are augmented by names given by the Australian aborigines: wombat, kangaroo, koala, bandicoot. The name "koala," which means "no water" to the aborigine, is rather more perceptive of the way this animal lives than the name given by scientists: *Phascolarctos,* the "pouched bear," a poor though inviting comparison.

THE CARNIVORES

One may ask which of the contemporary marsupials living in Australia and New Guinea best approximates the ancestral marsupials that managed to reach this continent, perhaps by land, perhaps by crossing narrow gaps of sea water. The answer is best provided by the four families of carnivores, the dasyuroids (6–1)—but what a variety of forms can be found within these families! All four have in common three unspecialized things: rear and front feet with no fusion among the five digits; a dentition consisting of numerous small sharp teeth on both upper and lower jaws; and a rudimentary pouch. The unspecialized feet reflect a claw-like structure, as in a cat's paw, for clutching and tearing prey, while the teeth are ideally savage, designed for shredding meat or insects or gnawing bones. The pouch of these primitively constructed carnivores is only a small fold of skin, a crescent which folds toward the rear, not at all like the capacious forward-opening pouch of kangaroos. Because the pouch is rudimentary and cannot accommodate large babies, the young often ride on their mothers' backs.

Marsupial Mice. Despite their small size, marsupial mice are fine examples of the carnivorous habit. *Antechinus flavipes* (6–2), for example, bristles with a ferocity which belies its timid appearance. As twilight signals the beginning of a night's work, it emerges from its nest of leaves, usually made amid the rubble of sandstone crannies. Soon quivering with the compulsiveness of a shrew, it lances out, predator on a microcosm of beetles, snails, grasshoppers, and even placental mice. The rapacious appetite of *Antechinus* springs from a brisk metabolism, and when active foraging is ended by the dawn, it creeps back to its nest and drops, exhausted, into a deep sleep.

Other marsupial mice show surprising adaptations. The flat-skulled marsupial mice, *Planigale,* have a head flattened to a degree almost unequaled in mammals, but very much like that of some lizards. Why? This modification permits the wedge-like face to poke into crevices in the ground—hiding places for insects and other prey. The smooth surface of the paws of *Planigale* reveals that it is a strictly terrestrial animal. An animal which customarily climbs, like *Antechinus,* has minutely ridged pads which help paws to cling to surfaces.

Among the catalogue of marsupial mice, the largest is *Phascogale,* often termed the brush-tailed marsupial rat. It exceeds other marsupial mice not only in size but in rapacity. Australian aborigines fear its bite, and European settlers in Australia discovered that chickens fall easy prey to *Phascogale.* So preoccupied is it with its prey that it can easily be caught, refusing to give up its catch; it successfully attacks animals twice its size. These habits have been commemorated in the common name "vampire marsupial." *Phascogale* lives in logs, and lines its nest with scraps stolen from everywhere.

The crest-tailed marsupial mouse, *Dasycercus,* is small, and simultaneously savage and dainty. It can ruthlessly kill a placental mouse, but before reducing it to a clean pile of bones and a neat skin, the crest-tail will carefully wash its face with its paws.

Antechinomys (6–3) is a marsupial mouse like a miniature kangaroo. Like its larger distant relative, it nervously hops about on rear legs, balancing with a long brush-tipped tail. Curiously, it is a perfect mimic of the rodents known as jerboas or kangaroo rats, placentals which people the deserts of the continental world— America, Africa, Asia. *Antechinomys* is also a desert animal, and its hopping gait matches the desert spaces it must cover in search of its widely scattered prey. This habit contrasts with *Antechinus,* which can find prey within a short radius of its home in cluttered woodland. *Antechinomys* shows anatomical adjustment to

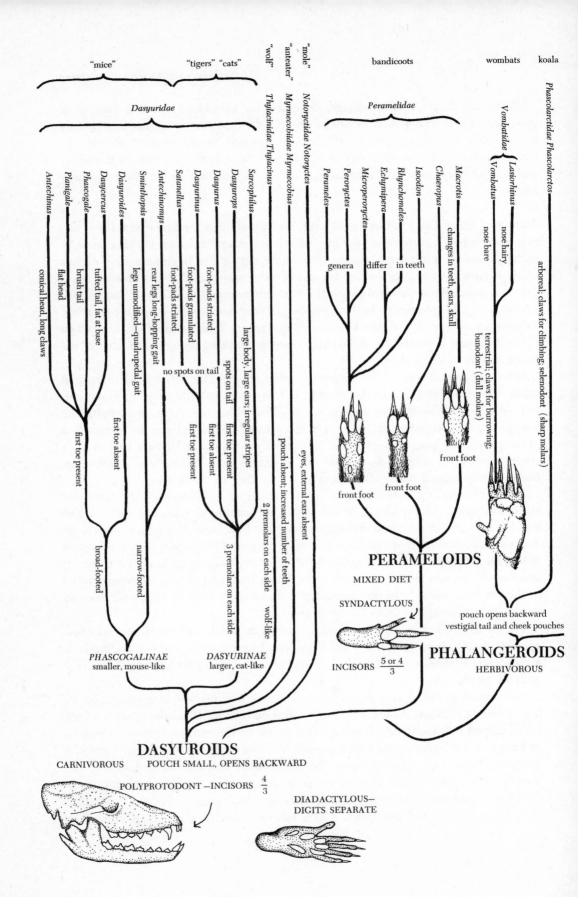

"mice"　"tigers" "cats"

"wolf"

"mole"
"anteater"

bandicoots

wombats　koala

Dasyuridae

Thylacinidae Thylacinus

Notoryctidae Notoryctes

Myrmecobiidae Myrmecobius

Peramelidae

Vombatidae

Phascolarctidae Phascolarctos

Antechinus

Planigale

Phascogale

Dasycercus

Dasyuroides

Sminthopsis

Antechinomys

Satanellus

Dasyurinus

Dasyurus

Dasyurops

Sarcophilus

Perameles

Peroryctes

Microperoryctes

Echymipera

Rhynchomeles

Isoodon

Chaeropus

Macrotis

Vombatus

Lasiorhinus

genera　differ　in teeth

changes in teeth, ears, skull

nose hairy

nose bare

arboreal; claws for climbing; selenodont (sharp molars)

terrestrial; claws for burrowing; bunodont (dull molars)

conical head, long claws

flat head

brush tail

tufted tail, fat at base

legs unmodified—quadrupedal gait

rear legs long-hopping gait

foot-pads striated

foot-pads granulated

foot-pads striated

large body, large ears; irregular stripes

spots on tail

no spots on tail

first toe present

first toe absent

first toe present

first toe absent

first toe present

2 premolars on each side

pouch absent; increased number of teeth

eyes, external ears absent

wolf-like

3 premolars on each side

front foot

front foot

front foot

PERAMELOIDS

MIXED DIET

SYNDACTYLOUS

INCISORS $\dfrac{5 \text{ or } 4}{3}$

broad-footed

narrow-footed

PHASCOGALINAE
smaller, mouse-like

DASYURINAE
larger, cat-like

pouch opens backward
vestigial tail and cheek pouches

PHALANGEROIDS

HERBIVOROUS

DASYUROIDS

CARNIVOROUS　POUCH SMALL, OPENS BACKWARD

POLYPROTODONT —INCISORS $\dfrac{4}{3}$

DIADACTYLOUS—
DIGITS SEPARATE

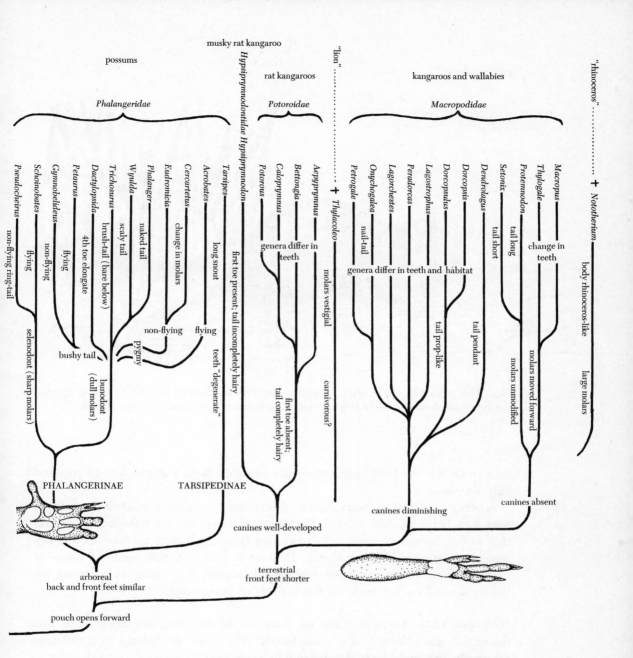

possums

musky rat kangaroo

rat kangaroos

"lion"

kangaroos and wallabies

"rhinoceros" ··············

Phalangeridae

Hypsiprymnodontidae *Hypsiprymnodon*

Potoroidae

Macropodidae

✝ *Nototherium*

Pseudocheirus
Schoinobates
Gymnobelideus
Petaurus
Dactylopsila
Trichosurus
Wyulda
Phalanger
Eudromicia
Cercartetus
Acrobates
Tarsipes
Potorous
Caloprymnus
Bettongia
Aepyprymnus
✝ *Thylacoleo*
Petrogale
Onychogalea
Lagorchestes
Peradorcas
Lagostrophus
Dorcopsulus
Dorcopsis
Dendrolagus
Setonix
Protemnodon
Thylogale
Macropus

non-flying ring-tail

flying

non-flying

flying

4th toe elongate

brush-tail (bare below)

scaly tail

naked tail

change in molars

long snout

first toe present; tail incompletely hairy

genera differ in teeth

molars vestigial

carnivorous?

nail-tail

genera differ in teeth and habitat

tail prop-like

tail pendant

tail short

tail long

change in teeth

molars unmodified

molars moved forward

body rhinoceros-like

large molars

selenodont (sharp molars)

bunodont (dull molars)

bushy tail

pygmy

teeth "degenerate"

first toe absent; tail completely hairy

PHALANGERINAE

TARSIPEDINAE

canines diminishing

canines absent

canines well-developed

terrestrial front feet shorter

arboreal back and front feet similar

pouch opens forward

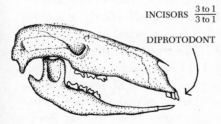

PHALANGERINAE

INCISORS $\frac{3 \text{ to } 1}{3 \text{ to } 1}$

DIPROTODONT

FASCICULUS ABERRANS (new structure in brain)

SYNDACTYLOUS

6-1. This evolutionary tree summarizes the way zoologists view the development of the Australian marsupials. Underlying the many different habits and diets of these animals are changes in the form of teeth, feet, and other parts: these are the tools marsupials have evolved in their varied and thorough exploitations of the many-faceted Australian environment. (Compiled from works by Tate, Raven and Gregory, Troughton, and Ride.)

6–2. The yellow-footed marsupial mouse *Antechinus flavipes* is, among living species, the type which most closely resembles the ancestors of the Australian marsupials.

its way of life: the hind foot is markedly elongate, with a single springy pad and only four toes.

Another group of marsupial mice, *Sminthopsis,* is closely related to *Antechinomys* and also inhabits deserts. The rigors of desert life are reflected in the fact that several species of *Sminthopsis* have fat tails which store up food for the dry season, when prey becomes scarce. Content to live in a nest made of grass—or even a crumpled newspaper—a *Sminthopsis* mother may carry as many as ten babies around on her back, in the fashion of an opossum.

Marsupial Cats. There is really no irony in the fact that marsupial mice and marsupial cats belong to the same family. The "cats" do belong to a different subfamily, but could be said to be simply more gigantic adaptations to the carnivorous way of life. The tiger cat, or native cat *Dasyurus quoll* (6–4), is a fine sample of these tendencies. Like the marsupial mice, it can equal in combat an animal larger in size, such as a placental tomcat. Like true cats, the marsupial cat *Dasyurops* can stalk its prey and can, snarling, hold off enemies such as dogs. Furtive yet aggressive, the tiger cat *Dasyurops* is powerful out of proportion to its size. Nevertheless, it is reported to be a rather clumsy animal, not fast in its movements. It compensates with its bite. Tiger cats often have "dining lairs" where piles of bones are evidence to its prowess as a carnivore. The tiger cat is distinctive by the spots on its tail. Other marsupial cats differ by lack of spots

6–3. The jerboa marsupial mouse *Antechinomys spenceri* mimics the hopping gait of placental jerboas and kangaroo rats in dry regions of continents other than Australia.

and, in the cases of *Dasyurus* and *Dasyurinus,* lacking foot pads. If pads are missing, the surface of the foot is granular in texture and is an adaptation to living primarily on the ground in rather open country.

The most spectacular of the marsupial cats is the Tasmanian devil, *Sarcophilus* (6–5), now extinct on the Australian mainland but still present in large numbers in Tasmania. A fierce-looking beast, it is about the size of a small dog, which it resembles further in its snarling habit and sharp teeth. The devil is black, with one or more white bands. Living in logs, it emerges to capture vertebrates, including its fellow marsupials, wallabies and rat-kangaroos, even birds and fish. Insatiable, the devil can make a single meal of a sheep. Sometimes it will follow a marsupial wolf in order to finish the remnants left behind by the wolf, whose victims are quite to the devil's liking. Despite its seemingly intractable behavior, *Sarcophilus* is full of amusing antics, and can easily be tamed if caught at an early age, a feature true of many marsupials. Like most marsupials, it is a very clean animal and washes either by bathing or by cupping its paws, wetting them with its tongue, and rubbing its face.

Tasmanian Wolf. Thylacinus, better known as the Tasmanian wolf, is a superb demonstration not only of adaptive radiation but of convergence. Not only has it evolved into a large, swiftly running carnivore, it has in the process made a remarkably close approach to wolf-like habits. The products of adaptive radiation

6–4. The Australian marsupials furnish a close approach to cathood in the eastern native cat, *Dasyurus quoll.*

6–5. The Tasmanian devil, *Sarcophilus harrisi,* is a carnivore which has survived on Tasmania, although fossils prove it once lived on the Australian mainland as well.

on islands (including Australia) are most frequently mimics of mainland plants and animals, and so it is with *Thylacinus*. If you saw one, you would undoubtedly think of it as a sort of dog or wolf, except for the banded back and the short lower portion of the hind legs. The Tasmanian wolf is three feet high at its shoulders and up to six feet in length. Although its footprints are still reported, one has not been captured since 1930. *Thylacinus* was once present on the Australian mainland, but the introduction by the aborigines of a similar but more efficient animal, the dingo, may have led to the disappearance of the thylacines. In prehuman times, the Tasmanian wolf preyed upon larger marsupials, but with man's introduction of chickens and sheep it proved such a good predator on livestock that settlers in Tasmania began a reign of extermination which has been almost completely successful. Thylacines attack dogs, but not man.

As the proportion of the parts of the hind legs hints, *Thylacinus* is a compromise between a bounding and a running animal. This compromise is well suited to the heavily thicketed forests of Tasmania. Cunning beyond that of a dog permits *Thylacinus* to capture even the wily banded anteater.

Marsupial Anteater. Two species of the genus *Myrmecobius* represent the Australian marsupials' entry into the anteater habit. Sometimes called a numbat or banded anteater, it even looks much like a placental anteater (6–7). Long a puzzle among marsupials, the numbat is now understood as a sort of degenerate carnivore. Because it has more than four molars on each side of both jaws, the banded anteater was once thought to be a very primitive remnant of the many-toothed marsupials outside of Australia, such as opossums. Now, zoologists favor the notion that the longer jaw is an innovation. Although a numbat's fifty-two

6–6. Among the evolutionary achievements of Australia's marsupials is a close approach to the wolf habit: the Tasmanian wolf, *Thylacinus cynocephalus*.

6–7. The banded anteater or numbat (*Myrmecobius fasciatus*) is a unique marsupial, specialized in many respects, which has no pouch.

teeth outnumber those of any other marsupial, they play little part in feeding. Termites are often swallowed without any chewing at all. More significant in its feeding habits is a long, extensible tongue with a cylindrical shape which permits it to probe into rotten wood and draw out termites. To secure this fare, the numbat slowly and deliberately scours the forest floor at night. Because it is accustomed to minute prey, *Myrmecobius* never bites human captors.

Not only are the numbat's teeth degenerate, the pouch is completely absent. Whereas the preceding carnivores have a modest crescent-shaped backward-facing flap of skin, *Myrmecobius* offers no such protection to its newborn, which must crawl to the nipples through coarse hair, which provides their only shield against the outside world. Because of unique features such as these, this marsupial falls in a family of its own (6–1).

Marsupial Mole. We have no real way of measuring the evolutionary distance or scope traversed by a given group, of assessing just how remarkable phylogenetic changes can be. Changes in size, shape, and function of parts may be slight, or they may represent the end-products of a complex genetic technology. Seen in these terms, however, the progressive conversion of creatures like marsupial mice into the marsupial mole *Notoryctes* is surely one of the great feats of the organic world. Its appearance alone (6–8) is most unusual. Like a mole, it is blind, and its eyes have, in fact, disappeared. Its rounded, short body is terminated not by a tail, but only a leathery tab. The legs are short, adapted closely to the digging process. Greatly enlarged nails on the third and fourth digits, like

6–8. A surprising end-product of evolutionary diversification is the marsupial mole, *Notoryctes typhlops*. This rare creature has no eyes or external ears, but has large claws for dredging beneath the surface of the ground.

a combination of pick and shovel, make *Notoryctes* an adept burrower. The marsupial mole is best described as a sort of animal dredge, sinking beneath the surface of the ground during its earth-moving activities. Completing its equipage for subterranean existence are a horny shield on its snout and a backwardly directed pouch which thus does not fill with dirt as the mole digs forward. *Notoryctes* has a silky coat, the color of which, white to reddish, matches the color of the sandy desert regions where it lives—perhaps a case of protective coloration. Rarely emerging from the ground, it stays in its burrows about three inches below the surface until after a rain, when the drenched soil forces him temporarily to abandon his subterranean habit. This may account for the fact that this marsupial curiosity was not discovered until 1888—indeed, a marsupial mole would certainly never have been expected. This creature mingles frenzy with torpor—furiously gobbling worms, insects, and larvae to feed an insatiable energy, it sinks momentarily into a fitful slumber, soon to awaken again, fulfilling a relentless cycle.

THE UNDECIDED CARNIVORES

The family Peramelidae encompasses creatures bearing the whimsical title of bandicoot. Bandicoots depart from the carnivore pattern in several respects. First, they, as well as the herbivores described later, are exponents of syndactyly —a condition in which two adjacent toes on each hind foot are combined into one (6–1). Secondly, although the bandicoots customarily consume adult insects, grubs, and larvae, they will also feed on roots and bulbs; they will even accept potatoes, pudding, or cake if offered them. The pig-footed bandicoot has even turned almost entirely to plant foods.

A mystery effectively hidden in evolution's archives is why the pair of adjacent toes should be joined in the bandicoots and in the herbivorous marsupials.

6–9. With its foreclaws, the short-nosed bandicoot *Isoodon obesulus* digs up insect larvae and other food items.

Syndactyly has received such ingenious explanations as that the paired toes provide a scratcher for lice, with which bandicoots are plagued, according to legend, and from which other syndactylous marsupials may suffer. Grooming has been alleged as another cause: the adherent toes serve as a narrow but effective comb. We may properly doubt if natural selection has indulged in considerations like these. Rather, a less fanciful explanation meets with more general approval—climbing. Still not entirely clear is why modification of two toes should benefit tree-climbers. Even those who accept this explanation must concede that bandicoots have diverged from tree-climbing ancestors and have taken to the ground.

Bandicoots have changed from their ancestors by developing more commodious pouches. These open downward and backward, as with the carnivorous marsupials.

In general appearance, a less-specialized bandicoot such as *Isoodon*, the short-nosed bandicoot (6–9), resembles a marsupial mouse. The long, conical snout is an easily noticed distinction shared by bandicoots, and is most pronounced in the other genera such as *Macrotis* (6–10) and *Chaeropus* (6–11). This pointed face is ideal for poking into the conical holes bandicoots dig in search of larvae. The front legs whir with activity when digging, but the excavations are mostly for exposing prey, and are usually too small to be useful as dens. Rather, bandicoots live in nests of stick or grass, secluded in underbrush, crevices, or rock piles. An exception to this is the bilby *Macrotis* (6–10), which can use both its broad-nailed forearms and its horn-tipped tail in digging, and thus manages to dig small burrows for nesting. Bilbies exceed other bandicoots in ear size, a fact that is

6–10. The rabbit-eared bandicoot, or bilby (*Macrotis lagotis*), has long ears which aid it in its nocturnal forays.

6–11. The rare pig-footed bandicoot, *Chaeropus ecaudatus,* has fewer toes than other marsupials, a fact perhaps related to its running gait.

celebrated in the nickname "rabbit-eared bandicoot." The bilby is also outstanding among bandicoots in its flattened molars, suited to a wider diet than the needle-tipped molars—almost like those of insectivores—found in other bandicoots.

The rare pig-footed bandicoot (6–11) combines a highly modified forefoot (6–1), ideal for scratching in the earth, with a specialized hindfoot. The slender limbs of *Chaeropus* may be likened to those of a deer. Digging nets it edible bulbs and roots; these bulk largest in its diet, which is supplemented by seeds, leaves, and an occasional insect.

Isoodon, Perameles, Macrotis, and *Chaeropus* are all terrestrial and are widespread throughout the Australian mainland. *Peroryctes, Microperoryctes,* and *Echymipera,* however, have managed to adapt to jungle-like conditions in New Guinea. One, *Peroryctes longicauda,* even manages to live as high as twelve thousand feet on Mount Wilhelmina. One genus, *Rhynchomeles,* is restricted to Ceram, an island west of New Guinea. Bandicoots thus manage a fantastic range of conditions, from snowy Tasmania to steamy tropics of northern Queensland and New Guinea, to New Guinea's alpine peaks; from wet rain forest in Queensland to the definitive aridity of Australia's "red center." In form, the bandicoots give little external indication of this range of ecological talents. Here is a story of adaptive radiation, but a cryptic story told in terms of physiological tolerance, not striking structures.

Endemic to small offshore islands of Australia are a series of bandicoots: a distinct species, *Isoodon barrowensis* (Barrow Island, Western Australia), a distinct subspecies, *I. obesulus nauticus* (Franklin Islands, South Australia), and a race of *Perameles bougainvillei* (islands near Shark Bay, Western Australia). All of these are appreciably smaller than their closest relatives on the mainland—perhaps for reasons discussed in Chapter 7.

THE HERBIVORES

Although much of it has now yielded to cities and to agriculture, a vast *Eucalyptus* forest stretches from one end of Australia to the other. This forest, the world's most distinctive, is a botanical labyrinth of a great variety of plants, some uncatalogued as yet, which accompany the eucalypts in their span across the continent. Although animal prey for the marsupials to hunt is somewhat limited in kind and quantity, the potential supply of plant food is enormous. However, the numerous spiny plants seem to defy consumption; the fibrous, oily leaves of the eucalypts seem unlikely forage. Time and the inexorable forces of evolution have permitted marsupials to poach on this rich reserve of vegetable matter. In details of teeth and digestive system alone we could read the ways in which the herbivores have exploited these resources, from roots to nectar.

A condition called diprotodonty (6–1) is a prime clue to how this has been accomplished. Somewhat in the fashion of rodents, the number of incisors has been reduced in the herbivores to three or fewer on each side on both upper and lower jaws, and their shape has become suited to chopping vegetable matter rather than tearing of meat. Marsupial herbivores possess another distinction, one not readily visible, a new brain structure (6–1).

Wombats. The wombat has been variously compared to badgers, beavers, and many other animals, but in truth no comparison fits very well. Wombats are large—up to eightly pounds—stubby and almost tailless, with short legs (6–12). The legs are powerful, equipped with long claws useful in digging for roots. Typically, wombats graze on grass, but they can vary their intake with such items as inner bark of certain trees or fungi. The burrowing ability of wombats is expressed not so much in food-seeking as in homemaking. Lying on its side, a wombat applies all four feet to the task of burrow-excavation. Burrows can be as much as one hundred feet in length. A nest made of bark finishes the artificial cavern.

Inefficient in reproduction, wombats bear only a single young each year. Unlike carnivores, wombats have only two nipples, but like carnivores, a backwardly opening pouch protects the infant. Although nocturnal and supposedly grumpy, wombats prove to be friendly, perhaps because they secure food by peacefully

6–12. A clumsy short-legged tailless animal, the wombat (*Vombatus hirsutus*) is well adapted to its ground-living habit. (New York Zoological Society photo.)

grazing, not killing. Like other herbivorous marsupials, they can be easily converted into pets by those who enjoy an oversized affectionate animal capable of tricks and antics but not easily broken of the burrow-digging habit. The ancestor of wombats may have lived in trees, if syndactyly is related to climbing ability. Moreover, the stub-like tail still contains vestiges of muscles which some tree-loving marsupials use in winding their prehensile tails around branches.

Koala. The koala, *Phascolarctos cinereus* (6–13), is often considered the lone representative of a family, Phascolarctidae. Although formerly similarities with phalangers were emphasized, some zoologists now feel evidence favors a closer relationship between wombats and the koala. Second only to the kangaroo as a symbol of Australia's wildlife, the koala appeals to many as a gentle creature (which it is), rather like a bear (which it is not). A koala might better be considered a sort of upended wombat (or perhaps the wombat should be considered a horizontalized koala).

Like a wombat, the koala has granular foot pads instead of the ridged ones one might expect in a tree-dwelling animal. The claws are geared to clinging rather than digging, however. Conforming to the wombat pattern, a koala's pouch opens backward—or rather, downward, since the animal is usually in an upright position. This would seem an "evolutionary mistake," because an infant might fall out; actually, strong muscles around the pouch prevent such a mishap. Koalas breed only every other year, and only a single young is produced in a breeding season. When old enough to leave the pouch, a baby (about seven inches in length) elects to cling to its mother's back, a habit common to many marsupials, but particularly picturesque in the koala.

Besides the low rate of reproduction, an extremely specialized diet makes the koala an effete or vulnerable creature. It not only prefers, it is restricted to the leaves of just a few species of *Eucalyptus.* Even these species sometimes have young leaves, as on sucker shoots, which contain a poison (hydrocyanic acid), so koalas must exercise further care in their choice of leaves. *Eucalyptus* leaves are thick, but filled with tough fibers and pungent oils, both features which lower digestive value and irritate intestines. To counter this problem, the koala has evolved an especially large appendix-like structure, the caecum, which effectively deals with eucalypt morsels, digesting them slowly. Also, a mucus-like substance secreted by the digestive tract may protect the koala against the roughness and pungency of the leaves.

Phalangers. The arboreal marsupials have found more than one way of taking to the trees. The koala depends on its claws to maintain its lofty position, but the phalangers have other means as well. Although the koala has a short, stubby tail, phalangers have tails which grasp, balance, even aid in gliding through the air. Far more agile than the koala, phalangers look quite different. Are they?

Authorities disagree about the classification of the greater glider (6–14) and

6-13. Australia's famed koala (*Phascolarctos cinereus*) is a tree-living vegetarian. Mammalogists now tend to believe that it is related to wombats, despite its quite different habits. (Australian National Travel Association.)

the ring-tail (*Pseudocheirus*); they reside insecurely in classification systems between the koala and the other phalangers. The reason for difficulty in placing them is that intermediate forms have died out, and so resemblances with both groups are evident. For those who classify, emphasizing differences often seems easier than discovering which relatives are closer. Zoologists now incline to place the greater glider and the ring-tail in a family, Phalangeridae, alongside the other phalangers. If we follow this view, we can regard the phalanger family as the group of herbivorous marsupials which have maintained the closest relationshp to trees. The tail of the koala may have dwindled during the period when its ancestors lived on the ground, but the phalangers have clearly spent a long uninterrupted history in the trees. They have strong nails, but the nailless great toe (6-1) can be opposed to the other toes, and thus is perfect for grasping a branch. The history of the phalangers has featured various sorts of tails. Moreover, gliding membranes like those of flying squirrels may have arisen three different times in phalangers. Phalangers do have in common a pouch which opens forward, seemingly a better adaptation to life in trees than the reverse condition in the koalas.

The greater glider *Schoinobates* (6–14) owes its name to its size and to the presence of winglike flaps. These membranes are attached to the front legs at the elbow, to the rear paws at the forepaw. In flight, the greater glider resembles a delta-winged aircraft. Among marsupials, it holds flight records—as much as 120 yards in a single glide. The gliding habit permits covering of a larger area in search of suitable food trees with tender leaves. The tail, as much as twenty inches in length, is evenly fluffy and perpetually in motion although it is not truly prehensile. On the ground, the greater glider is awkward and slow. Almost strictly a vegetarian, it dines on leaf tips and flowers of selected eucalypts, especially the peppermint gums. Appropriately, it nests in hollows high up in dead or living *Eucalyptus* trees. Like koalas, greater gliders bear only one young during a year.

Ring-tails (*Pseudocheirus*) are related to the greater glider but are smaller. Lacking hair on their tails, they are free to use the tail as a grapple or hook when climbing. Moreover, ring-tails lack gliding membranes. Searching for food at night, they sense their way with whiskers to various fruits and flowers, even invading orchards and gardens. Chattering or bird-like noises, diet, prehensile tail, arboreal habit—these are all features which render the ring-tails a marsupial ap-

6–14. The greater glider, *Schoinobates volans*, eats Eucalyptus leaves like the koala. A narrow gliding membrane permits it to widen its search for these leaves by means of short "flights."

proach to monkeyhood. Monkeys are absent in Australia and New Guinea, so the ring-tails are a logical evolutionary substitute. They are successful, ranging from cool Tasmania to hot Queensland, and in New Guinea from low forests to icy scrub at twelve thousand feet.

Smaller and more squirrel-like than the greater glider are the lesser gliders, which belong to the genus *Petaurus*. Like the greater gliders, species of *Petaurus* bear flying membranes, but have apparently evolved them independently. Lesser gliders seem to have evolved from something like the non-flying *Gymnobelideus*, Leadbeater's possum. Lesser gliders differ from the greater glider in diet and, appropriately, teeth: they have the teeth of insect-eating animals. In addition to insects, they choose buds, blossoms, and fruits. In captivity lesser gliders greedily accept cake and cookies and, given a chance, they will also rifle a vase of flowers in search of nectar. One species aptly bears the name of sugar glider.

Unique among phalangers is the striped possum *Dactylopsida* (6–15). Not only is it distinctive in the skunk-like black-and-white markings, it has a markedly elongate fourth finger. This specialized digit permits the striped possum literally to reach into new dietary realms. Larvae deep in wood crevices can be probed and pried out, and the love of nectar for which phalangers are notorious can be satisfied by dipping into beehives deep in hollows of trees and with its nimble fingers, extracting wild honey. Leaves and berries round out Dactylopsida's fare.

Notably fox-like are the three species of *Trichosurus*, the brush-tail possums. Long ears and a canine snout enhance this illusion. The brush-tails are deprived of gliding membranes, but are skilled in using prehensile tails for swinging from limb to limb. A hairy tail would seem ill-suited for this; in fact, the brush-tails lack hair on the undersurface of the tail, which thus can grasp branches firmly.

An equally remarkable tail is possessed by the scaly-tailed possum, *Wyulda*. As the name implies, the tail is scaly rather than hairy; this adaptation is like that of the ring-tail possums, but has occurred independently. Wyulda's teeth suggest that it is intermediate between the brush-tails and the cuscus.

The cuscus, *Spilocuscus* (6–16), is sometimes known by the scientific name *Phalanger*, a name which reminds us of its digits which, like those of all arboreal marsupials, have well-articulated fingers. The cuscus is rather large, and its bare tail is a classical example of what a prehensile tail should be. Despite its size it has managed to achieve a wide pattern of distribution in the Australian-New Guinean tropics. From tropical Queensland, it reaches into New Guinea, into the Solomon Islands on the east, into Timor and Celebes on the west. Cuscuses relish small mammals and birds as well as leaves and fruit. In their leafy warm forests, they can be found curled up, sleepy during the day, like sloths.

A marked contrast is furnished by the agile pygmy possums *Cercartetus* and *Eudromicia*, which resemble mice with prehensile tails. Corresponding to their size, these animals elect a delicate diet—nectar, small fruits, insects. However, it is a rich and varied diet, and the pygmy possums grow fat. They seem accustomed to drinking water in the form of raindrops as they run down leaves. About

6–15. The striped possum (*Dactylopsida trivirgata*) has a long fourth toe which enables extraction of larvae from wood. It locates insects by drumming on branches with its toes.

twice a year, they may sleep for weeks in a sort of hibernation, finally rousing themselves for another round of eager feeding. One species, *Cercartetus nanus*, stores fat in its tail during winter months in the same way as the marsupial mouse *Sminthopsis*. Because they are capable of digesting a wide variety of foods, they can afford to become selective, and often develop narrow preferences in captivity. They are equally particular about which kinds of bark they employ to "feather" their nests high in trees.

A close relative of the pygmy possums which has evolved its gliding membrane independently of the other gliders is *Acrobates*, the minute pygmy glider (6–17). The membranes are wide, reaching from front forepaws to rear forepaws. The tail is curiously winged with bristles, its flattened expanse noted in the common name "feather-tail glider." *Acrobates* can carry leaves rolled up in its tail. An animal the size of the bowl of a tablespoon, the pygmy glider plies gracefully from twig to twig. The small nectar-filled cups of *Eucalyptus* or bottle-brush

6–16. The spotted cuscus (*Spilocuscus maculatus*) is a tropical marsupial much like a monkey in its habits, prehensile tail, and diet. (New York Zoological Society photo.)

flowers offer meals in keeping with the pygmy glider's size. To balance its intake with proteins, a world of small insects suits *Acrobates*. The nest is constructed from leaves, which can be pushed up around the entrance to shut out daylight when the pygmy glider is asleep inside. These minute animals can be found in forests of eastern and southern Australia.

Isolated in forests of Western Australia is an anomalous phalanger, *Tarsipes*, the honey possum (6–18). Its teeth are described as "degenerate," in keeping with its diet, composed mostly of nectar. Its pointed snout, narrow mouth, and long, cylindrical tongue (see also 10–19) betray it as an animal basically devoted to the craft of extracting nectar from tubular flowers. Like that of a moth or bird, its tongue is extensible, skillfully darting down a narrow flower. The narrow mouth of the honey possum is modified into a sort of tube for sucking up nectar. *Tarsipes* is also agile at catching flies and moths and eats pollen as well; these are easily taken during its nectar-seeking rounds. Delicate feet and a prehensile tail

6–17. Smallest of the gliding marsupials, the feather-tail glider (*Acrobates pygmaeus*) is an agile nocturnal nectar-seeker.

aid *Tarsipes* in its flower-to-flower forays. Although certain bats are known to pollinate flowers, *Tarsipes* is well-nigh unique among land mammals in its pollination activities (Chapter 10).

Kangaroos and Their Allies. If kangaroos were not such common animals, we would be much more impressed with them. We would recognize them for what they are, among the unlikeliest of animals. One feature which is so obvious as to escape notice is that kangaroos are large animals—on a scale with the vast and open plains of Australia itself. Kangaroos, however, are not without smaller antecedents; the stature they have attained derives from a steady evolutionary progress. Fortunately, many stages in this series are still alive for our observation.

The most unspecialized ancestors in the kangaroo line appear like marsupial mice, and are called rat kangaroos. Unlike marsupial mice, they are syndactylous and diprotodont. The most primitive living form in the line leading to kangaroos is probably *Hypsiprymnodon*, the musky rat kangaroo. Like phalangers, it possesses on its hind foot a great toe opposable to the fingers, which aid phalangers in climbing but are no longer of such use to *Hypsiprymnodon*. Despite the fact that we could call it a non-missing link between the phalangers and the rat kangaroos, its appearance is very much like that of a true rat kangaroo, such as *Bettongia* (6–19).

Basic toward conversion to the kangaroo habit is change in legs and feet. On other continents, grazing animals of the plains are merely swift four-footed creatures, speedy versions of the general placental type; Australia's answer differs. Long rear legs are for flying hops, short front legs are for grasping, and a large muscular tail serves for balance and for defense. Undeniably successful in the

6–18. Western Australia's conical-nosed honey possum *Tarsipes spenserae* is perfectly designed for poking into flowers in search of nectar and insects.

Australian environment, these characteristics can be traced in stages: gradual elongation of rear feet, the gradual raising of the body trunk above the ground, propped upon powerful jumping legs. Progressive changes in teeth, inconspicuous at first glance, loom large to the zoologist who traces the history of kangaroos. These changes are directed toward the grazing habit. Secure protection of the young in a hopping marsupial seems essential. In response to this need, the forwardly directed pouch has been redirected into an upwardly oriented one, corresponding to the upright stance of most kangaroo-family members. As might be expected, larger members of the family have more capacious pouches. These deep pockets are in marked contrast with the tiny flap, hardly deserving the name pouch, in the primitive marsupial carnivores.

Rat kangaroos look something like experimental scale models of their larger relatives. In a similar way, their diet is scaled down to smaller items. Rat kangaroos graze on smaller grasses, roots, and fungi. Distinctions, particularly in teeth, compel zoologists to recognize rat kangaroos as a family, Potoroidae (6–1), or sometimes as a subfamily of the kangaroo family, Macropodidae. The short-nosed rat kangaroo, *Bettongia* (6–19), lives in open country but makes burrows. These burrows are lined with such nesting materials as sticks and bark. *Bettongia* has a curious habit: it carries such nesting materials in a curled-up tail, a habit probably carried over from its phalanger-like ancestors.

Rufous (rust-colored) rat kangaroos (*Aepyprymnus*) inhabit Queensland

6–19. The brush-tailed rat kangaroo (*Bettongia penicillata*) can carry nesting material with its tail. The bounding gait of this animal makes it resemble a miniature kangaroo.

forests, while potoroos (*Potorous*) inhabit swamps or streamside spots of south-eastern Australia. Another genus, *Caloprymnus*, haunts the most barren regions of southern and central Australia, but does not burrow—it nests in grass tussocks which sparsely dot the desert stretches.

Incredible as it seems, the fierce-looking extinct animal *Thylacoleo* (6–20) is thought to be related to the rat kangaroos. Much larger, it had teeth which suggest that it regressed to the carnivorous habit. It may have eaten, as 6–20 suggests, a kangaroo, *Procoptodon*, which also became extinct in the Pleistocene. We can only guess at some aspects of its appearance from the skeletal remains in existence, but the marsupial lion, as *Thylacoleo* is sometimes called, was a large animal. We can imagine it skulking through forests, attacking and scavenging. Larger than true carnivorous marsupials, such as dasyurids, *Thylacoleo* adds another dimension to the adaptive achievements of the marsupials.

Rat kangaroos lead almost imperceptibly into wallabies in size and general appearance. The smallest of the wallabies occupy an ecological niche much like that of a rabbit. In fact the name "hare wallaby" is applied to two genera, *Lagorchestes* and *Lagostrophus*. Inhabitants of scrubby plains, they even assume the sitting posture of a rabbit.

A striking case of reversion is shown by the tree kangaroo, *Dendrolagus* (6–21), a testimonial to the fact that marsupials have found the tree-living habit an avenue susceptible to repeated exploitation. Apparently the tree kangaroo's history, if we look far enough back, included a phase in the trees, followed by the terrestrial habit typical of kangaroos, then back into the trees again. While on the ground, ancestral forms lost the clinging toe—as have all members of the kangaroo and potoroo families. Adaptation to trees by *Dendrolagus* has been

6–20. Sometimes called a "marsupial lion," the extinct *Thylacoleo* was a sort of kangaroo-turned-carnivore.

accompanied by increased emphasis on molars like those of other arboreal marsupials. Toenails likewise are longer and more curved than in terrestrial counterparts, footpads bear rough surfaces, and hind legs are reduced because the hopping habit has been abandoned. Larger than phalangers, tree kangaroos do not compete with Australia's possums, for food articles are roughly in proportion to body size. *Dendrolagus* (literally, the "tree rabbit") does feed on fruits, leaves, and ferns, however.

Rock wallabies (*Petrogale* and *Peradorcas*) are upright and use their tails for both balancing and "steering." The name "rock wallaby" is especially appropriate, for they inhabit rocky, hilly regions. Telltale feet reveal this: particularly thick pads protect rear feet; soles are like sandpaper. These feet have left their mark on the Australian landscape—floors of caves frequented by rock wallabies become polished like marble. Rock wallabies have diversified agility: they are known to make skillful leaps in rocky or open country, but climb and perch in trees. When a rock wallaby is aloft in a tree, its tail acts like that of the tree kangaroo. Rock wallabies occur only on the Australian mainland.

Nail-tails (*Onychogalea*) are silky-haired wallabies provided with a horny tail tip. Curiously, no clear notion of the function of this "nail" has yet been formulated, but some have suggested it might resist the rough wear possible when the tail is used in nest-building or as a lever in jumping. The species of *Onychogalea* with the longest nail, the northern nail-tail wallaby, faces the most rugged terrain.

6–21. This tree kangaroo (*Dendrolagus matschiei*) from New Guinea's highlands represents a switch in habit from the plains to the trees by a segment of the kangaroo family.

Scrub wallabies (*Setonix* and *Thylogale*) are relatively small, and prefer open shrubby forest. In size and general appearance they are almost squirrel-like. The quokka, *Setonix brachyurus* (6–22), is easily seen on offshore islands of Western Australia; it has almost vanished on the mainland. On Rottnest Island, it has abandoned nocturnal habits in favor of accepting daytime handouts from tourists, who find it will eat almost anything and prove very friendly in the bargain.

Larger and more robust than the quokka are the pademelons, *Thylogale* (6–23). Pademelons live only on the eastern fringe of the Australian mainland

6–22. The easily tamed quokka (*Setonix brachyurus*) is a diminutive short-tailed kangaroo from Western Australia.

and on Tasmania; they frequent the denser forests whose floor is covered with tough-leaved shrubs.

Largest of the wallabies belong to the genus *Protemnodon* (6–23). Differing from tree kangaroos basically in dental matters, the true wallabies would probably be identified by the uninitiated as kangaroos. Wallabies tend to be more upright; some of them frequent forests and scrub, whereas kangaroos prefer plains. Some wallabies even cope with thicketed forest. Wallabies, then, are vegetarians of the scrub or grazers of the forest.

Some species of *Macropus,* the genus to which true kangaroos belong, are so wallaby-like that they enjoy the hybrid name "wallaroo" (6–24). The true kangaroos, however, are animals of the open plain; corresponding to the breadth of the terrain, the trunk of the kangaroo body is more nearly horizontal than is that of wallabies. Living "parallel" to the ground in this fashion, their loping forward gait can at times yield to fantastic vaulting—a leap over a lumber pile twenty-seven feet long and ten feet high has been reported. Statistics show a kangaroo can attain thirty miles per hour; so great is its muscular mastery of level ground that while running, it is airborne 70 per cent of the time. Specifications on aquatic locomotion—which one ordinarily does not associate with kangaroos—would be equally impressive. Not generally appreciated is the great versatility of a kangaroo's limbs. Males have been seen to fight with both hind legs, standing on their tails. When kangaroos move slowly, hind legs move forward, momentarily resting on the arms, while the tail pushes the body forward. Profiting from the shade of a tree or rock to sleep during the morning, kangaroos begin to graze in late afternoon. Small wisps of vegetation, eaten in sufficient quantity, suffice quite well. Kangaroos weigh up to two hundred pounds, and thus are the largest of living marsupials. Perhaps among the most specialized of Australia's marsupials also, kangaroos form the logical apex for the marsupial phylogenetic tree (6–1).

6–23. Above, a rare albino individual of the Tasmania pademelon, *Thylogale billardieri.* (Australian National Travel Association.) Below, the dark-gray swamp wallaby, *Protemnodon bicolor.* Kangaroo-like in appearance, *Protemnodon* stands more upright, does not lope over long distances as kangaroos do (New York Zoological Society photo).

6–24. The wallaroo or euro (*Macropus robustus*) above, is large, shorter-tailed, upright. It frequents rocky country and is good at climbing. The red kangaroo (*Macropus rufus*) below has a long tail, a body nearly horizontal when standing; capable of enormous forward leaps, it is an ideal plains animal. (Australian National Travel Association.)

A Rhinoceros Parallel. Fossil remains of a huge marsupial beast, *Nototherium* (6–25), have caused some zoologists to envision this animal as an approach to the rhinoceros habit. The comparison is tempting, if rather superficial. *Nototherium* did approximate the rhinoceros in size, but its appearance must have been somewhat more like that of an overgrown wombat. We can imagine this animal, alive as recently as the Pleistocene, sluggishly grazing in swampy areas. Climatic changes may have caused its extinction; *Nototherium* probably needed wide stretches of suitable grassy fodder which have now disappeared. Less able to adapt to changing conditions than the smaller marsupials, it nevertheless was a high-water mark in demonstrating the capability of the marsupials, aided by isolation, to reproduce the adaptive modes of placentals. The systematic position of *Nototherium* is not clear; it is a member of the phalangeroid line, and may, if certain details in teeth can be trusted, be closer to the phalangers (in the wider sense).

THE EPIC OF RADIATION

We can no longer suppose, as Darwin did, that Australia's marsupials are "divided into groups differing but little from each other, and feebly representing . . . carnivorous, ruminant and rodent mammals." This opinion is far from the mark, probably because Darwin and his contemporaries were overawed with the way in which placental mammals, when introduced into Australia, succeeded in overwhelming the marsupials. Because they evolved in isolation, Australia's marsupials never evolved superiority in competition for particular niches. On continents dominated by placentals, relentless selection has hammered out placentals able to compete well for particular niches, able to compete even on continents to which they are not native but have been introduced. The Australian marsupials have "made the mistake" not of differentiating poorly, but of winning campaigns for special habitats unopposed and thus never developing ways of countering potential competitors.

The epic of Australian marsupials goes beyond other examples of adaptive radiation on islands in several ways. The scale of radiation is larger because the area is larger, time has been longer, and the greater complexity of mammals permit more spectacular results when they undergo adaptive radiation. Radiation has occurred not in a single explosion, but in successive cycles. Invasion of habits and ways of life has taken place more than once: this can be seen in the history of a particular group, such as the line leading to tree kangaroos, where ancestors went through phases in trees, on the ground, and in trees again. Or, viewing a particular way of life, we can see groups which have made parallel approaches to it: *Thylacoleo* appears to have been an entry into the carnivorous habit which the Tasmanian wolf and Tasmanian devil also occupy. A mixture of beetles and herbs is favored by some bandicoots—and then again by some of the phalangers, but the former are terrestrial, the latter arboreal. The same

6–25. *Nototherium mitchelli,* a marsupial often likened to a rhinoceros, became extinct in the pleistocene. This huge animal once roamed grasslands and swamps, and probably grazed on low-lying greenery.

habitat has been exploited in more than one way by the marsupials: a small animal, a medium animal, and a large one, for example. A bandicoot, a hare wallaby, and a kangaroo can coexist on the same piece of ground, even eating some of the same things, but they will each place somewhat different demands on that piece of ground.

Geographic isolation on a large scale has magnified the amount of radiation performed by the marsupials. The rift which for a very long period of time existed between western and eastern Australia induced separate development among marsupials of the two halves—sometimes with similar, sometimes with very different results. In some cases, marsupials evolved on one half migrated to the other with retreat of the sea covering the center; in other cases, the separation has been maintained. Here, for example, are genera which are confined only to one part:

EASTERN	WESTERN
Dasyurus	*Wyulda*
Dasyurops	*Tarsipes*
Phascolarctos	*Setonix*
Gymnobelideus	*Lagostrophus*
Dactylopsida	
Acrobates	
Hypsiprymnodon	
Aepyprymnus	
Thylogale	

The greater richness of the eastern part in endemic genera is due to the greater expanse of forests on that coast. The same patterns of east-west separation is evident at the species level. For example, two species of the potoroo (*Potorous*) are confined to the west, one to the east. Some genera, known by fossils to have been from both west and east, now live only in the east: *Thylacinus* and *Sarcophilus*, for example. Many marsupial species are restricted to small, isolated pockets: the hare-wallaby *Lagorchestes*, for example.

The separation of New Guinea from Australia and Tasmania from Australia has had relatively few effects upon the marsupials because it is such a recent happening. Nevertheless, some species are confined to only one of these three regions.

Those who manage to juggle mentally the many known facts about structure, size, diet, habitat, and various habit features will agree that the Australian marsupials viewed as a whole are a monument to unlikelihood. They are perhaps not so striking individually, but in their entirety they are a summation of many paradoxes, a unique evolutionary story produced by a unique land.

7 The Inadvertent Giants—and Dwarfs

ANY island is, for its immigrants, a new situation. Smaller land area, different food sources, freedom from competitors, maritime climate—these are among the changes a continental animal will "notice" upon migration to an island. This "notice" takes the form of evolutionary change. If an animal species is plastic, capable of change, its descendants will fit themselves to the pattern of the island environment. Among land animals, reptiles are more abundant on islands than other vertebrates; they are also more changeable. Reptiles are both ancient survivors and modern opportunists.

We may look to reptiles, then, as particularly sensitive indicators of the island influence. The story island reptiles tell is by no means a uniform one—which one would expect, for island situations differ markedly one from another. The world's largest lizard (nine feet long) is an island species. Two species of island lizards, one in the Old World, one in the New, vie for the title of world's smallest lizard: they are only a little more than an inch long at maturity. If these results of evolution on islands seem contradictory, they do agree in differing from their mainland relatives. The lesson is clear: an island species with even a modest amount of "evolutionary momentum" will change, given time. Island reptiles, like those on mainland areas, are capable of evolutionary change, and the directions this change takes is governed by the island environment. Gigantism and dwarfism have not happened once, they have happened many times, independently, on islands all over the world. Something in the island situation promotes these two kinds of changes, and we must search for the causes.

GIGANTISM

Lizards. Varying from subtle to startling is the increased size of island reptiles when compared with their closest mainland relatives. The giant of them all is the Komodo dragon, *Varanus komodoensis,* an enormous beast that lives on Komodo and a few neighboring islands in the Lesser Sunda Islands of Indonesia (7–6); males attain nine feet in length, females, six feet. Although monitor lizards, of which the dragon is one, are large, the Komodo species exceeds the others by far.

Geckos are well represented on islands, so we might expect a number of giant island geckos. Although geckos as a whole average perhaps less than six inches in length, *Rhacodactylus* on New Caledonia attains fourteen inches and *Phyl-*

lodactylus riebeckii on Socotra is twelve inches long. On the Mascarene Islands Reunion and Mauritius, *Phelsuma cepediana* attains six inches, but on the nearby smaller island Rodriguez the closely related *P. guentheri* is almost twice that long, eleven inches. Other large geckos include *Gehyra* from New Zealand (7–10), *Tarentola gigas* from the Cape Verde Islands, and two species of *Aristelliger* (*A. lar, A. nelsoni*) from the West Indies.

Even more conspicuous for gigantism are the iguanid lizards. Among the most famous example are the two Galápagos genera: *Conolophus,* the land iguana (15–13, 15–14) and *Amblyrhynchus,* the marine iguana (15–12). Because their ancestors have long since been left behind, these giant iguanas are difficult to compare with mainland relatives, which must have been smaller. Examples of iguanids which can be easily compared are pairs of species which live on islands in the Gulf of California and on nearby mainland Mexico, respectively. On the barren and massive island Angel de la Guardia is *Sauromalus hispidus,* markedly larger than mainland relations such as *S. obesus* (7–1). Huge and easily captured is the spotted chuckawalla of San Esteban Island, *S. varius.* These lizards live under rocky ledges and piles of lava, can be pulled out of their lairs by the tail, and make no attempt to bite. In most cases, the Gulf of California island iguanids differ less strikingly, but appreciably, from their continental relatives:

Island Species	Length, mm.	Length, mm.	Continental Relative
Crotaphytus insularis (Angel de la Guardia I.)	357	335	*C. collaris baileyi*
Uta slevinii (Angel de la Guardia I.)	297	278	*U. mearnsi*
U. squamata (Santa Catalina I.)	154	105–148	*U. stansburiana*
U. mannophorus (Carmen I.)	162	"	" "
U. stellata (San Benito Is.)	159	"	" "
U. martinensis (San Martin I.)	172	"	" "
U. palmeri (San Pedro Martir I.)	183	"	" "
U. nolascensis (San Pedro Nolasco I.)	131	"	" "

Some would say that these island species should be regarded merely as races of mainland species; they would also contend that the ranges in their length overlap those of mainland populations. Both claims may be true, but at least statistically, the island iguanids are larger. One genus of large iguanid lizards, *Sator,* is confined to two islands in the Gulf of California. The West Indies also contributes some sizable iguanids: the giant anoles (*Anolis equestris,* Cuba; *A. garmani,* Jamaica; *A. cuvieri,* Puerto Rico).

The night lizards, Xantusiidae, have also achieved marked gigantism on

7–1. Islands in the Gulf of California, Mexico, host unusually large chuckawalla lizards. At left, Captain Allan Hancock captures the rather docile piebald chuckawalla *Sauromalus varius* in its lava den on San Esteban Island. The spiny chuckawalla *Sauromalus hispidus,* right, is found on Angel de la Guardia Island; the curled-up specimen of a typical mainland chuckawalla (*S. obesus*) beside it gives a size comparison. (Left: Allan Hancock Foundation photo.)

islands (7–2). *Xantusia riversiana,* which occurs on three islands of Southern California (San Clemente, Santa Barbara, San Nicolas), far outclasses any of the mainland Xantusias in size. This species is photographically contrasted with *X. henshawi* in 7–2; the maximum sizes of these species are 179 mm. and 148 mm., respectively.

Among anguid lizards, *celestus occiduus* on Jamaica must be reckoned a giant. The wall lizards *Lacerta* (Lacertidae) in the Mediterranean region are represented by many island forms. Some of these are appreciably larger than those on the continent or on nearby larger islands.

Skinks, well represented on islands, number many island giants among them. *Riopa bocourti* from New Caledonia attains twenty-three inches; *R. garnieri* from the nearby Loyalty Islands reaches sixteen inches. The Cape Verde Islands boast an endemic genus, *Macroscincus,* whose name simply means "large skink." The Australian skinks, two of which are illustrated here (7–7), are remarkably large; some reach two feet in length. Other sizable skinks include *Didosaurus mauritianus* of Mauritius, *Coruscia,* a genus endemic to the Solomon Islands, and *Eumeces kishinouyei* of the Ryukyu Islands.

7–2. California's mainland night lizards are all small elusive creatures like the trio of *Xantusia henshawi* shown above. One species of this genus, *X. riversiana*, occurs on California's offshore islands; it is much larger than mainland species, and can be seen prowling in the day as well as night. (Photographs by John Van Denburgh.)

Snakes. Snakes are rarer than lizards on islands, and thus offer fewer examples of any phenomenon. One example of snake gigantism is the tiger snake *Notechis scutatus* from Australia. The dark-colored race on offshore Kangaroo Island is appreciably larger than those on the mainland. More striking are two genera of boid snakes, *Bolyeria* and *Casarea,* endemic to a tiny mound of rock, Round Island near Mauritius. Perhaps once connected with Mauritius, Round Island is a refuge for these peculiar snakes, which once may have existed on both islands. Angel de la Guardia Island, home of giant lizards, also bears an exceptionally large rattlesnake (*Crotalus mitchelii angelensis*).

Tortoises. Tortoises are no exception to the gigantism trend. Largest in the world are the renowned Galápagos tortoises (15–15). Close rivals are furnished by *Testudo elephantina,* the elephant tortoise of Aldabra Island, *T. daudinii,* from other islands nearby, and *T. indica* from Mauritius. The islands of the West Indies are littered with fossil remains of now-vanished tortoises. Some tortoises obviously survive better, or longer on islands, and the giant tortoises are among these. The ancestors which migrated to islands were probably, at least in some cases, much smaller, and a gradual shift to huge size has taken place in these cases since their dates of arrival.

If the above roster of island giants seems bulky and thereby dull, the list itself is an impressive one, and strongly suggests the effect islands do have.

OUT OF PROPORTION

Tails. Reptiles as practitioners of gigantism on islands express increase in size not only in terms of length, but in terms of various body proportions. "Plump," "stubby," "broad," and "fat" are among the words used to describe the distinctive condensed appearance of many island reptiles. The Australian geckos (7–3) are good examples, as are the Australian skinks (7–7). The tail, instead of being lean and tapered, the hallmark of a swift and agile continental lizard, is broader, more abruptly tapered, or even rounded and stubby, and often fat. A swelling near the base characterizes some, such as that of *Gymnodactylus* (7–3). The leaf-like tail of *Phyllurus* (7–11) could also come under this description, but it is also markedly flattened, an adaptation which goes beyond that of a mere storage device. The knob tail (7–3) has a tail which is almost nonexistent in its shortness. The stumpy tail (7–7) has a tail which is little more than a lump of fat, while *Egernia* (7–7), less modified, has an abruptly tapered broad tail.

Those who object that Australia's large size puts it beyond the scope of an island will find that the same phenomena occur on the smallest islands also. The West Indian gecko *Sphaerodactylus* (7–4) shows this. Appreciably more robust in its dimensions is S. *gibbus* from Exuma Cays (Bahamas), or S. *exsul,* from Little Swan Island. When these are compared with a continental type, such as S. *lineolatus,* the difference becomes apparent.

Heads and Bodies. The tail is only one indicator of a stocky form, however. Some island reptiles have larger heads, such as the rattlesnake *Crotalus exsul* of Cerros Island (Gulf of California). The Cuban crocodile *Crocodylus rhombifer* has a strikingly compressed and broadened form. Markedly wider head and body distinguish the Australian gecko *Nephrurus* (7–3). The fatness of the tail in *Sphaerodactylus* (7–4) extends to the body as well. *Phelsuma newtonii* on Rodriguez is not only larger and plumper than its relative *P. cepediana,* it has a shorter snout. The list of lizards with a more rounded form includes *Lacerta lilfordi conejerae* (Conejera, near Cabrera Island, Balearic Islands), *Lygodactylus madagascariensis* (Juan de Nova Island, near Madagascar), *Ctenosaura bakeri* (Utella Island, Honduras), *Uta palmeri* (San Pedro Martir Island, Gulf of California), *Xantusia riversiana* (Southern California Islands), *Riopa bocourtii* (New Caledonia), *R. mentovaria* (Halmahera Island, Indonesia), and the skinks illustrated in 7–7. This list does not at all match the list of lizards which are greater in length.

Genetically, changes influencing one part of the body may involve another. A gene or group of genes which make for a plump torso may also determine that the tail is short and wide. Gigantism, then, is not merely an enlargement

7–3. Markedly unlike other geckos in form are these two from Australia. The knob-tailed gecko *Nephrurus asper*, top, is a large-headed warty lizard. Its compact, plump shape may be related to habits peculiar for a gecko: it burrows beneath logs and rocks. The fat-tailed gecko *Gymnodactylus milii*, bottom, lies in rocky crevices. Its fat tail can become two-thirds the length of the rest of the body.

to scale. It may or may not be accompanied by a condensation of form, such as shortening of the tail, which would, in fact, make a lizard or snake comparatively shorter even though it is larger.

GIANTS OTHER THAN REPTILES

Other groups of animals support these tendencies. The larger Australian marsupials are giants compared with all other marsupials. Many island birds show gigantism. If they do, however, they are almost invariably the flightless ones—a topic discussed in Chapter 9. Gigantism in island insects is not unusual; it is in fact, a frequent part of their evolutionary curriculum. New Zealand's wetas (9–4) illustrate this tendency. The evocatively named *Macropanesthia rhinoceros* (7–5) is a giant burrowing cockroach from Australia. Females exceed two inches in length. It is entirely flightless. The Australian insect fauna is littered with

7–4. Geckos of the genus *Sphaerodactylus* are ideal for studying changes in form related to island habitats. The many species are native to West Indian islands and neighboring mainland areas. A typical mainland form is represented here by S. *lineolatus* from Costa Rica, above left. *Sphaerodactylus exsul*, below, is from Little Swan Island; its thick body and stubby legs are distinctive. At right is S. *gibbus* from Exuma Cays, Bahama Islands; its head, body, and tail are short and plump. (Drawings courtesy of Museum of Comparative Zoology, Harvard University.)

examples of gigantism, such as the mammoth walking sticks (Phasmidae), more than a foot in length in some cases.

A walking stick relative which mingles gigantism with self-protection is the leaf insect *Phyllium* (7–5). In dense rain forest of islands surrounding Southeast Asia, *Phyllium* perfectly mimics in its green color, flattened shape, and even the net-like pattern of veins on its wing covers the finest details of the leaves among which it lives. The flattened legs look like insect-chewed leaves; such leaves are very common in tropical rain forests. *Phyllium* individuals are between three and four inches long. If they were smaller, they would not match the sizes of rain-forest leaves, so gigantism is a compulsory part of a scheme of protective coloration, pattern, and shape for *Phyllium*. Most leaf insects (family Phylliidae) are island residents. *Phyllium* occurs on Ceylon, the Seychelles Islands, the Philippines, and the larger islands of Indonesia. A close relative, *Pulchriphyllum,* lives in India and Indo-China, while *Chitoniscus* occurs on is-

7–5. Typical of gigantism in Australia's insect fauna is a huge flightless cockroach, *Macropanesthia rhinoceros*, left (photography by Robert F. Thorne). *Phyllium siccifolium*, right, a relative of the walking sticks, is a native of Amboina in Indonesia's Moluccas Islands. In its shape, color, texture, and large size it ingeniously mimics rain forest leaves, which average about three or four inches in length.

lands north and east of Australia. Although leaf insects must have originated in Southeast Asia, they have survived mostly on islands, a fact which suggests that their evolutionary exercise in leaf-mimicking, although effective, has not been able to succeed as mightily on continental areas as in the relatively protected environments of islands.

Even a tiny islet, Marotiri (Austral Islands) shares in the phenomenon of gigantism. Visiting this islet, the Bishop Museum entomologist Elwood C. Zimmerman noted: "On the smallest of all the islands on which we collected, the largest species of beetle (*Rhynchogonus*) was collected."

DWARFISM

Before examining the reasons for gigantism in island creatures, we must take into account the reverse phenomenon. Especially among island reptiles, we find species which go well beyond condensation in form. The West Indian gecko *Sphaerodactylus elegans* has the common name in Cuba of *salamanquita de la Virgen*, (little salamander of the Virgin) because it is reputed to hide behind portraits of the Virgin, so common in Cuba. It can hide in wall crevices easily, because it is only 34 mm. (1¼ inches) long.

A small island near Madagascar, Nossi-Bé, is the home of 32-mm. *Brookesia minima*, a tiny representative of the chameleon family. Other dwarf insular lizards include *Lacerta lilfordi planae* (Plana Island, Balaeric Is.), *Phelsuma madagascariensis abbottii* on Aldabra Island (127 mm. long, compared with 200 mm. in Madagascar relatives), *Geckolepis typica* (St. Marie Island, near

Madagascar), *Chalcides ocellatus tiligugu* on Pantelleria Island, in the Mediterranean, and *Scelotes astrolabi stumpfi* on Nossi-Bé (200 mm., as compared to up to 500 mm. for this species on Madagascar). Most of these dwarfs occupy small islands which lie off the shores of larger islands.

Monitor lizards of the genus *Varanus* never attain the size on the islands of the Bismarck Archipelago that they do on nearby New Guinea. On islands of the Gulf of California, *Cnemidophorus canus, C. martyris, C. bacatus,* and *C. catalinensis* are little more than dwarf island forms of the whiptail lizard *C. tessellatus.*

Snakes show diminution in size on islands just as prominently as lizards. The rattlesnake *Crotalus tortugensis* (Tortuga Island, Gulf of California) attains forty inches in length; its mainland relative *C. atrox* grows to fifty-five inches. On the Greek island Milos (Cyclades Islands), the viper *Vipera lebetina* is only about half the length of the mainland relative: thirty-two inches vs. sixty inches. Similar dwarfing is shown by *Crotalus exsul* in the Gulf of California, the Hainan Island (China) keelback *Natrix subminiata,* and the Florida Keys racer *Elaphe quadrivirgata.*

Some islands or island groups are characterized by an entire series of smaller reptiles. The Lesser Sunda Islands of Indonesia and the Monte Bello Islands, off Western Australia, have been reported as having such assemblages. The Komodo dragon, however, is from the Lesser Sunda Islands. Evidently both trends can occur on a single island or island group.

Narrower body form characterizes a few island reptiles, such as the Bermuda skink *Eumeces longirostris,* which combines a slender snout with a short, thick tail.

REASONS FOR CHANGES IN SIZE AND SHAPE

Why should so many island reptiles be subject to these tendencies of enlargement or diminution in size, of alteration in proportions? These changes are only testimonials to particular conditions, faithful symbols of a new range of ecological conditions. What are these conditions?

Any particular area has a spectrum of animals. They represent various habits and sizes, food preferences, and periods of inactivity and activity. A few of these grades and types might fall within the ranges suggested by the following diagram:

> Small carnivore. . . . . .Large carnivore
> Small herbivore. . . . . .Large herbivore
> Nocturnal. . . . . . . .Diurnal
>   etc.

On a continental area, these and other gamuts of animal life are fully filled with suitable candidates—in general all that the food supply and space will bear. On islands, the chances of dispersal dump an uneven and impoverished assortment of animals. Do they match all the niches available to them? No. It would be strange indeed if they did. Instead, only a few immigrants arrive. If they establish, they reproduce rapidly, and are abundant. Biologists visiting islands on expeditions often note the great abundance of, for example, lizards. Even making allowance for the fearlessness of island animals, which would make them appear more abundant, populations do seem denser on islands than on mainland areas—in some cases. The explanation for this is probably (a) abundance of food sources; and (b) lack of other species competing for the same food. Reptiles on islands almost appear "released" from the competition which exists on continents. They are also often released from the depredations of continental predators, but not always. One author claims that owls on Jamaica have influenced the development of smaller size in the gecko *Aristelliger*, which is sought by owls. Smaller individuals might escape notice, hide more easily. Some cases of dwarfism on islands do not seem related to predation, but to nutrition. Snakes usually do not live on very small islands (provided they could have been dispersed there) because there is too limited a quantity of prey to support a successful self-perpetuating population of snakes.

Just as positions available are not the same in number and kind as job-seekers who present themselves, the opportunities on an island not only are unsuited for some immigrants, they do not favor all aspects of an immigrant which does manage to establish. Just as a man may be acceptable for a position, but must gain new skills to fulfill his occupation, an island environment "urges" an immigrant lizard to change in some direction. Some hypothetical stories may be used by way of illustration:

On an oceanic island, no mammals are present. Various lizards, including some moderately large ones, arrive. One of these larger lizard species is gradually able to occupy the role of a large herbivorous mammal. Changing its diet by omitting insects and tolerating a wide variety of plant foods, from flowers to cactus pads, it becomes the reptile equivalent of a sheep or goat. This may have been the story of *Conolophus*, the "giant" land iguana of the Galápagos Islands or the seaweed-eating marine iguana *Amblyrhynchus*, of these islands (Chapter 15). A similar history may have been experienced by the giant vegetarian chuckawallas of the genus *Sauromalus* (7–1).

On another island or group of islands, we can imagine a similar story. This island does have some large herbivorous mammals, so that niche is filled. These herbivores, however, do represent potential prey for a lizard—provided it could reach sufficient dimensions to conquer them. A large monitor lizard, following arrival, is able to evolve into just such an audacious habit. Living in rocky dens, it roams the steep, grassy, palm-clad hillsides in search of various animals. This scenario may be a biography of the Komodo dragon, *Varanus komodoensis* (7–6). Today this giant lizard feeds upon Komodo's pigs and antelopes. It is a reptile substitute for the large carnivorous mammals, such as leopards and other large cats, which have not been able to cross Wallace's Line. The strange habits of the

7–6. World's largest lizard, the Komodo dragon (*Varanus komodoensis*), can reach nine feet in length. Many expeditions have visited Komodo Island (Indonesia) to study the habits of this giant carnivore. (San Diego Zoo photo.)

Komodo dragon, native to Komodo and nearby Flores Island, make it one of the world's great curiosities. It became known to science only about fifty years ago. Since then it has been the object of many expeditions, which have elaborately reported and photographed this animal and its ways.

Gigantism in some reptiles may be tied not merely to conversion to an entirely new diet, but a widening of food preferences. A lizard increasing its size may be able to catch and eat larger morsels than its smaller ancestors, but it may also be able to eat all of the things its ancestors did as well. It can poach on the assortment of larger food items if there is no opposition from well-established competitors.

Also, gigantism in reptiles may be related to territorialism. An individual animal tends to guard an area it regards as its own. A larger animal could police a larger territory, which could furnish it with a more abundant food supply. Another possible inducement to gigantism is offered by the perpetual battles in which males are engaged at mating time. Lizards, as mentioned earlier, often densely populate islands, and specimens with bodies and tails damaged, perhaps by such combat, are common. Natural selection of a sort may well favor a larger male, and thus what may be termed sexual selection can be a catalyst to evolution. We may note in this regard that males of the Komodo dragon are appreciably larger than females. This process, of course, would be expected to happen on continents as well as islands, but it may happen more easily on islands because competition on mainland areas would circumscribe the changes which a group of lizards could make. Some have suggested another form of sexual selection: louder voices possessed by larger males would be more advantageous during courtship.

Taking another tack, we can imagine a hypothetical lizard on a small island with a strongly seasonal climate. Shrubs, herbs, and flowers appear rapidly following rains and then quickly vanish, as do the insects to which these plants play host. Ants, however, are relatively constant in numbers throughout the year, and provide some nutrition even during the dry season. To compensate for the unequal supply of nutrition during the year, the lizard evolves a thick fat-storing tail, and develops other aspects of corpulence as well. Hind legs become shorter, fatter. This body form is poorly suited to rapid movement, but for the insular lizard this is no disadvantage. The sluggish habit suits island conditions: there is not far to go for food on a small island, and birds of prey are absent, so there is no cause for sudden escape—except from a visiting biologist. This path has apparently been followed by a number of lizards. Some of the *Sphaerodactylus* species on small West Indian islands have this aspect (7–4). Several of the island representatives of the Mediterranean wall lizards, *Lacerta* (7–13) appear participants in such a program, as does the giant skink *Macroscincus* from the Cape Verde Islands. The Australian skinks (7–7) and geckos (7–3) are not inhabitants of a small island. Nevertheless, they have a dry season to endure, and thus storage of fat is appropriate. Moreover, these Australian lizards are relatively large

7–7. Australia harbors some very distinctive skinks. *Egernia major*, above, is commonly known as the land mullet because of its fish-like scales. It has an extremely fat, short tail. The stumpy-tail skink *Tiliqua rugosa*, below, is quite common in drier Australia. Extremely plump and well-armored, it is a sluggish storehouse of fat. (Above, New York Zoological Society photo; below, photograph by Robert F. Thorne.)

as skinks and geckos go, and their gigantism may be related, as with the Galápagos iguanas, to a new niche, which on other continents would be occupied by animals other than reptiles. Australian skinks are not exclusively vegetarians, but some of them, like *Tiliqua* (7–7), tend strongly in this direction.

There is a possibility that longevity may be related to gigantism. The Galápagos tortoises are of undetermined lifespan, but some must be ancient. A short lifespan, a quick life cycle, and perhaps thereby a small size might be advantageous if predation were heavy. But on islands, organisms are often released from the attrition of predation—predation by snakes, for example. Older individuals could be expected. A fast life cycle is no longer advantageous, and with such pressures gone, a longer juvenile period, a bigger adult size might well be the outcome.

Predation may explain natural selection for smaller size, as with the Jamaican gecko *Aristelliger* sought by an owl. There is, however, an explanation which may apply to more cases of island reptiles which have changed to the miniature mode. Size of animals tends to be roughly in proportion to the area they occupy. Elephants, bison, and lions require huge stretches of territory. This tendency for proportioning can even be traced in a smaller model, wall lizards on four of the Canary Islands:

| Species | Length, head + body, mm. | | Island | Area, |
	Males	Females		sq. km.
Lacerta galloti galloti	135	126	Tenerife	2030
L. g. palmae	112	98	Palma	715
L. g. gomerae	102	83	Gomera	370
L. g. caesaris	82	78	Hierro	275

7–8. Dwarfism is sometimes produced in the course of evolution on islands. The sphinx moth of North America (*Deiliphila lineata*) is represented on the Galápagos Islands by much smaller-sized individuals (left).

How can size of islands influence size? The explanation is surely not of collective starvation into a smaller size—not directly, anyway. Rather, we can envision a population gradually coerced into smaller size by natural selection. Just as the island giants are breakthroughs into new ways of life, so the dwarfs may represent penetrations into a miniature world of prey—or other conditions. The miniature island gecko *Sphaerodactylus elegans* and the minute chameleon *Brookesia minima* eat smaller insects, in keeping with their size—insects which a larger lizard, such as a monitor, would overlook. Thus, by gradually becoming smaller, a lizard species can escape into an uncontested world where tiny gnats are acceptable fodder. Island reptiles which have experienced gigantism and dwarfism have been prodded by natural selection to exploit large or small articles of food, respectively.

The smaller size of the Galápagos moths (7–8) and butterflies may relate to the very brief rainy season on those islands. After the rains, a profusion of short-lived flowers bursts upon the Galápagos scene, providing food for moths and insects only for a limited time. A moth which rapidly matures can complete its life cycle before the flowers fade and is thus at an advantage. This adjustment to the short Galápagos spring by moths may apply to other island dwarfs as well.

OBSOLESCENT LEGS

A strange turn of events which one probably would not have predicted has overtaken certain lizards. Skinks, which have made more numerous successful establishments on islands than other lizards (except geckos) might be expected to furnish more numerous evolutionary demonstrations than other groups of lizards. One of these experiments by skinks which at first glance appears a flirtation with disaster is the loss of legs in certain genera. *Brachymeles*, a genus endemic to the Philippines, shows a perfect series in degeneration of legs (7–9). Biologists are fond of such a series because it shows "non-missing links" in evolution. One may ask not only why this direction has been taken, but why incomplete—and therefore perhaps partly adapted—stages in a series should be left behind. The legless habit in *Brachymeles* signals a progression underground. Legless species are burrowing creatures, living beneath the ground surface much of the time. Those which still possess legs are terrestrial, seen at the surface, but they furtively scamper under leaves, into rock crevices, beneath logs. The small vestigial legs probably do not help much in these endeavors, for *Brachymeles* does not seem to suffer from their smallness, and the presence of such ineffectual appendages does not, apparently, disadvantage this creature, either. This tolerance has permitted a fairly slow loss, reminiscent of the loss of wings in flightless birds (Chapter 9).

Curiously, the loss of limbs related to "going underground" has occurred, independently, in other groups of island skinks. On Madagascar the endemic genus *Grandidierina* shows a series like that of *Brachymeles*. Front legs are lost in all

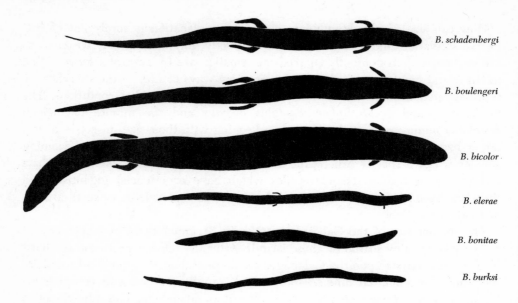

B. schadenbergi

B. boulengeri

B. bicolor

B. elerae

B. bonitae

B. burksi

7–9. On the Philippine Islands the skink genus *Brachymeles* contains species which form a progressive series toward leglessness. Evolutionary changeover to a burrowing habit is believed responsible for this alteration.

species; the hind legs are present in *G. fierinensis,* very reduced in *G. petiti,* and absent in *G. rubropunctata* and *G. lineata.* Isolated on tiny Barkuda Island in the Indian Ocean is the genus *Barkudia,* consisting of a single species, *B. insularis:* a skink with no legs.

Skinks with small legs (*Lygosoma* and *Siaphos*) occupy Australia, which is also the home of a distinct family of legless lizards, Pygopodidae. One of these, *Pygopus lepidopodus,* reminds one of the way in which Australia's marsupials have invaded and reinvaded a particular habitat. This legless lizard occasionally makes forays into trees, like a snake, in search of insects, spiders, and even small snakes.

There are legless lizards belonging to other families (Dibamidae, Anguidae) which occur on the Asiatic continent, but they are well represented on the islands of Indo-Malaya as well.

Statistical surveys of the wall lizards (*Lacerta*) show decrease in length of hind legs (7–13). This is interpreted as a regression: the pressure for rapid locomotion to escape from predators, to seek food, has vanished, so dwindling of hind legs can be afforded. Hind legs are shortest on flat islets, such as Monacone, and show an intermediate condition on steep, rocky islets, such as the Faraglione islets, where climbing ability is still valuable but need for rapid movement is not at a premium.

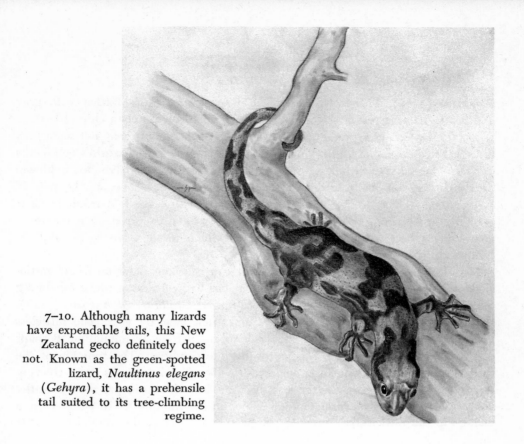

7–10. Although many lizards have expendable tails, this New Zealand gecko definitely does not. Known as the green-spotted lizard, *Naultinus elegans* (*Gehyra*), it has a prehensile tail suited to its tree-climbing regime.

TAILS WITH A TWIST

Change in size, as we have seen, connotes functional changes. Changes in form other than pure gigantism have affected reptile tails—tails whose owners have responded to some island situation. Lizards which inhabit trees are no novelty in tropical countries—but ones with prehensile tails are a decided departure. Two of these are very rare: *Cophotis* of Sumatra and *Hylagama* of Borneo. Although these islands are not free of prehensile-tailed animals other than lizards, these lizards (family Agamidae) have been able to enter the same way of life as monkeys and phalangers.

The opportunities for a prehensile-tailed animal were completely open in New Zealand, however. The only other vertebrates on New Zealand which have obvious adaptations to life in trees are birds. Development of a gecko into a prehensile-tailed creature under these circumstances was entirely logical. Not only has the tail of this gecko, *Gehyra* (7–10), taken on the attributes of a tail owned by a climbing animal, the color of the lizard has changed as well. Cleverly mottled with green like the leafy surroundings in which it has elected to live, *Gehyra* is very well concealed.

Protective coloration is joined to change in shape in an Australian gecko,

Phyllurus (7–11). This lizard has a flat, heart-shaped tail. Mottled with gray and brown like the rest of the animal, this tail would seem only a chip of bark to a casual observer—or a predator. An adaptation of this nature may not seem very remarkable, because examples of protective coloration on the world's continents are so common. Nevertheless, geckos on other continents have not achieved nearly the remarkable record that the Australian geckos have, as the pair in 7–3 also show. The great diversity of the Australian geckos is a result of their evolving in isolation, and probably would never have occurred on a continent containing a large roster of lizards, each of which would have its possibilities limited by the others.

Not all cases are easy to interpret. What can be claimed for an island rattle-snake which has lost its rattle? This is what has happened to a snake inhabiting Santa Catalina Island in the Gulf of California, *Crotalus catalinensis* (7–12). Ordinarily, rattlesnakes collect a series of rattles, year by year. The rattleless rattlesnake evidently discards—or does not form—such an accumulation. Perhaps one can think of this as a permanently juvenile condition. The function of the rattle in a normal rattlesnake is not certain: does it galvanize its prey, freezing its victims' attention so as better to strike? Or does the rattle protect the rattle-snake by frightening off large animals which might trample it? In either case, a change in the rattlesnake's predator or prey would effect the value of a rattle

7–11. The leaf-tailed gecko of Australia, *Phyllurus platurus*, is a fine example of changes in form which have been fostered in isolated conditions. The flat tail may be a storage mechanism, although it may also serve in protective coloration when the lizard lies upon bark or rocks.

as seen by natural selection. If capture of prey is not aided by a rattle on Santa Catalina Island, or if large animals which might prey on the rattlesnake are absent there, the rattle could be evolutionarily discarded. Discontinuation of useless organs is common enough on islands, as wingless insects and birds indicate (Chapter 9).

THE DUSKY ISLANDERS

Not only change in shape, but also prominent change in color affects some island reptiles. Like changes to gigantism and dwarfism, this alteration appears to have swept island reptiles, and therefore would seem to reflect something peculiar in the island situation. Why should island reptiles be black? Certainly this phenomenon is an extensive one, for a listing of island reptiles notably darker or blacker than their mainland relatives would probably take several pages. A few cases could be explained as protective coloration, but most blackish reptiles form all too blatant a contrast with their environment. This is certainly true in the Lacertas of 7–13; they are boldly in contrast with the weathered rocks, grayish to white, which they frequent. The Galápagos marine iguana (15–12) is dark in general tone, matching to a certain extent its lava habitat, but this is anything but protection, because it has no enemies. Other attempts to explain black-

7–12. A seemingly diabolical animal, this rattleless rattlesnake (*Crotalus catalinensis*) is native to Santa Catalina Island in the Gulf of California. The lack of rattles may be a sort of permanently juvenile condition (San Diego Zoo Photo).

7-13. On tiny rocky islets near Capri in the Mediterranean, individuals of the wall lizard *Lacerta serpa* are different from mainland individuals. The islet-inhabiting lizards mostly have shorter rear legs, shorter tails, and darker color. These differences are closely correlated with the requirements of life on small rocky islets.

ening of island lizards point to the predominance of insects or salty foods in their diet, but such hypotheses fail in too many cases to be taken seriously.

There is a relatively simple and satisfying explanation for melanism, as darkening in skin color is scientifically termed. This explanation has to do with regulation of the heat of an island reptile. Reptiles, being cold-blooded, avail themselves of sunlight as a means of heating. Black is the color most effective in absorbing heat. Lizards such as chameleons which are capable of quick color changes have been used experimentally to show that in practice a deep tone does have such a utility. In such lizards, color changes from pale to dark at dawn; when sunlight becomes quite bright, the color fades again. Few lizards, however, have ability for rapid color change, so a built-in color change is the only alternative.

Why should Galápagos lizards, such as *Tropidurus* and the marine iguana, benefit from such a thermal mechanism when they live on the equator? The Galápagos Islands are actually rather cool, thanks to the cold Humboldt Current which flows past the archipelago. Despite the fact that rocks do heat up during the day, the land can be cool on a Galápagos morning. The function of melanism on an extremely hot island like Socotra, home of a giant dark tortoise, is more difficult to explain. Such cases are few, however, and most melanistic reptiles seem explainable by the thermal theory. Most insular lizards enjoy a climate more even than that of continental areas. Cooler in summer, warmer in winter, island temperatures are greatly modified by surrounding water which neither gains or loses heat as fast as land areas, and passes on this effect to shores it surrounds.

A day which begins cool on an island will stay cool; midday and afternoon would be warmer on an inland area on the same day. Moreover, island shores are often whipped by cooling breezes, and always there is moister air which withdraws heat from a body more effectively than dry air. Under conditions like these, an island reptile would clearly benefit from any increase in warmth deriving from greater heat-absorbing capacity of a dark skin. Moreover, the increased body size of gigantic lizards provides problems. When a rounded object doubles in volume, its surface is not doubled—it is increased less than that. Coming full circle to the issue of gigantism, we might see how melanism would aid a bulky reptile. On a cold or crisp morning, a dark skin would come to the aid of a thick, fat reptile, drawing more warmth from the early sunlight, activating it more quickly for another day of island life.

8 Some Remodeled Plants

A FAMILIAR fact of island life is the tendency for a new island, ready to receive plant immigrants, to find itself in receipt of ill-assorted waifs of vegetation. Instead of depositing a broad spectrum of plants on an island, long-distance dispersal favors non-woody plants—herbs—most; it favors trees least. Why?

On continents, forest trees mostly have large seeds, poor for dispersal. Because these seeds tend to drop mostly within the forest where they were formed, they are not at a disadvantage. If seeds of forest trees dropped mostly outside of a forest, most would be wasted—a poor scheme for survival, because few forest species can grow in pioneer situations. Most forest trees require stable conditions, built up over long periods of time. A tree seedling in a forest encounters a difficulty: growing up into better-lit upper reaches of a forest, very shady conditions must at first be endured. To go through these earliest stages, to develop quickly a spread of leaves to cope with the shade, the food storage of a large seed is often providential. Herbs and shrubs, in contrast, often take advantage of open situations; indeed, they often require them. Seedlings of such plants can be found in the open sun; as soon as they sprout, they enter sunlight sufficient for their food-manufacturing needs. Large quantities of food stored in seeds would be wasted in plants of open situations—as soon as they germinate, seedlings can manufacture their own food from sunlight. Many herbs are most successful when they reach new, pioneer situations. On two grounds, then, herbs tend to have smaller seeds: better dispersibility so as to reach pioneer situations, lessened food storage because it is unnecessary in such places.

Those who are botanically acute will detect many exceptions to this plan, but as a generalization, it seems true—acorns are larger than poppy seeds. There are some small-seeded forest trees, and some have been successful at reaching islands (*Metrosideros,* for example). Others, larger-seeded but possessing fleshy fruits, secure transport by birds. Most trees, however, are misfits in long-distance dispersal and are left far behind in transportation to islands.

If islands are to simulate the varied vegetation of continents, occupants for vacant niches must be fabricated from the spotty collection of immigrants long-distance dispersal offers them. Tree arrivals will remain trees. The few which establish can easily sweep over their adopted islands. They may even form races, enter new environments. In the Hawaiian Islands, *Metrosideros* grows in bare lowland lava and also in high wet bogs—the same species, in fact. In the bogs, it forms small shrubs. One or two tree species, however, do not make a forest. Other

8–1. On Rarotonga (Cook Islands), a woody sunflower relative *Fitchia speciosa* (left) is a sizable tree. It has probably developed from shrubby ancestors such as *Fitchia cordata* (right), a species which is endemic on the summits of Bora Bora (see 4–3).

species, with other ecological talents, will find varied ways of exploiting the forest situation, ways tolerated by the dominant trees. These other, additional tree species can be recruited by natural selection from two sources: shrubs and herbs.

TREES MADE TO ORDER

The opportunity for treehood is often accepted by shrubs, which can accomplish this by increasing in height and developing a single main trunk. The products of this access to greater stature are not particularly startling—a large shrub is sometimes imperceptibly different from a small tree. The changeover can be clearly seen in some cases. On Bora-Bora, the sunflower-relative *Fitchia cordata* is only a shrub (8–1). As a shrub, it is well suited to the cloudy upper slopes of Bora-Bora, open and covered with low ferns or grasses. On Rarotonga, however, a deep forest clothes the slopes. From shrubby ancestors like *F. cordata*, a *Fitchia* equal to the situation has been evolved. *Fitchia speciosa* is a true tree (8–1) with a tough woody trunk. It is the giant of its genus, unlike any of the other species of this Polynesian genus.

A curious, but true tree has been evolved on Samoa by a family noted mostly for shrubs—Rubiaceae, the family to which coffee and gardenias belong. *Sarcopygme* (8–2) is literally yards away from its ancestors, which were probably shrubs with relatively small leaves. *Sarcopygme* plunges upward to the top of Samoa's thick, jungle-like forest with its single stout trunk. Sarcopygme's trunk

8–2. *Sarcopygme* is a genus of trees, native only to Samoa, which belongs to the coffee family. *Sarcopygme pacifica* has many aspects suggesting it is converted to the tree habit from a shrubby ancestor; few branches, huge leaves, congested heads of flowers are among its peculiarities. The tree, left, is about 25 feet tall; the heads, center, contain young fruits; the shoot at right includes a cap-shaped bud which will open into a head of flowers.

branches only a few times—or not at all—certainly the most efficient way to reach the upper portions of a forest. This habit, some will say, is not that of a true tree, but a substitute tree. Perhaps one might better say it has a palm habit, a crown of tremendous leaves borne in a rosette atop the stem. Corresponding with this growth form, flowers are borne not on thin stalks scattered over the plant, but on thick lateral stems, clumped into a head. Fruits are not only aggregated into this head, they are united with each other. *Sarcopygme* is clearly a recent entry into the tree habit, and one which is autochthonous on Samoa; the fact that it is strictly a Samoan tree helps in proving that it originated from shrubby ancestors.

Islands hold other such examples. The family Araliaceae, to which ivy belongs, is well represented on islands. These representatives usually have pole-like trunks, towering up through the forest, branching only when they reach the light. Such a plant is New Zealand's *Pseudopanax ferox* (8–3). This plant appears distinctly wilted, because the leaves point downward. As though to discourage leaf-eating animals, these leaves are armed with sharp teeth, so that leaves look like weird, corroded saws. The function of these teeth is difficult to understand, be-

8–3. Young plants of *Pseudopanax ferox*, an ivy-relative native to New Zealand, have downwardly directed leaves. These narrow leaves have saw-toothed margins. The strange habits of this tree have evolved on New Zealand, and may be related to the change from shrub to tree in the island environment.

cause New Zealand is relatively poor in leaf-eaters—although some do exist. When *Pseudopanax ferox* reaches tree height, the sawtooth leaves gradually give way to more normal shorter, wider leaves. Although there is no incontrovertible proof, circumstantial evidence suggests that *Pseudopanax* and other New Zealand trees belonging to Araliaceae arose from shrubs.

How many island trees can be traced to shrubby origins? Certainly some. Looking at the flora of islands, particularly oceanic islands, a discerning botanist would find that a certain percentage falls in this category, but clear evidence on this point is difficult to find. One criterion would be an island tree whose closest mainland relative is a shrub. The plant body of a flowering plant is relatively plastic, and contains few traces of whether its antecedents were shrublike or tree-like in mode of construction.

HERBS TO TREES

More spectacular and perhaps rarer is the phenomenon of herbs which change into trees on islands. Many botanists now believe that on continents, the great trend of evolution in flowering plants is from woody plants to herbs. This trend is undoubtedly valid, but believing that this is exclusively a one-way process, and that the reverse cannot occur under certain circumstances, would be foolish. In fact, conversion of herbs to shrubs and trees is not unexpected on islands, as well as on a few continental mountaintops. Those unwilling to believe this have to claim that the peculiar shrubs and trees illustrated in 8–6, 8–8, and 8–9 are not autochthonous, originating on islands, but are, in fact, remnants of some peculiar antediluvian flora. Actually, origin of these types from overgrown herbs is easy to imagine. Anatomical studies—few of which have been made on these interesting plants as yet—can also demonstrate this. As suggested earlier, opportunities for treehood on islands, vacancies open to whatever groups can evolve into trees, are definitely present. If ecological opportunity is aiding this change in habit, climate is, in a way, also catalyzing it.

For example, what would happen to a sugarbeet or a cabbage if you grew it in a climate with the same temperature all year? This has been done, both naturally and artificially. The results are curious, because these plants, instead of ending a year by flowering and dying, continue building stems, the leafy crowns pushed ever upward on a thick stem. Sugarbeets will look like the *Plantago robusta* of 8–4, except that flowers will be lacking. Cabbages under these conditions resemble *Dendroseris macrophylla* or *D. litoralis* (8–7). Changes in temperature, changes in day length corresponding to the annual cycle of the temperate zone trigger flowering. Where these conditions fluctuate less drastically, a plant may fail to flower for one year, several years, or indefinitely. Islands often offer these mild, uniform conditions, and so for a herb immigrant the necessities for flowering before the onset of winter vanish.

Herbs are not merely passive; they evolve so as to take advantage of these conditions. For example, the weedy *Plantago*, *P. lanceolata* (8–4) flowers, then dies, typical of an annual. *Plantago robusta* from St. Helena Island flowers every year, but continues growing (8–4, right). This habit reminds one of an annual which has been released from a compulsive annual cycle: the "pressure is off." An annual habit would be wasteful in a uniform climate: an annual would have to be formed anew each year, beginning with a seed. A perennial is not only possible in a uniform climate, it is more efficient—it can continue growth directly from its last-formed stem and leaves, bypassing seedling stages.

St. Helena Island is not the only island where this has happened. Independently, big perennial Plantagos have evolved on the Juan Fernandez Islands, on the Hawaiian Islands, and on the Canary Islands. *Plantago princeps* on the Hawaiian Islands and *P. fernandeziana* on the Juan Fernandez Islands have pole-like stems, crowned by a rosette of long, narrow, leathery leaves. The Canary Island *P. arborescens* is a shrub with narrow, almost needle-like leaves.

Transitions can be seen in a genus of succulents from the Canary Islands. *Aeonium* (8–5) exhibits a wide spread of growth forms. *Aeonium tabulaeforme* is not only a rosette plant which is flat, but its disc of leaves is closely flattened against its rocky habitat. After it builds the rosette it flowers and then dies.

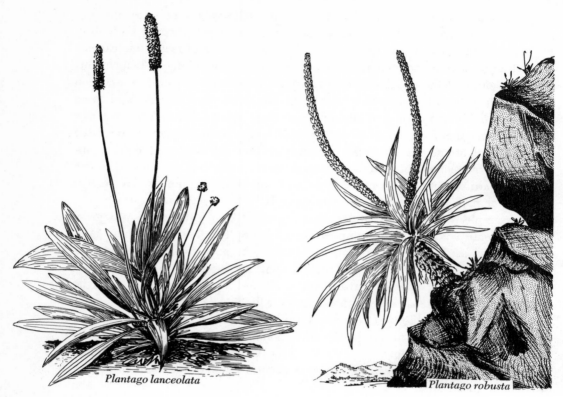

Plantago lanceolata

Plantago robusta

8–4. *Plantago lanceolata*, left, is a common weed familiar to many as the "plantain." On islands there are many species of *Plantago* which instead of being annual weeds, are perennial shrubs with rosettes of large leaves crowning thick stems. Such a species is *P. robusta*, right, from St. Helena. *Plantago robusta* has leaves approximately twice as long as those of *P. lanceolata*.

Aeonium glutinosum and *A. haworthii* represent essays in increased plant size. They could be defined as rosette shrubs: sparsely branched, leaves clustered at the tips of branches, stems somewhat succulent. *Aeonium glutinosum* has a long, thick stem and large leaves; *A. haworthii*, on the other hand, has numerous rosettes of smaller leaves, borne on thinner stems. Neither of these terminate their lives in flowering, but flower annually without discontinuing growth. The name of *A. arborescens* (8–5, right) suggests that it is a tree. Although it can be three feet tall, it is at best only a miniature tree. The branches are indefinite in length; flowers occur annually. The succulent stems are apparently not capable of good woody growth, and this appears to limit the push to treehood by the genus *Aeonium*. As a compensation for their lack of tough woody stems and roots, Aeoniums can form roots along the stems. These grow down to the ground

8–5. On the Canary Islands, the genus of succulents *Aeonium* has achieved a variety of forms: *A. tabulaeforme*, left, forms a flat leafy disc, closely appressed to rocks. A small dense shrub is the habit of *A. haworthii*; *A. glutinosum* has few but thick, tall stems, and *A. arboreum* (right) can form "miniature trees" about four feet in height. Aeoniums are popular in gardens.

and form prop roots, perpetually rerooting the plant as it grows up—and even when, because of its vulnerable succulent stems, it falls over.

The rosette-shrub habit is a successful one in the Canary Islands, and the story of *Aeonium* has, in various ways, been duplicated by other genera: *Echium*, *Kleinia*, *Euphorbia*, and *Campanula*, for example.

In Southern California, the offshore islands have a Mediterranean climate much like that of the Canaries. These California islands host a variety of endemic herbs-turned-shrubs. The roster includes the buckwheats *Eriogonum arborescens* and *E. giganteum,* and the sunflower-relatives *Eriophyllum nevinii* and *Coreopsis giganteum.*

There can be no doubt that lettuces are true herbs. At its woodiest, a lettuce plant would never qualify as a shrub. Because the lettuce and its relatives epitomize the herb habit, instances in which they have been converted into true shrubs—or even trees—would be particularly informative. As it happens, the world's woodiest lettuces are island genera.

Some, like *Thamnoseris* (8–6), are not very woody. *Thamnoseris* inhabits dry lava islands west of northern Chile—the Desventuradas Islands. In rocky crevices, *Thamnoseris* forms low, stunted, succulent shrubs; leaves and flowers emerge whenever moisture permits, followed by spherical bunches of flower heads. The erratic periods of growth and flowering are well suited to the erratic rainfall of these dry islands; the perennial habit permits rapid resumption of growth soon after a shower.

On one of California's islands, San Clemente, a peculiar woody lettuce has evolved. Not closely related to mainland genera, its distinctness has been appreciated only recently; it was named as a new genus, *Munzothamnus*. *Munzothamnus* is definitely a woody plant, its rounded shrubs reaching six feet. Large lobed leaves, up to eight inches in length, crowd the branch tips. During California's short spring, bright pink flower heads cover the plant.

The Canary Islands have produced a series of woody lettuces also. The starting point of these *Sonchus* species must have been somewhat like the European weed, widely known in temperate lands today as the sow thistle (*Sonchus oleraceus*). From this base, a group of true shrubs has evolved (8–6). *Sonchus arboreus* has a form rather like that of *Munzothamnus,* to which it is not closely related. Leaves are fern-like, and the heads of flowers are large and chrome yellow. *Sonchus leptocephalus* is quite different in appearance. The leaves have very narrow segments, a reduction in leaf surface which probably corresponds to the hot, drying lava beds where this shrub grows. Branched from the base, *S. leptocephalus* reminds one of an ocotillo. Flower heads are small, borne on wiry stalks. Stems of both the Canary *Sonchus* species are succulent and help tide plants through the dry season, when leaves wither and die.

The woody lettuces of the Juan Fernandez Islands located west of central Chile, however, offer an incomparable display of oddities (8–7). This is all the more curious when one realizes that the Juan Fernandez Islands are essentially a pair of small, isolated islands, which seem an unlikely spot to have spawned this assemblage. The genus *Rea* is a rosette shrub with leathery, narrow, smooth-edged leaves, quite unlike a lettuce in appearance. It grows in shady portions of the rain forest. Its flower heads, however, are small and rather like those of a cultivated lettuce. Similar in habit but quite different in flower structure is *Hesperoseris*, which is probably extinct now. *Dendroseris litoralis* has large leaves—a foot or more in length. It bears huge yellow flower heads and has thick succulent stems. In sum, it presents an ungainly sight in the grassy sea level

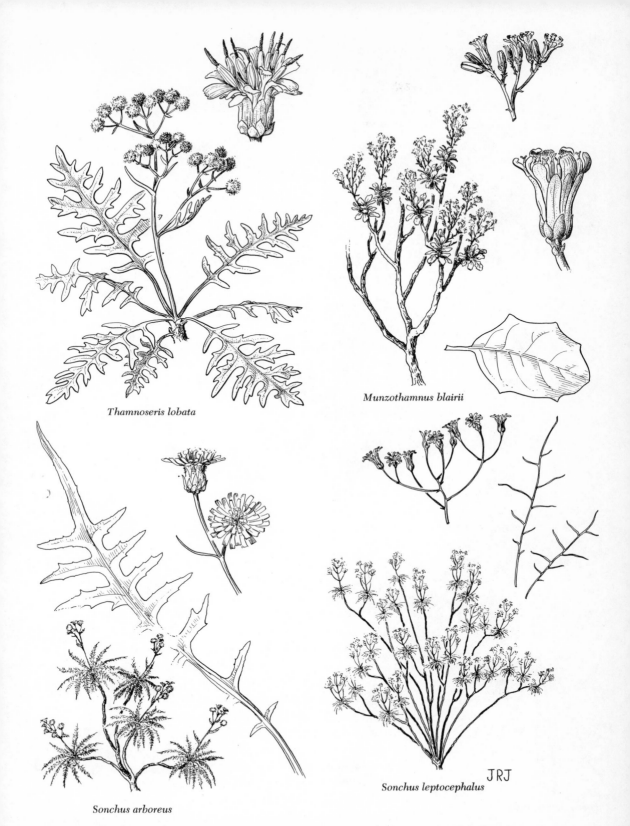

Thamnoseris lobata

Munzothamnus blairii

Sonchus arboreus

Sonchus leptocephalus

JRJ

8–6. Lettuce relatives have turned into curious awkward shrubs on islands all over the world. *Thamnoseris* forms low succulent shrubs (a single branch is shown) on Chile's Desventuradas Islands. *Munzothamnus* is found only on San Clemente Island, California. On the Canary Islands a distinctive series of shrubs is formed by species of *Sonchus*, a genus familiar to the world's gardeners through an annual weed, the sow thistle.

197

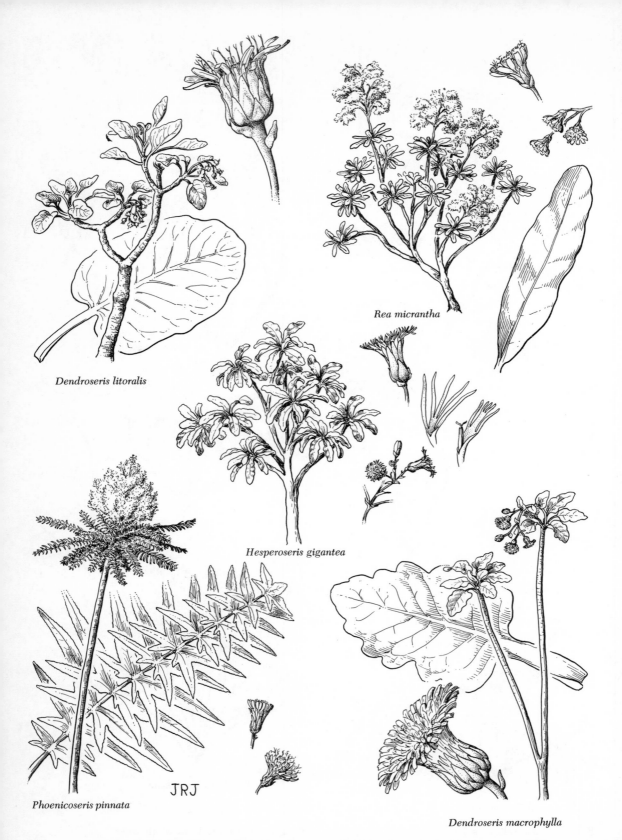

Dendroseris litoralis

Rea micrantha

Hesperoseris gigantea

Phoenicoseris pinnata

JRJ

Dendroseris macrophylla

8–7. The Juan Fernandez Islands, west of Chile, have fostered some remarkable tree- and shrub-lettuces. Differing markedly from each other in habit, leaf shape, and size, and details of the flower heads, they are probably all descendants of a single immigrant to these islands.

198

meadows of dry Santa Clara Island, a tiny islet near Másatierra Island. *Dendroseris macrophylla* is an even larger plant. It has fewer branches, larger stems, and heavy scalloped leaves—characteristics of a plant reaching into the light in foggy cloud-forest.

Unlike any other plant in the world is *Phoenicoseris pinnata* (8–7, lower left). Amid the scrubby vegetation of steep slopes of the Juan Fernandez cloud forest, it bears a crown of long leaves, their feather-like pattern unlike that of any other lettuce relatives. The stem is thick and unbranched, and after rising for years above the neighboring shrubs, it suddenly bursts into a cone of small white flower heads. This event, followed by maturing of seeds, terminates the life of the plant. *Phoenicoseris* differs in this single-flowering habit from the other Juan Fernandez lettuces. Another species of *Phoenicoseris* (8–8), *P. regia*, shows how the large leaf size is related to the single thick stem, as in palms. Leaves in *P. regia* are irregular in shape, almost like those of some fantastic variety of lettuce; they represent a stage leading to the finely and precisely cut leaves of *P. pinnata*.

The metamorphosis of these lettuces into shrubs or trees invites comparison with what has happened on other islands, to other plants. The Hawaiian lobeliads (Chapter 5) provide an almost exact parallel to the Juan Fernandez lettuces. Each growth form and leaf type can be roughly matched, showing that islands with a particular climate and a particular degree of isolation tend to promote these forms, these sizes.

Lobeliads in southeastern Polynesia prove that these trends are not unique to the Hawaiian Islands. *Apetahia*, on Raiatea in the Society Islands, and *Sclerotheca*, stretching from Rapa in the Austral Islands to Rarotonga in the Cook Islands, are shrubby lobeliads like Clermontias in their form.

Does anything like this happen on continental areas? Yes, but in rather special cases. On Africa's high alps are lobelias which look like huge enlargements of ordinary rosette herbs. Their solitary trunks, long strap-shaped leaves, clustered at the tip, have the habit of a yucca or an aloe. Mimicking this same habit in this region are senecios, members of Compositae, the family which has provided the high Andean meadows of South America with palm-shaped species of *Espeletia*, kin to sunflowers. Why have these plant forms, so much like some on islands—and representing the same families as these island forms—evolved on equatorial alps of the world?

A high mountain near the equator has a different climate from one in the temperate zone. Days near the equator do not vary much in length from month to month, the weather is cool, but almost uniformly so the year around. Thus, the climate is rather like the moderate conditions on islands. A rosette herb of indefinite longevity suits mountains with less pronounced seasons. Above the timber line herbs succeed, and woody rosette herbs succeed where true trees fail—because they belong to groups capable of rapid evolution to suit the unique environment of equatorial highlands. Lowland forest trees have apparently not been able to do this. The ancestors of the equatorial alpine rosette trees are temperate zone herbs, which arrived on the equatorial peaks by long-distance dispersal, just as did the ancestors of island rosette trees.

A FAMILY AFFAIR

Among the great surprises of the island world are the ways in which the family Compositae has performed under stimuli of island situations. To this family belong asters, sunflowers, thistles, chrysanthemums, marigolds, chicory, and even lettuce. Thus, the lettuce relatives of the Juan Fernandez, Canary, Desventuradas, and Southern California islands are but a few samples of the versatility of this family. The majority of the practitioners of the herb-to-shrub or herb-to-tree gambit on islands are members of this family. Going back to the Juan Fernandez Islands, we can see how two other immigrants belonging to this family have, independently, been drawn into this evolutionary endeavor. Representing the senecio allies of the family are three endemic genera: *Robinsonia*, *Rhetinodendron*, and *Symphyochaeta*. As if to prove the efficacy of the form taken by *Rea* (8–7) on these islands, *Robinsonia* simulates it (8–8). *Rhetinodendron* and *Symphyochaeta*, with similar forms, are closely related, probably derived from the same ancestors. Turning to the thistle tribe, we find the Juan Fernandez Islands bear two endemic genera: *Centaurodendron* (8–8) and *Yunquea*. *Centaurodendron* has much the same habit as *Phoenicoseris* (8–7) or *Wilkesia* (5–6). A single stalk, large leaves, and a profusion of thistle-like heads which terminate the life of a *Centaurodendron* plant are among the resemblances. *Yunquea* has this same habit, combined with leaves like those of *Dendroseris macrophylla* or *D. litoralis* (8–7). *Centaurodendron* and *Yunquea* were probably derived from a sort of South American bachelor's button (*Centaurea*).

The Hawaiian Islands harbor a number of Compositae which tend toward trees. The tarweed genera *Dubautia* and *Wilkesia* (Chapter 5) are excellent examples. Quite a different genus from this family, also a Hawaiian endemic, *Hesperomannia* has achieved the rosette tree form. Its nearest relatives are in South America.

However, St. Helena Island, a mere rock compared with most islands, provides us with a picture too remarkable to ignore. On this island there is a constellation of woody Compositae completely beyond any reasonable expectation. They stem not from one, but perhaps four immigrants representing different parts of the family. We have no way of knowing exactly how herbaceous or shrubby these ancestors were, but there seems no question that the stature of St. Helena's Compositae is greater than that of the immigrants which gave rise to them (8–9).

Three of St. Helena's woody Compositae—*Commidendron burchellii*, *C. glutinosum*, and *C. gummiferum*—are shrubs and reach six, four, and nine feet respectively. Their closest mainland relatives are asters. *Commidendron robustum* goes one step farther: it forms gnarled trees twenty feet tall, flat-topped and umbrella-like. Its large yellowish flower heads are pendulous, and its resinous foliage gave the name "gum tree" to this species.

A close relative of *Commidendron, Melanodendron,* is a spreading tree, fifteen feet or more in height. Large succulent leaves and blackish stems are commemorated in the name "black cabbage tree." Flower heads are white. Although *Commidendron* and *Melanodendron* are endemic genera, St. Helena's *Psiadia rotundifolia* is only one of many species of *Psiadia,* a genus of aster-relatives which grows in Africa and on islands of the Indian Ocean. *Psiadia rotundifolia* grows to twenty feet, and is distinctive in its numerous small flower heads.

Quite different is St. Helena's *Petrobium,* a genus of one species. Its closest relatives? Perhaps, oddly enough, they are *Fitchia* (8–1) and *Oparanthus* of Polynesia. Like *Fitchia,* it is truly woody; trees up to twenty feet in height have been reported.

Different specimens of a tree from St. Helena were once called two endemic genera—*Pladaroxylon* and *Lachanodes.* Today, botanists think they are only an endemic species of a worldwide genus, *Senecio. Senecio leucadendron* is a tree fifteen feet in height, both woodier and larger-leaved than its relatives on the African mainland.

The Galápagos Islands offer a similar assemblage of Compositae: *Scalesia,*

8–8. From small-sized ancestors belonging to three different parts of the sunflower family (Compositae), these odd trees have evolved on the Juan Fernandez Islands. Shown here are *Phoenicoseris regia,* left, a kin of chicory or lettuce; *Robinsonia masafuerae,* related to the groundsels (*Senecio*); and *Centaurodendron dracaenoides,* a relative of thistles or the bachelor's button. (Left and middle, photographs by Carl Skottsberg; right, photography by H. Weber.)

Aster burchellii

Psiadia rotu[...]
cabbage[...]

"Lachanodes"
she-cabbage-tree

"Pladaroxylon"
he-cabbage-tree

Senecio leucadendron

202

Commidendron robustum
gumwood

Melanodendron integrifolium
black cabbage-tree

Aster gummiferus
little gumwood

Petrobium arboreum
whitewood cabbage-tree

8–9. On tiny St. Helena Island, a bewildering group of trees belonging to the sun-flower family (Compositae) have evolved. Mainland relatives of all of these would be small, herbaceous plants. A minimum of four different immigrants probably formed the basis for this insular essay into the tree habit.

Macraea, Lecocarpus, and *Darwiniothamnus* (Chapter 15). They are all endemic, all woody.

Why have Compositae made this sudden venture into woodiness on islands, why do they have so many endemic genera to their credit? Darwin, in his *On the Origin of Species,* claimed:

"Trees would be little likely to reach distant oceanic islands; and an herbaceous plant, though it would have no chance of competing in stature with a fully developed tree, when established on an island and having to compete with herbaceous plants alone, might readily gain an advantage by growing taller and taller and overtopping the other plants. If so, natural selection would often tend to add to the stature of herbaceous plants when growing on an island, to whatever order they belonged, and thus convert them first into bushes and ultimately into trees."

Darwin's hypothesis was based upon his observations of the Galápagos Compositae. Compositae are exceptionally good exemplars of this process because: (1) they are a family of mostly herbaceous plants; some are clearly herbs, like the lettuces; others are somewhat woody, like sunflowers; (2) Compositae have small fruits with very good dispersal mechanisms, and are thus unusually well represented on islands; (3) the family Compositae is a large one, so that many species are constantly dispersing; (4) Compositae are very weedy in nature; they are suited to pioneer situations other plants could not tolerate; and (5) they evolve very quickly into new forms.

These specifications explain why Compositae have excelled as tree- or shrub-forming herbs. One can, however, question Darwin's claim that overtopping has forced increase in height. This would be a meaningless process unless a tree could be supported by the ecology of an island. Although ecological circumstances are vague and difficult to define, they may come closer to the true explanation. The Galápagos woody sunflower *Scalesia,* which influenced Darwin's thinking, actually grows most frequently in thinly populated open situations. With this widely spaced habit, overtopping of a distant neighboring bush would be difficult indeed. The tree species of the genus, *S. pedunculata* (15–3, 15–4), often is the only important tree species where it grows, so there are no competing species of any significance which it could have overtopped. Nevertheless, the direction from small shrub to large shrub to tree which Darwin hypothesized is, according to all available evidence, the correct one. There is no evidence favoring reduction of *Scalesia* trees downward to the shrub category.

Ancestrally, Compositae was probably a family of shrubs. Today both shrubs and herbs are common in the family. These have retained various degrees of woodiness, and various potentials for increasing their woodiness when provoked to do so by natural selection. Some herbs in the family have been wedded to the herb habit for long periods of time—the lettuce tribe, for example. When these increase plant size, they do so in an awkward and inadequate manner; apparently they cannot develop into true trees. This would explain the odd and succulent growth forms of the Juan Fernandez genera *Dendroseris, Rea, Hesperoseris,* and *Phoenicoseris* (8–7). *Fitchia* (8–1) has retained more wood-forming ability, and this explains why *F. speciosa* has been able to become a true tree.

TREES VIA A LOOPHOLE

There are some groups of herbs which have apparently completely lost the knack of forming normal woody stems. In such a plant, the cambium, the wood-producing layer of a woody stem, ceases to function almost as soon as it is formed. How to develop more? Produce a second cambium, then a third, and so forth, each with a little wood. This is how beets widen, as one can see from the ring-like markings in a beet. Imagine a relative of a beet which is developed into a tree fifteen feet tall. This is approximately what has happened in the case of *Chenopodium sandwichense,* a Hawaiian tree. Its ancestors were not beets, but were related to them: the genus *Chenopodium* is known to gardeners from species which are weedy, such as "lamb's quarters." A Juan Fernandez *Chenopodium, C. nesodendron,* has succeeded in becoming a shrub up to nine feet in height. The evolutionary factors which produced other trees, as in Compositae, from herbs are the same for these Chenopodiums, only the means of developing a trunk is different.

In a similar predicament are the amaranths (cockscombs, etc.). On the Hawaiian Islands, one of these has evolved a large tree, *Charpentiera* (8–10). The ring-like wood of this stem is exactly the same phenomenon seen in the rings of a beet, although with a little more wood and a little less soft tissue. Seen externally, this stem looks like any ordinary tree trunk, and gives no hint that it is basically only a herb which has built up a stem in a very peculiar fashion. Another Hawaiian amaranth genus, also an endemic, has managed this same trick: *Nototrichum.*

Another family, Nyctaginaceae (four-o'clocks, bougainvilleas) has also participated in this program. Genera sometimes segregated from *Pisonia—Heimerliodrendron* (New Zealand), *Rockia* and *Ceodes* (Hawaiian Islands)—are among the Pacific island genera from this family which have been built according to this plan.

Although tree ferns do occur on continents, they are particularly common on islands (8–11). Many areas in Hawaii, Tahiti, New Guinea, Samoa, and other Pacific islands are literally tree-fern forests. A tree fern is a sort of masquerade of a true tree. Ferns cannot widen their stems by producing more wood, as seed plants can. Therefore, a tree fern continues to grow upward without adding more wood to its trunk. How can it maintain a strong stem? Tough tissues other than wood may be present. More importantly, new roots are continually developing from the crown. The lower portion of a tree fern trunk is dead and does not conduct water to the leafy rosette. Therefore, these roots must grow

8–10. The Hawaiian tree *Charpentiera* must stem from a herb ancestor. The trunk of this endemic genus of trees is not really woody: the rings of woody tissue composing the stem are akin to the rings one sees in a beet.

from the newer, upper trunk all the way down, inside the stem, until they reach the base. They contribute to the strengthening of the trunk, and the base of an old tree fern is a mass of roots. Cut open a tree fern stem and you will find it is filled with roots. A tree fern, then, is only a rosette fern which lives atop its old dead trunk.

Tree ferns seem particularly suited to islands. First, the superior dispersal power of all fern spores enable them to arrive on islands before seeds can. If the spores are those of tree ferns, they may establish a forest, and tend to remain in spite of later invasions by seed plants. If the spores were those of lower rosette ferns, such ferns might evolve into tall tree species. The great height of tree ferns in New Zealand, Samoa, and other islands suggests that this has, to some extent, happened. Secondly, tree ferns are well-adapted to moist cool uplands in tropical regions, and are likely to succeed on islands which provide these conditions.

THE PARTIAL GIANTS

Just as insular reptiles have bodies which show over-all gigantism or enlargement of particular portions such as the tail, so do plants. Conditions on subantarctic islands favor large leaf size, but not a large plant. An island in far southern oceans is like alpine regions above the timber line having cold, whipping winds which inhibit any growth more than a few inches above the surface of the ground. The long days of summer near Antarctica, however, permit plants to grow almost continuously, day and night, for a short season. The mammoth cabbages which can be produced above the Arctic circle in Alaska are evidence of how polar climates promote this manner of growth. Because of these climatic

8–11. Tree ferns are not the exclusive property of islands, but they are a tree form especially abundant in these isolated areas. Tree ferns are not true woody trees; they are more like rosette ferns which live atop their own dead stem. Above, a forest of tree ferns gives the cool heights of alpine New Guinea a strange aspect. The fern shown, enlarged below left, is *Cyathea hymenophylloides*. New Zealand's forests are rich in tree ferns. One is *Dicksonia antarctica*, right, which has become familiar to horticulturalists all over the world.

circumstances, a subantarctic island might be expected to bear plants of the cabbage habit. One such plant is *Pringlea* (8–12), a native of the Kerguelen Islands in the southern Indian Ocean. *Pringlea* belongs to the same family as the cabbage (Cruciferae), but its cabbage-like form has been developed independently of that of the cabbage. Ancestors of *Pringlea* probably looked much like mustard or radish plants, and adopted the cabbage form in reponse to the natural selection exerted by the peculiar climate of subantarctic latitudes. The same course has been followed by other plants which inhabit these islands—the aster relatives *Celmisia* and *Pleurophyllum* on New Zealand's subantarctic islands have a rosette form much like that of *Pringlea*.

A simple explanation will not serve for *Brighamia* (8–12), a genus endemic to the Hawaiian Islands. In almost inaccessible crevices up the steep cliffs that form the northern faces of the islands Kauai and Molokai, you will find *Brighamia*, a plant that looks like a bowling pin surmounted by a head of lettuce. This is *Brighamia*, a member of the Lobeliaceae, the family which has furnished the Hawaiian Islands with many bizarre trees and shrubs (Chapter 5).

The stems of *Brighamia* are thick and succulent, often as much as three feet tall. Sometimes the base of the plant is rounded, permitting the stem to sway back and forth in the stiff winds that sweep the cliffs. The leaves also are thick and succulent, perhaps better to resist the drying effect of the constant winds and salt spray. Beach plants often show such modifications toward succulent leaves. Succulence is also desirable because the crevices where this plant grows offer little moisture. The size of the leaves varies with the amount of moisture available at any particular season of the year.

Brighamia is unique, and few similar plants can be found. On Guadalupe Island, Mexico, there is, however, a stem succulent which shows adaptation to coastal conditions in its peculiar growth form. This is *Talinum guadalupense* (8–13), a member of the *Portulaca* family. Talinums are small rosette plants, living close to the ground, but on Guadalupe Island this shrub-like species has evolved. Its long, gangling stems attest to the fact that continual growth is possible, winter or summer. Although temperatures are even on Guadalupe Island, moisture is not and this *Talinum* survives the dry months with water stored in its thick stems. At such times, the rosettes of succulent leaves shrink to a group of smaller leaves, which will yield to larger leaves and flowers when rainfall permits.

A giant stem is the hallmark of *Dendrosicyos* (8–14), an endemic of Socotra Island in the Indian Ocean. Like an elephant's leg or an ungainly column, this stem can be as much as twelve feet high. Undoubtedly it is a sort of gigantic succulent, storing water against the aridity of Socotra's desert-like conditions. To be sure, various plants in dry regions of the African mainland, belonging to various families, have this water tank type of construction. What is surprising about *Dendrosicyos* is that it represents a conversion into a huge tree-like succulent from a vine! *Dendrosicyos* is a representative of a family of vines, Cucurbitaceae, to

Pringlea antiscorbutica

Brighamia insignis

8–12. Among the many incomparable oddities of plant form on islands are the Kerguelen Island cabbage *Pringlea* and the Hawaiian lobeliad *Brighamia*. Pringlea's rosettes have evolved to suit the fierce Antarctic climate of Kerguelen. *Brighamia*, resembling no other plant in the world, is a succulent cliff plant. Topped by lettuce-like rosettes and long tubular white flowers, the stems rock upon rounded bases as the wind buffets them.

8–13. On Islote Negro, a tiny islet off Guadalupe Island, Mexico, sprawl the thick, succulent stems of *Talinum guadalupense*. The flowers, right, show that this plant belongs to the portulaca family. This species is a giant insular representative of the family.

which squash, pumpkins, and gourds belong. At the top of the stem of *Dendrosicyos* is a shrub-like collection of shoots, the leaves and flowers of which clearly illustrate that this is, in fact, its botanical relationship. Socotra's plants are derived, of course, only from those which once arrived on the island. Thus, it is a cactus substitute, created from some sort of squash relative which once arrived on Socotra.

DWARFS WITH A REASON

An alpine region, perpetually cool but moist, swept by winds and sometimes faced with brilliant sunshine, tends to evolve a particular type of plant. Below the timber line in such a region, a conifer is the answer—evergreen leaves permit use of sunlight throughout the year, condensed needle-like or scale-like leaves resist drying winds, freezing cold, and burning sunshine. Above the timber line, a shrub or herb-like conifer ought to be the best type of plant. With few exceptions, however, conifers seem unable to evolve into herbs of this sort, so various other groups of plants have accepted this role. Proof of a "need" for a conifer-like plant is suggested by the fact that in Tasmania the ever-plastic Compositae has evolved a genus of shrubs, *Ozothamnus*. The shrubs look identical to a cypress or juniper when they are not in flower.

Approaches both conifer-like and unique are offered by the flowering plant *Hebe*, relative of garden veronicas, which has adapted to virtually every niche New Zealand has to offer. Some *Hebe* species are known as "whiplash" species, because with their narrow branches, covered with scale-like leaves, they have the cord-like appearance of cypress branches (8–17). These vicarious conifers are well adapted to the whipping winds of alpine New Zealand; they are a vindication among flowering plants of the ecological adeptness of conifers.

Another solution to problems offered by climates of the subantarctic islands is demonstrated by *Raoulia*, one species of which has been given the name "vegetable sheep" (8–15). This mound-like "shrub" is formed of hundreds of stems, crowded densely and growing at the same rate, so that the surface of the mound appears very smooth. On each of these stems there is a dense clothing of minute, scale-like woolly leaves, so closely appressed to each other and the stems that each individual leaf is almost imperceptible. The compact cushion-like habit, a miracle of condensation, provides a minimum exposure of plant sur-

8–14. The family to which melons and cucumbers belong (Cucurbitaceae) consists mostly of vines. On Socotra Island, however, the vining habit is exchanged for that of an elephantine tree. This genus, *Dendrosicyos*, stands out in this family in its huge proportions and is endemic to Socotra.

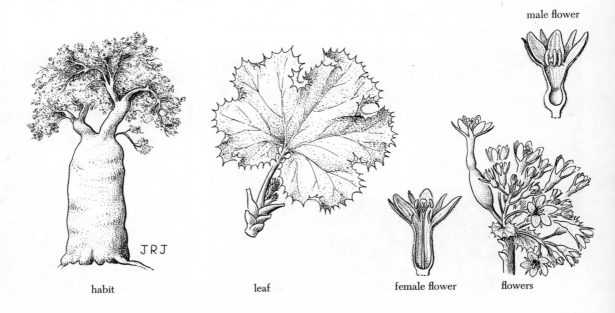

male flower

habit   leaf   female flower   flowers

8–15. Thousands of tiny stems, millions of minute woolly leaves make up this dense, tough cushion plant, *Raoulia eximia*, New Zealand's famous "vegetable sheep." This plant, a radical departure in growth form, belongs to the sunflower family (Compositae), a family of great plasticity in evolving new plant forms.

8–16. Typical of the shape of cushion plants is *Donatia novae-zealandiae*, inhabitant of New Zealand's Southern Alps. Dotted with many white flowers, Donatia's strange alterations of form make it difficult for plant classifiers. The hundreds of stems which compose a cushion are not soft; a saw is required to cut into the mat.

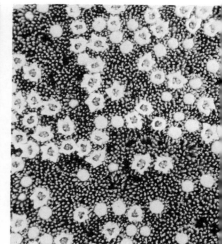

8–17. New Zealand's *Hebe* species range from leafy shrubs to this "whiplash" species, which mimics a cypress in its stems. The conifer habit of twigs represents an adaptation to the climate of alpine New Zealand.

face. The woolly hairs not only protect against drying winds, they reflect excessively bright sunshine. *Raoulia* is the world's most distinctive cushion plant—and it stems from ancestors one would not, at first, expect. The reader of this book, however, will by now believe that the family Compositae is capable of anything, and so the invention of the "vegetable sheep" by this family is understandable. *Raoulia* is, in fact, closely related to the papery "everlasting flowers" familiar to gardeners.

Other New Zealand cushion plants show that this type of plant form represents a definite pattern toward which many immigrants have evolved. *Donatia* (8–16) comes from the snowy mountains of New Zealand, Tasmania, and Tierra del Fuego. It forms tough, dense cushions like those of *Raoulia,* but its leaves are not hairy; they are bright green, and wedge-shaped. Because of this extreme growth form, *Donatia* plants look quite unlike their relatives. This difference in form, in fact, has confused botanists. Is *Donatia,* as some have claimed, in a family by itself, not closely related to other plants? Recent evidence favors the view that it is, instead, related to saxifrages. The small white flowers, although somewhat different from saxifrage blooms, seem clearly of this affinity.

An endemic cushion plant of the Kerguelen Islands, *Lyallia* (8–18), is a product of Caryophyllaceae, the family to which *Gypsophila* and *Silene* belong. The flowers and fruits of *Lyallia* clearly demonstrate this relationship, and other, not very dissimilar cushion plants belong to this family. On the other hand, *Hec-*

branch   flower   flower   leaves   branch

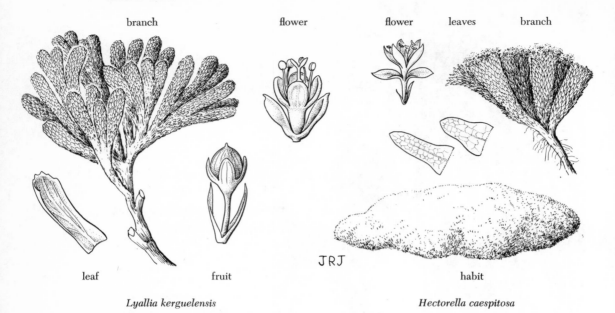

JRJ

leaf   fruit   habit

Lyallia kerguelensis   *Hectorella caespitosa*

8–18. Endemic to Kerguelen Island is the cushion plant *Lyallia,* a member of the family Caryophyllaceae. Is New Zealand's similar-looking *Hectorella* closely related? Plant taxonomists have been unable to decide in which of two families (Caryophyllaceae and Portulacaceae) *Hectorella* belongs.

torella (8–18) from New Zealand is a puzzle for taxonomists. Is it close to *Lyallia,* or is it allied to the *Portulaca* family? Or does it belong in a family by itself? *Raoulia, Donatia, Hectorella,* and *Lyallia* are all genera endemic to relatively small island regions. In the course of changing to the cushion habit, they have diverged to such a degree that they must be called new genera. Even flowers are altered, and this has furnished examples of how change in growth form can obscure the true relationships of island genera. Where an entire series from "normal" to specialized growth forms are present, as in *Hebe* (8–17), the situation is much easier to interpret. Trying to find the mainland relatives of island plants with bizarre growth forms provides an intriguing challenge, because one often must look for a plant with an entirely different appearance. Flowering plants change their vegetative appearance rapidly in an evolutionary sense, but flowers, upon which the classification system rests, change much more slowly. In looking for relatives of island plants we not only learn about the devious pathways of evolution on islands, we also learn a great deal about the island situation, the conditions which induce an everlasting flower to become a *Raoulia* or a lettuce relative to turn into a *Dendroseris.*

9 They Can't Go Home Again

IF WE want to see how islands affect or change the evolution of a plant or animal, the best place to look is among a group notorious for rapid evolution, for quickly invading and adapting to new places, new climates. The candidates which may come to mind first are insects. Because most insects are flying animals, they can give us an answer to the question, "How do islands affect the ability to fly?" This is a question which might not occur to us as one to ask, except for the fact that some perceptive naturalists have observed some peculiar modifications of insects and birds. One such naturalist was Darwin. Upon reading a book on the beetles of the Madeira Islands, he became surprised: "There is a very curious point in the astounding proportion of the Coleoptera that are apterous (wingless). . . ."

Far from unique, we find this situation repeated on islands everywhere. As if to provide us with a double, in fact a multiple, proof, class after class, family upon family of insects that are perfectly normal on continents have taken up the wingless, or at least flightless, habit on islands. A list of insects falling in this category on the Hawaiian Islands is rather startling:

LEPIDOPTERA (moths, butterflies)
    One species (*Hodegia apatela*)
DIPTERA (flies)
    Emperoptera (an island relative of *Campicnemus*)
HYMENOPTERA (bees, wasps, ants)
    Many flightless species; the Hawaiian Diapriidae are more flightless than continental ones.
HEMIPTERA (true bugs)
    among *Heteroptera:* one species of *Metrarga;* terrestrial Emesidae; *Acanthia;* many or most endemic Delphacidae
NEUROPTERA (nerve-winged insects)
    Hemerobiidae: *Pseudopsectra, Nesomicromus, Nesothauma* (9-1)
ORTHOPTERA (grasshoppers, etc.)
    Locustidae: *Banza* (*Brachymetopa*)
    Gryllidae: *Paratrigonidium, Prognathogryllus*

COLEOPTERA (beetles)
  Curculionidae: *Proterorhinus, Heteramphus, Oodemas*
  Cioidae: *Apterocis* (a derivative of *Cis*)
  Elateridae: *Dromaeolus, Dacnitus*
  Lucanidae: *Apterocyclus* (a relative of *Dorcus*)
  Nitulidae: wingless forms in four genera containing nine species
  Histeridae: some species of *Acritus*
  Staphylinidae: *Myllaena* (some species)
  Carabidae: of the endemic species, 184 are flightelss, only 20 fully winged

More could probably be added to this list, now that Hawaiian insects are becoming better known. *Coleoptera* (beetles) ought to offer the best illustrations of flightlessness, if the above list is any criterion. Perhaps non-flying beetles are more numerous than other groups of insects on islands, but because beetles have wing covers, this fact is more difficult to see at first glance. More obvious in their degeneration of flying ability are such insects as the Hawaiian *Neuroptera* (nerve-winged insects, 9-1).

Of these *Neuroptera, Nesomicromus vagus* is a fair example of how flying ancestors of the family Hemerobiidae may have looked. Its somewhat angular wing contours hint a loss of flying ability; a good flier would have rounded wing outlines. Nevertheless, the relatively intact wings of this species might account, in part, for the fact that this species is the only *Nesomicromus* which occupies all the major islands from Kauai to the island of Hawaii. *Nesomicromus drepanoides,* an endemic of Kauai forests, shows loss of flying ability in its wings—they are wide, shorter, and angular. Curiously, a parallel to these two species occurs in the Juan Fernandez *Neuroptera:* the flightless endemic *Gayomyia* and the flying *Chrysopa* match closely the *Nesomicromus* pair in wing pattern.

Further stages in wing malfunction are shown in genera closely related to *Nesomicromus* (9-1). Although *Pseuopsectra usingeri* apparently has good front wings, the back wings are reduced to tiny triangular vestiges. Without back wings, flight is clearly impossible. This species is a native of the Humuula region of the island of Hawaii. *Pseudopsectra cookeorum* is like *P. usingeri,* but suffers further deficiencies: large spines, which would certainly hamper flight, stud the wings. *Pseudopsectra cookeorum* is an endemic of Maui, and has been found only on *Dubautia* plants just inside the west rim of Haleakala crater (5-3). Both *P. cookeorum* and *P. swezeyi* share another defect: the wing veins are coarse and densely crowded together, making the wings unmanageably heavy. *Pseudopsectra swezeyi* has odd-shaped wings, undulate in contour, decidedly not tailored to flight, which would be quite impossible even if back wings were present. Incapable of anything more than a weak flutter, this species has a thorax covered with cone-like tubercles. *Pseudopsectra swezeyi* lives on the cluttered floor of Kauai forests. All vestiges of hind wings have been lost in a genus related to *Pseudopsectra, Nesothauma.*

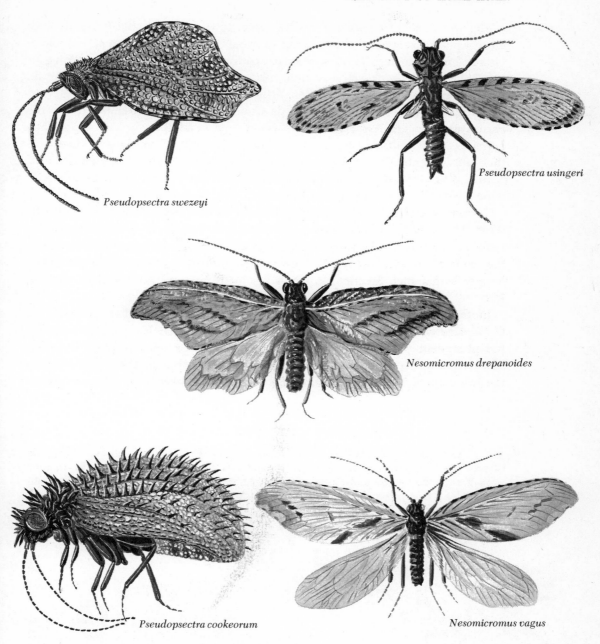

Pseudopsectra swezeyi

Pseudopsectra usingeri

Nesomicromus drepanoides

Pseudopsectra cookeorum

Nesomicromus vagus

9–1. These Hawaiian genera of lacewings (Neuroptera: Hemerobiidae) show strange alterations of form related to their flightless habit. *Nesomicromus vagus* is the least altered of the types shown here. Because insects evolve rapidly, they clearly show how flightlessness has been induced by island circumstances.

Flightlessness, then, need not involve complete winglessness, but it usually does mean some curtailing or abbreviating of wings, conditions known to entomologists as brachypterism. This evolutionary pathway usually involves shortening or narrowing of wings, as well as various malformations, and finally no wings at all. This can be seen in two island flies. *Tristanomyia* (9–2) is a genus retricted to the bleak islands Gough and Tristan da Cunha in the South Atlantic. It has the narrowest of wings. Not related to *Tristanomyia* is another fly, *Acropsilus borboroides,* which not only has lost its wings, it has lost all vestiges of them and their attachments. One would never guess that, in fact, this is a derivative of normal flies. *Acropsilus borboroides* lives on an island swept by fierce antarctic winds—New Zealand's Campbell Island.

Turning to *Orthoptera* (grasshoppers, etc.), we find similar but distinctive patterns. The Galápagos grasshopper *Halmenus robustus* (9–3) shows wing covers reduced to a quarter the length of those in a normal grasshopper, and the wings they conceal are even briefer. Perhaps the most surprising thing about this grasshopper is that such functionless wings and wing covers have not been entirely lost.

In the family Gryllidae, to which crickets belong, are other examples of *Orthoptera* with degenerate or lost wings. The normal cricket (9–4, lower left) has prominent wing covers, useful for making chirps when rubbed together. Crickets, of course, also have powerful hind legs for hopping. These legs must be the only form of locomotion for the Juan Fernandez cricket *Haplosphyrum skotts-*

9–2. Flightlessness has evolved many times independently among insects living on islands. The strap-winged fly at left, *Tristanomyia frustulifera,* is a fruit fly relative from Tristan da Cunha and Gough Islands. At right is *Acropsilus borboroides* (Dolichopodidae) from New Zealand's Campbell Island; this fly has no vestiges of wings at all.

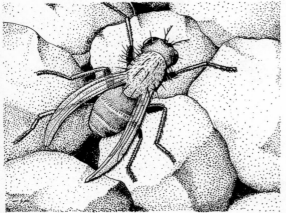
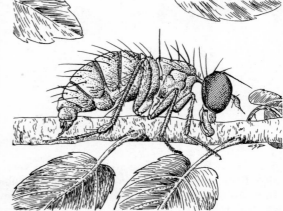

bergi (9–4); it must also be chirpless. The normal and flightless crickets form a pair much like the Galápagos grasshoppers in degree to which wings have been shortened. Curiously, another wingless cricket exists on one of the smallest and most remote islands of the Pacific—Morotiri (Austral Islands).

New Zealand's wetas (9–4, above) belong to the orthopterous family Tettigoniidae. They are large crickets which have long ago lost the ability to fly. They have no wings, no wing covers. Two, *Hemideina megacephala* and *Deinacrida heteracantha,* are dwellers of the forest floor. Stubby and almost grublike, their bulging forms would be poorly suited to flight even if they had adequate wings. *Hemideina megacephala* is found widely in New Zealand's forests, within rotten logs, under loose bark, or in old trees. It can make a grating sound by scraping legs against body. *Deinacrida heteracantha,* gross and clumsy, has a four-inch body and long, spiny legs. It hides beneath rocks and browses on grass at night. Both *Deinacrida* and *Hemideina* use short hopping movements, well-suited to a littered forest floor.

The cave weta *Pachyrhamma fuscifer* (9–4) shows many adjustments to life

9–3. Stages in flightlessness can be seen in the Galápagos grasshoppers. The giant painted grasshopper (*Schistocera melanocera*) below can fly well, but the short-winged grasshopper above (*Halmenus robustus*) is quite incapable of anything more than a short hop.

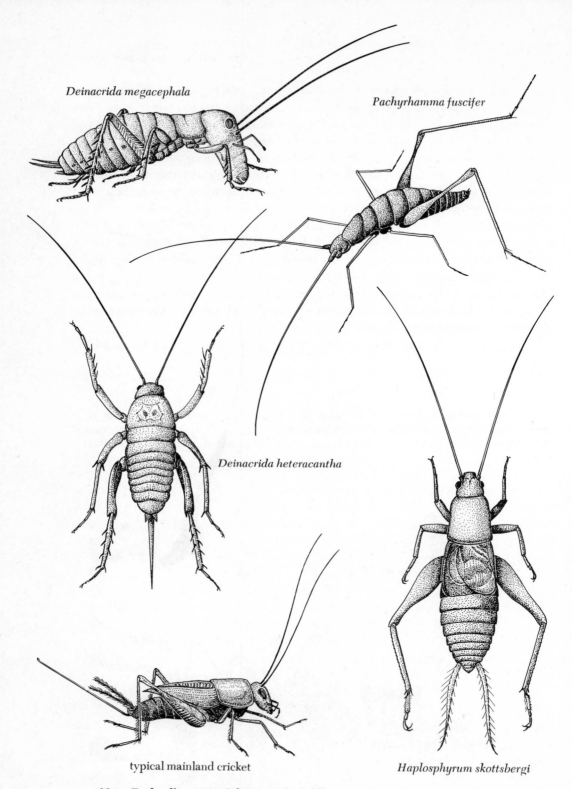

Deinacrida megacephala

Pachyrhamma fuscifer

Deinacrida heteracantha

typical mainland cricket

Haplosphyrum skottsbergi

9–4. New Zealand's wetas (above and middle) are giant wingless crickets, specially adapted to situations where flight is not required, such as a cluttered quiet forest floor (*Deinacrida*) or a cave (*Pachyrhamma*). Although not completely wingless, Juan Fernandez's *Haplosphyrum* (below right) is quite incapable of flight.

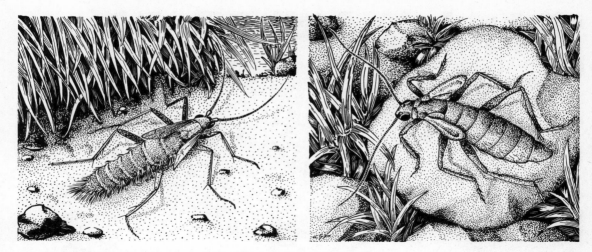

9–5. A fascinating phenomenon of islands near Antarctica is their abundance of large moths which have only tiny vestigial wings. At left is *Dimorphinoctua cunhaensis* from Tristan da Cunha in the South Atlantic. *Brachyapteragrotis patricei* at right is a native of Amsterdam Island, far south in the Indian Ocean.

in caverns beyond mere winglessness. Highly attenuated limbs and antennae give these insects a length of twelve to fourteen inches. They have no ears and have lost a characteristic part of the cricket heritage, a sound-producing apparatus.

DISINHERITED MOTHS

An equally spectacular story is revealed by island moths. Moths of large tropical islands differ but little in form from those on tropical mainland areas. But on the exposed subantarctic islands of the Southern Hemisphere, they tell another story (9–5, 9–6). They invariably show reduction in wing size. Two moths, belonging to the same family (Phalaenidae), but on islands half a world apart, tell the same tale: Both pairs of wings reduced to a minimum. Each was probably derived from a normal phalaenid moth independently of the other. At first glance, neither *Brachyapteragrotis patricei* of Amsterdam Islands nor *Dimorphinoctua cunhaensis* of Tristan da Cunha and nearby islands looks like a moth. The large abdomen and strong legs, which would be overshadowed by wings in other moths, are not only exposed, they are larger than those of an average moth.

Not all moths on these islands have so completely abandoned their wings, although many have. Only a slight deterioration of wings is necessary to cancel flying ability. The more prominent wing curtailment among moths of New Zealand's subantarctic islands often takes the form of smaller wings with a tapered, pointed outline, like the female *Xanthorhoe* of 9–6. Observations by J. T. Salmon and J. D. Bradley on these flightless moths reveal that although non-flying, they are lively: "occur amongst the tussock, and springs like a grass-hopper"; "It jumps with agility and shams death if disturbed"; "The moths leap with great

9–6. From New Zealand's southerly Campbell and Auckland Islands comes this geometrid moth, *Xanthorhoe oxyoptera*, as well as a host of other flightless moths. An interesting question is why the male (left) has much more nearly normal wings than the female (right) in this species.

agility, and when their wings are folded along the body their appearance and manner of behavior could lead them to be mistaken for small grasshoppers. When touched they instantly drop to the ground and remain still. These moths are disturbed in countless numbers when walking through the tussock in September. They leap away in all directions."

Virtually all of the flightless moths on these islands, regardless of the family to which they belong, or on which island they live, show wings more reduced in the females than in the males. This is clearly shown in *Xanthorhoe oxyoptera* from Campbell and the Auckland Islands (9–6). Even in the one moth from the Hawaiian Islands which shows flightless tendencies, *Hodegia apatela*, the male appears normal while the female has reduced wings. Why? The reason appears to be part of the broader picture of "grounded" island insects.

MAKING SOME EXPLANATIONS

Charles Darwin said, regarding flightless island insects: "I think I have guessed the reason, viz., that powers of flight would be injurious to insects inhabiting a confined locality, and expose them to be blown to the sea; to test this, I find that the insects inhabiting the Dezerte Grande, a quite small island [in the Madeiras Islands] would be still more exposed to this danger, and here the proportion of apterous insects is even considerably greater than on Madeira proper." Nearly one hundred years later, the Norwegian entomologist Per Brinck added, "it can hardly be doubted that the ability of a species to stay in a place is strongly increased if the spreading-contributive flying power vanishes. The emigration from a locality offering advantageous possibilities of living must be highly decreased."

Supporting this idea is an experiment with that famous laboratory animal, the fruit fly *Drosophila*. An artificial population composed of 87.5 per cent normal and 12.5 per cent vestigial-winged individuals was exposed to the open air, where breezes could pass over them. After thirty-eight days, the proportion of flightless vestigial-winged flies had risen from 12.5 per cent to 67 per cent of the population.

If by losing their wings, insects "save their skins" and avoid being blown off a favorable island which is limited in size, extremely windy islands ought to be the richest in flightless insects. On Tristan da Cunha, only two of the twenty autochthonous species of insects have well-developed flying wings. The stress of winds on subantarctic islands must be particularly great. Too cold for trees (the timber line is literally at sea level on many of them), these islands offer insects only minimal protection from gales. Perhaps this climate is the reason for the prevalence on such islands of moths whose females have much smaller wings than males. Females would be less expendable than males because they carry eggs, and a population could afford the loss of some males, especially after mating, without being threatened with decimation of offspring for the following year. In the case of the moths of 9–6, winds sweeping up from Antarctica would rip no females away from their islands, and probably only a few males—males don't fly in these species, but might sail away like kites. Interestingly, a high proportion of females to males is seen in the birds of Tristan da Cunha (Chapter 10).

As so often seems true in biology, the explanation of flightlessness as a protection from being blown away to certain doom does not seem to account for all insect non-fliers on islands. If winglessness is a safeguard against passive transport, one would expect that forest insects might not be flying forms, for in their sheltered location they would be in less danger of being blown away. The opposite seems true. Many of the Hawaiian non-fliers are forest species. However, there may be nothing contradictory in this fact. Many Hawaiian forest insects are described as "sluggish," although there are exceptions and some entomologists question this description. Sluggishness, flightlessness, or both would be advantageous for a forest insect living in a stable environment with just the right food plants handy. A tendency to move away from a good source of nutrition would, in fact, be suicidal.

Moreover, new diets acquired by island insects may indirectly alter the pattern of flight. If food can be acquired by sitting and chewing rather than hunting and capturing, flight loses its value. Tristan da Cunha is an island of plant-eating insects, and plant-eating insects seem strongly favored on other islands as well. On an island covered only by low tussocks, like Campbell Island, moths might be expected to take over the grasshopper habit. Where all plants can be reached by hopping and many favorable ones are nearby, why fly?

Loss of flight would be disastrous for insects constantly sought by birds or lizards. As the number of such predators is lessened on islands, flightlessness becomes a scheme progressively less perilous. An alternative, where predators are present, is acquisition of new habits to avoid predators. William Beebe reported that on the Galápagos Islands, where flightless insects abound, hunting for insects is a business of looking under stones and in other secluded niches. Degeneration of flight among island insects, then, may combine several factors: insurance against being swept away; tendency to remain near good and readily available food sources; freedom from predators; freedom from floods; and perhaps many other changes in habits as yet poorly understood.

THE AWKWARD AVIFAUNA

A *Tale of Rails.* The irony of fliers becoming flightless as they evolve on islands is magnified in the case of birds. Are the reasons the same as they are for insects? The number of flightless birds on islands is truly startling. Often rare or inconspicuous, they form a well-hidden but constant component of oceanic island faunas. One group of birds possesses a special penchant for losing flight during evolution on islands—the family Rallidae (rails, coots, waterhens). Island rails and rail relatives reported by one or more authors to be flightless are as follows:

PACIFIC OCEAN

Porzanula palmeri (9–7)**	Laysan rail	Laysan I. (Hawaiian Is.)
*Pennula sandwichensis***	Hawaiian rail	Hawaiian Is.
*Rallus wakensis***	Wake I. rail	Wake I.
*Aphanolimnas monasa***	Kusaie I. crake	Kusaie I.
*Rallus owstoni**	Guam rail	Guam I.
Nesophylax ater	Henderson I. rail	Henderson I.
*Pareudiastes pacificus***	Samoan wood rail	Samoa
Rallina (*Nesoclopeus*) *poeciloptera***	Fiji barred-wing rail	Fiji
*Tricholimnas lafresnayanus**	New Caledonia wood rail	New Caledonia
*Tricholimnas sylvestris**	Lord Howe wood rail	Lord Howe I.
Gallirallus australis (9–11)	weka	New Zealand
Gallirallus hectori	buff weka	New Zealand
Porphyrio (*Notornis*)* *mantelli* (9–10)	takahe	New Zealand

*Nesolimnas dieffenbachi***	Chatham Is. banded wood rail	Chatham Is.
*Rallus modestus***	Chatham Is. rail	Chatham Is.
*Rallus muelleri***	Auckland Is. rail	Auckland Is.
Habroptilus wallacii	Halmahera rail	Halmahera (Moluccas)
Edithornis sylvestris	Solomon I. wood rail	San Cristobal I. (Solomon Is.)
Tribonyx mortieri	Tasmanian native hen	Tasmania

ATLANTIC OCEAN

Atlantisea rogersi (9–9)*	Inaccessible I. rail	Inaccessible I. (near Tristan da Cunha I.)
Porphyriornis comeri	Gough Island gallinule	Gough I.
*Porphyriornis nesiotis**	Tristan da Cunha gallinule	Tristan da Cunha I.

INDIAN OCEAN

Dryolimnas cuvieri	Mascarene wood rail	Aldabra & Assumption Is.

* Rare; in danger of extinction
** Extinct or probably extinct

Many extinct rails, known from bones only, could be added to this list. Some of these were almost certainly flightless. Fossil rails from New Zealand include *Capelirallus karamu, Diaphorapteryx hawkinsi, Gallirallus minor, Pyramidia hodgeni, Aptornis defossor, A. otidiformis,* and *Paleolimnas chathamensis.* Ascension

9–7. *Porzanula palmeri* is a completely flightless rail from Laysan Island in the Hawaiian chain.

Island in the Atlantic Ocean once claimed a flightless rail. On the Mascarene Islands (Mauritius, Réunion, and Rodriguez) there must have been a number of rails, some or all flightless. Some Mascarene rails are known from bones, but others exist only as paintings and descriptions of travelers—descriptions made before concepts of unequivocal scientific descriptions were developed. Those of which bones are known, and which certainly did exist, include *Aphanapteryx broecki* (9–8), *Erythromachus* (*Aphanapteryx*) *leguati* (9–8), and *Fulica* (*Paludiphilus*) *newtoni*.

Many island rails are described as "probably non-flying" or "poor fliers." Others may fly, but have not been reported to do so, perhaps because field observations are lacking. Rails in such categories include *Rallus pacificus* (Tahiti), *Poliolimnas cinereus brevipes* (Iwo Jima), *Nesoclopeus woodfordi* (Solomon Islands), *Rallus philippensis pelewensis* (Palau Islands), *R. philippensis macquariensis* (Macquarie Island), *Porphyrio porphyrio albus* (Lord Howe Island), *Laterallus jamaicensis* (Jamaica), and *Amaurolimnas concolor* (Jamaica).

Even continental rails and their relatives are notoriously poor fliers. When chased, they would rather run than fly. In the air, their flight seems heavy, labored, irregular. Yet rails, denizens of marshy grassland and scrubby regions, do manage to migrate. Indeed, the abundance of rails on distant islands seems at first a contradiction to their sporadic flying habits. Perhaps it is not a contradiction at all. Caught up by a storm, good fliers might often fight successfully against strong winds and manage to return home. A poorer flier, like a rail, could well be swept along with a gale, flying sufficiently to keep aloft but not enough to fly against the weather, only to follow it until, exhausted, one would reach an island. The recent immigration by natural means of the purple gallinule *Porphyrula* from America to Tristan da Cunha shows that this family does indeed possess remarkable migratory ability, for whatever reasons. Rails obviously also do

9–8. Now extinct are these flightless rails from the Mascarene Islands. *Aphanapteryx*, from Mauritius, disappeared in the seventeenth century. *Erythromachus*, closely related, vanished from Rodriguez at about the same time.

Aphanapteryx broeckii
Van der Broecke's red rail

Erythromachus leguati
flightless blue rail

well in island situations; perhaps their demands on the environment are less specialized than those of forest birds.

The island rails have taken advantage of the most diverse possible opportunities. On Laysan Island, the extinct rail *Porzanula palmeri* (9–7) was reported to scurry among grasses. Its nest was a hollow sphere, open at one end, made of grass leaves. *Porzanula* fed on eggs of sea birds, moths and caterpillars, and even the flesh of dead birds. This diet, easily obtainable without flying, and the hot, dry climate of Laysan are the circumstances to which *Porzanula* adapted.

Inaccessible Island, home to the tiny flightless rail *Atlantisea* (9–9), is a cold, windy island in the South Atlantic. *Atlantisea* haunts the grassy tussocks and shrubs, searching mostly for insect larvae, but also consuming large quantities of seeds. Its nests are actual subterranean burrows in the soft ground underneath grass clumps. Detailed study of wings and feathers shows that *Atlantisea* has gone farther than most rails toward degeneration of wings. Wings are still useful to this bird for braking, when it jumps, or for climbing—it uses its wings somewhat as clumsy arms.

The takahe, *Porphyrio (Notornis) mantelli hochstetteri* (9–10), likes grassy tussocks, but at 2000 to 3500 feet in cold areas of southern New Zealand. At an opposite pole from *Porzanula*, the takahe eats larvae only as a nestling. As an adult it ravages a great variety of plants with its strong bill, suited for seed-crushing. It even consumes large quantities of grass, as though the takahe is substituting for herbivorous mammals, which are not native to New Zealand.

The weka, *Gallirallus australis* (9–11), is native to the west forest fiordland and other areas of New Zealand's South Island—a habitat unlike the treeless islands where *Porzanula* and *Atlantisea* make their homes. Quite flightless, the weka pokes furtively through scrub in search of rabbits, mice, lizards, eggs, and insects, almost as though it were a sort of cat. Some of the animals it seeks were

9–9. Smallest of the flightless rails is *Atlantisea rogersi*, endemic of Inaccessible Island (near Tristan da Cunha) in the South Atlantic.

9–10. Once thought to be extinct, but recently rediscovered in New Zealand's fiordland is the takahe, *Porphyrio mantelli*, a member of the rail family (Rallidae).

introduced in historical time, but it has easily adapted to them. The weka's curiosity leads it to raid rivers for fish, snails, mussels, and crayfish. Nests are grass mats concealed under tree trunks or in dense patches of ferns or rushes. Many other distinctive members of the rail family could be described, and we will never know what diverse habits the extinct genera, such as those of the Mascarene Islands (9–8), may have possessed. Why have rails slipped into flightlessness so easily? Rallidae clearly qualify for first place among birds in the number of flightless species on islands.

The answer lies in the reluctance of rails to fly, hallmark of the family either on islands or continents. This habit is in turn tied to the predilection of rails for foods easily secured without flying. Rails might well have become flightless on continents except for the pressure of enemies that make flight an occasional necessity. Also, migration to better feeding grounds make flights worthy of retention on continents, whereas on small islands the choice of feeding grounds is severely limited. Even if the habit of flight is no longer a necessity or even desirable on islands, we still might ask why wings lose their function. What is the driving force which leads to decadence in wing structure and usefulness?

Part of the answer may be suggested by an analogy with aircraft. Airplanes

9–11. New Zealand's weka (*Gallirallus australis*) is a flightless rail which persists in various habitats. Shown here is one which frequents streams, eats various aquatic creatures.

must be able to fly when delivered by a manufacturer to an airline. But this is not enough. Flight of aircraft depends on constant maintenance of numerous parts, any one of which may be vital for performance. A genus of island birds is like an airline company without a maintenance department. With natural selection no longer enforcing flying ability, any change in body form and structure may be critical. With only small changes, a bird or insect may be pushed over the threshold from where flight is still possible to where it is not. Once over the threshold, changes of wings to vestiges can take place with impunity. The threshold between flying and non-flying may be crossed almost imperceptibly, as the island rails, some of which can still fly, show.

What pushes a bird or insect down the path from flightlessness to virtual winglessness? This path has been traveled to its conclusion by some, such as the kiwi (9–14), which is virtually wingless. Mere disuse of wings does not afford a positive "push" to loss of already functionless wings. Rather, a pressure is exerted by changes in living patterns. An analogy is again in order. The body of a bird represents a limited budget of energy, also of potential activities. If greater demands are put on one item of a budget, less can be expended on other items of a budget. If running becomes valuable, the evolutionary economy of a bird may invest more in stronger, longer legs, less in wings. The native hen of Tasmania, *Tribonyx mortieri,* has been clocked by automobiles at thirty miles per hour, and is a much more powerful runner than other species of rails on Tasmania; it is also the only one which is completely flightless.

Another possibility is based on genetics. A gene which controls one feature sometimes has a variety of other influences. One part of a body is not totally independent of another, and genetically a large body size or larger legs may automatically have the consequences of diminishing wings. In small insects, loss of wings is a much simpler matter. In birds, wings are complex structures—bones, muscles, skin, feathers. Erasing these structures and the numerous genes which control them requires more time than the discontinuation of an insect wing. Complexity of bird wings may in part account for the fact that in no flightless island birds have all vestiges of wings completely vanished. When functionless wings become very small, however, they become unimportant—they neither help nor hinder a bird appreciably. Therefore, natural selection would be less likely to expunge wing vestiges entirely than to make marked changes leading from large wings to small wings. The effects of single genes in insects can be very drastic. A single gene in the fruit fly *Drosophila* is all that is needed to change from normal wings to tiny shriveled remnants or virtually none at all. Therefore, insects do not have a complex of genes which govern wing vestiges, as birds do, because insect wings are far simpler.

New Projects for Non-Fliers. If the insular situation leads to reduction of wings in one family of birds, Rallidae, others might be expected to be susceptible also. They are. In the process of this change, these birds often engage in unexpected new habits. The list of flightless or near-flightless island birds other than rails looks like this:

SPHENISCIDAE (penguins) six genera, eighteen species	penguins (9–18)	far-south islands (see 9–19)
CASUARIIDAE (cassowaries) *Casuarius* (five species) (9–16)	cassowaries	Australia, New Guinea
DROMICEIIDAE (emus) *Dromiceius novae-hollandiae* (9–15)	emu	Australia, Tasmania
APTERYGIDAE (kiwis) *Apteryx* (two species) (9–14)	kiwis	New Zealand
DINORNITHIDAE (moas) six genera (see Chapter 14)	moas (14–4)	New Zealand
AEPYORNITHIDAE (elephant birds) two genera (Chapter 16)	elephant birds (16– 9)	Madagascar

PHALACROCORACIDAE (cormorants)		
Phalacrocorax harrisi (Chapter 15)	flightless cormorant (15–21)	Galápagos Is.
ANATIDAE (ducks)		
Anas aucklandica	flightless duck	Campbell, Auckland Is., N.Z.
Tachyeres brachypterus	steamer duck	Tierra del Fuego, Falkland Is.
MESOENATIDAE (mesites)		
Monias benschi (Chapter 16)	mesite (Plate V)	Madagascar
RHYNOCHETIDAE (kagus)		
Rhynochetos jubatus (9–12)	kagu	New Caledonia
ALCIDAE (auks)		
Alca impennis	great auk	Islands of N. Atlantic; adjacent mainland
RAPHIDAE (dodos)		
Raphus cucullatus (9–17)	Mauritius dodo	Mauritius I.
"Victoriornis imperialis" (9–17)	white dodo	Réunion I.
"Ornithaptera solitaria" (9–17)	Réunion solitaire	Réunion I.
Pezophaps solitarius (9–17)	Rodriguez solitaire	Rodriguez I.
PSITTACIDAE (parrots)		
Strigops habroptilus (9–13)	kakapo	New Zealand
ACANTHISITTIDAE (New Zealand wrens)		
Xenicus lyallii (Chapter 14)	Stephen I. wren (14–8)	Stephen I., N.Z.

Others could be added to such a list. The collared hemipode of Australia, *Pedionomus* (Pedionomidae), is a weak flier. The wattlebird *Callaeas* from New Zealand has been described as "halfway toward becoming flightless." The depreciation of flight by wattlebirds is evidently recent, for it is only subtly evident in the structure of wings. *Callaeas* has long legs, and "by means of these long legs they actually swing themselves from branch to branch, and very rarely use their wings as a means of locomotion. In moving through the bush they simply run—using the wings to balance—in great bounding hops through the interlacing branches, and in this way can move at a greater pace above than one can walk below. It is doubtful if the [wattled] crow can make any sustained flight." Another genus, the huia *Heteralocha* (10–6), related to *Callaeas*, "never rises, like other birds, above the tree tops."

The Laysan Island duck, *Anas wyvilliana laysanensis*, can be frightened into a rather labored flight, but only with great difficulty.

In addition to the fossil moas, elephant birds, and rails listed above, paleontology provides some curious examples of insular non-flying birds. Among the most startling is a recently discovered owl from Cuba, currently under study by Dr. Bryan Patterson of Harvard University's Museum of Comparative Zoology.

Dr. Patterson found that the owl was flightless, stood three feet high, and belonged to the family Strigidae. The spectacle of an enormous owl, awkwardly hopping over Cuba's landscape in search of animal prey, perhaps rodents, is intriguing. A hint as to why Cuba should have hosted this bird is offered by the fact that other large fossil birds occurred in Cuba at the same time: a large crane, a giant eagle, a condor, and a turkey. Lacking large mammals, Cuba evolved birds to take their places. Without danger of being captured by, for example, a large cat, an owl could "afford" to be flightless.

The Almost-Fliers. New Caledonia's kagu (9–12) gives us an idea how opening stages in wing loss may have looked. It apparently cannot fly, but still has well-developed wings. These may prove somewhat advantageous in display during courtship procedures, for the kagu also has prominent head feathers which suggest that function. *Rhynochetos* prowls forests in search of insects, snails, worms, and frogs, all foods which certain mammals could utilize, so the kagu's foraging may represent a compensation for New Caledonia's lack of mammals. With terrestrial animals readily available to the kagu as food, it no longer needs to take to the air.

The steamer ducks of subantarctic New World islands belong to two species: *Tachyeres brachypterus* and *T. patachonicus.* They are similar in appearance, but *T. brachypterus* cannot fly. Both species have wings of the same length,

9–12. Lone occupant of the family Rhynochetidae is New Caledonia's kagu (*Rhynochetos jubatus*). Its wings, although conspicuous when extended, are incapable of flight.

but *T. brachypterus* weighs appreciably more. As the name "steamer duck" implies, *Tachyeres* is a bird of the ocean surface. It can flap upon the sea surface "at a great pace, throwing up so much spray that at a distance, it is the flying water rather than the bird that draws the eye." Steamer ducks attack their prey from beneath the surface of the water. One may say that in adopting the flightless habit, *T. brachypterus* has abandoned flight in air in favor of flight on the surface of the water.

Also looking like a normal bird, but actually a non-flier, is New Zealand's kakapo (9–13). A parrot is not a bird one would expect to lose the power of flight, but the kakapo proves that given rich forest conditions and long isolation, this can happen. This bird favors berries, leaves, twigs, and nectar as articles of diet, and it climbs, instead of flies, to get them. Surprisingly, it feeds at night, and after filling itself with these plant foods it creeps down to a den, usually a hollow at the base of a tree, to sleep during the day. Habits like these seem strange for a parrot, and more like those of a tree-living marsupial.

Flight Long Lost. Sharing the same islands with the kakapo is the kiwi (9–14), which has become renowned as a symbol of flightlessness and of New Zealand's animal life. Like the kakapo, kiwis feed at night, returning by dawn to their burrows or nests in hollow logs. When sleeping, it tucks its bill to the side of its body, where a wing would be if it had one. It has no externally visible

9–13. Although parrots seem unlikely candidates for flightlessness, one on New Zealand has acquired this habit, lives on or near the ground: the kakapo (*Strigops habroptilus*).

9–14. Famous as a symbol of flightlessless is this kiwi (*Apteryx mantelli*). Kiwis are nervous ground birds of New Zealand's wet forests. (San Diego Zoo photo.)

wings, and its feathers, with bare barbs lacking flat surfaces like those of a normal bird, are as degenerate in their way as the stubs of wings are. Kiwis are unlike kakapos in that they have a long, narrow beak—which suggests distinctive habits. Moreover, the nostrils are in the tip of the kiwi's beak, not at its base, as in other birds. The nostrils permit the kiwi to detect prey by smell, a unique ability. Thus, the kiwi beak becomes a sensitive probe, aided by whisker-like barbless feathers at the base of the beak. With this apparatus the kiwi pokes into leaf mold and moss, extracting insects and grubs. "In searching for earthworms they showed a considerable ingenuity. The hunt opened with the usual tapping. When by this means the bird discovered the burrow of one of these worms it set to work at once enlarging the opening, using its bill as a workman uses a crowbar. When it had formed a funnel-like depression, it inserted its bill and took a good hold of the worm. With a steady pull it often succeeded in bringing its victim to the surface." Feats such as these, compensating for its lack of flight as a means of finding food, show the depth of its adaptation to foraging on the forest floor, an adaptation which has con-

9–15. Sharing Australia's plains with kangaroos, emus are giant non-flying birds suited to great open spaces. They are still abundant in many parts of Australia. (New York Zoological Society photo.)

tributed heavily to the kiwi's flightlessness. The kiwi has no competition for its niche, and rather reminds one of a bird equivalent of an insectivore or anteater.

Another extreme is represented by the striding giants of Australia and New Guinea, emus (9–15) and cassowaries (9–16). They are to this region what ostriches are to Africa, what rheas are to Argentina. Emus are restricted to the plains country of temperate Australia and (formerly) Tasmania, whereas cassowaries inhabit forests of tropical northern Australia (Queensland) and New Guinea and nearby islands. Thus, the two bird groups do not overlap at all. Their large size often seems related to large land expanse. Controversy has clouded whether emus, ostriches, rheas, etc. are closely related and whether their history has always been a flightless one. The answer to both parts of the question appears to be "no." They represent giant forms which originated from normal ancestors, and if they all came from a single ancestral group, it would have been a flying bird widespread over the Southern Hemisphere.

Emus are swift runners, and are entries into the deer or antelope habit. Emus consume various types of vegetable matter, supplementing plant foods with

9–16. Cassowaries are tropical equivalents of emus, occupy forest areas in northern Queensland and New Guinea. Shown here is *Casuarius casuarius aruensis* from the Aru Islands near New Guinea. Cassowaries can easily be recognized by the horny head crest, blue and red neck wattles, and shining black plumage. (Below: New York Zoological Society photo.)

caterpillars and insects. This is also true of cassowaries, which find fruits abundant in their forest habitats. The shapes of emus and cassowaries seem to indicate that wings have vanished in favor of legs. Correlated with the large size and way of life of emus is their long life span—about fifteen years in the wild, up to thirty years in zoos. Also related to large size is slow maturation of infants. The incubation period for eggs is long—eight weeks to three months.

The diet of cassowaries is fruits, but unlike parrots, they have no special adaptation of beaks to crush fruits. They rely instead on a vigorous digestive system. As those who have tangled with them can testify, cassowaries are quite capable of defending themselves by kicking, and the dagger-like hind claw can shred an opponent. Cassowaries have been known to deal fatal blows in this manner. The hard, horn-like crest on the head (9–16) is a protective mechanism. Thus, the cassowary has shifted from the evasive flight which defends most birds to potent confrontation by kicking and tearing. This confrontation, however, occurs not between the birds and their natural enemies—for they apparently have none. Rather, individuals within a flock use these mechanisms for fighting among themselves.

The Underwater Fliers. Of the world's penguins, all are Southern Hemisphere creatures (9–19). One, a Galápagos Islands species, lives astride the equator (15–20). Some penguins are migratory, others remain all year on a single island or archipelago, such as the Galápagos penguin. Even though they migrate to sea in winter, penguins tend to show a strong fidelity to particular islands, even to particular nesting places on islands, to which they may return year after year. Only four species of penguins could be said to frequent continental shores (other than Antarctica). The jackass penguin, *Spheniscus demersus,* patronizes the coasts of South Africa; *S. humboldtii,* the magellanic penguin, follows the cool Humboldt waters north along the South American shoreline; and the two species of *Eudyptula* touch the southern coasts of Australia. Why are all other penguins exclusively island creatures?

One obvious answer lies in the fact that in the coldest portions of the southern oceans, there is no continent other than Antarctica. Going one step further, one could ask why penguins favor such cold regions. Biologists generally concede that penguins are descended from birds capable of flight. Perhaps as a flightless bird it has found the lack of predators and competitors on the far-southern islands convenient. Constant annoyance by land carnivores would, in time, be their undoing. The price penguins pay for this convenience is adjustment to extremely cold climates. The penguin is the seal of the bird world. Penguins may tend to prefer fishing at different depths, or for different fish, than seals, and may not appreciably compete with them, although there are some parallels in their diet and migratory patterns. Even if they are competitors, there seems to be room for both.

Important to remember is that penguins, although often supposed to be an ancient group of birds, have not lost their wings; the function has changed to that of flippers instead—a remodeling, not a degeneration. One paleontologist views penguins as capable of "submarine flight." There is a possibility that penguins may have originated directly from flying birds, without going through a non-flying stage on land.

In the Miocene, there were penguins five feet tall: *Pachydyptes* and *Anthroportis.* Fossil penguins are abundant in South America. Perhaps penguins originated farther north than most of them now live, and were forced by competition into the southern oceans. Island habitats and ways of life which seem extreme may have been beyond the reach of many other vertebrates, but may have permitted survival of the penguins.

The recently extinct great auk of the North Atlantic offers an interesting

Raphus cucullatus
Mauritius dodo

"Victoriornis imperialis"
"white dodo"

"Ornithaptera solitaria"
"Reunion solitaire"

Pezophaps solitarius
Rodriguez solitaire

9–17. The famous dodo of Mauritius had flightless relatives on the other Mascarene Islands. The Rodriguez solitaire was a taller bird, also flightless. Both the dodo and the solitaire are known from skeletal remains. On Reunion, some dodo-like or solitaire-like birds definitely existed, but they are known only from drawings and descriptions. The "white dodo" and the "Reunion solitaire" may actually be one and the same.

9–18. Most species of penguins inhabit islands of the far southern oceans. Shown here are the small macaroni penguin *Eudyptes chrysolophus* (upper left), the Adelie penguin *Pygoscelis adeliae* (upper right), and Antarctica's great Emperor penguin *Aptenodytes forsteri* (lower left). (Above: San Diego Zoo photo; below: New York Zoological Society photo.)

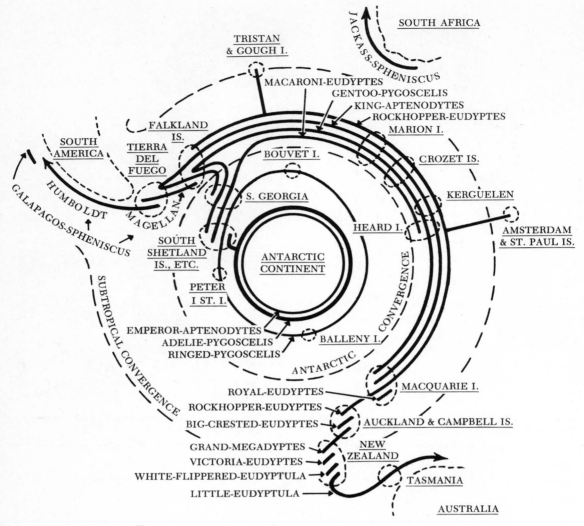

9–19. Penguins are migratory ocean birds, but some have very limited ranges, and some frequent only a few islands. This summary, prepared by MacIntosh, shows the range of each species. Only three species form nesting colonies on mainland areas, such as South America, Africa, or Australia.

parallel. Unlike penguins, it was the only non-flying member of its family. Like penguins, however, it had "submarine flight," migrated, and although its distribution included mainland areas, most of the stations from which it was known were offshore islands. Perhaps it clung to life as long as it did by taking advantage of relatively "safe" island conditions. The great auk represented a relatively recent adaptation to the penguin habit, perhaps compensating in northern oceans for lack of penguins. The great auk's wings were not nearly as specialized as those of penguins, but it used them with remarkable effectiveness in swimming as do flying species of auks. Although the great auk was a short-lived evolutionary experiment (thanks to deliberate killing of this remarkable bird by hunters), it must be ranked as a striking adaptation, perhaps made possible by insular habitats.

One more flightless aquatic bird provides a somewhat inverted example of island life. In and around Lake Titicaca, the high fresh water lake of the Andes, lives a grebe, *Centropelma micropterum*. Lake Titicaca is the only major lake of the high Andes, and so for a grebe suited to fishing in its waters, there is no choice: Lake Titicaca is an island to the grebe. Flightlessness under these circumstances is readily understandable. With abundant food provided by the waters of the lake, but similar food supplies far away, the grebe probably took to the air little, but exercised its swimming abilities increasingly. Now, it has been overtaken by flightlessness.

An example of a fishing bird which has taken the turn to flightlessness on a true island area is offered by the Galápagos flightless cormorant (Chapter 15).

FRUITS ONLY FOR FALLING

Plants too lose flying ability: they lose their dispersal mechanisms. Compositae, because of their excellent dispersal mechanisms, might be expected to show loss more conspicuously, if this principle is true. They do. The mainland *Bidens* (2–10) discussed earlier has a good means of fruit transport; what has happened to its relatives on islands? One relative of *Bidens* is the Polynesian sunflower *Fitchia*. Most species of *Fitchia* have fruits like those of *F. cuneata* (9–20). The fruits of *F. cuneata* are markedly hairy, and the two needle-like prongs are evident. These prongs, however, are delicate, and they do not bear barbs. In several respects, then, the fruits of *F. cuneata* are more poorly designed for dispersal than are the smaller fruits, with stout prongs bearing barbs of such a *Bidens* as *B. frondosa* (9–20). *Fitchia cuneata* appears to have diminished its ability for long-distance transport because all evidence points to *Bidens*-like ancestors for *Fitchia*. If *F. cuneata* is poor at dispersal, *F. speciosa* (9–20, right) is worse. Its fruits can attain three inches in length. The seeds contained in these fruits are the largest in the entire family Compositae, a family of more than twenty thousand species. *Fitchia speciosa* on Rarotonga Island represents the farthest penetration of this genus into the Pacific (3–1), and it also is the only tree of its genus (8–1). With its huge fruits, *F. speciosa* could never have arrived on Rarotonga—its gigantic state has been evolved there. Increased fruit size suits a species of deep forest, for abundant food storage in seeds helps boost a young seedling into the better-lighted canopy of the forest where it can compete for light. Factors such as these probably explain why *F. speciosa* is a large plant as well as why it has large fruits—it has taken on all aspects of a typical forest tree. *Fitchia cuneata* grows in shrubby, low forests, and so its smaller plant size and smaller fruits are proportionate to the habit and habitat, adequate for its needs.

The Hawaiian tarweeds offer other good examples. Ancestors of Hawaiian

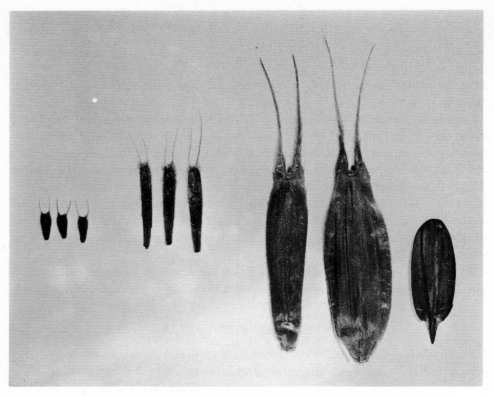

9–20. Progressive loss of dispersal ability is illustrated by this series of fruits of closely related members of the sunflower family (Compositae). At left is the "Spanish needle" (*Bidens frondosa*), fruits of which catch easily on clothing (see 2–10). *Fitchia cuneata* (middle) from Tahaa Island has much larger fruits which do not attach easily to feathers or animal fur. *Fitchia speciosa* (right) from Rarotonga Island has the largest fruits in the family; these fruits are virtually ineffective in dispersal much beyond the base of the tree on which they grow. The seeds they contain (extreme right) are heavy.

tarweeds probably had bristles or scales atop their fruits, as shown for the mainland tarweed in 9–21. In comparison, *Wilkesia* (9–21, right) has much longer, heavier fruits, bearing much shorter appendages. Fruits of *Wilkesia* are crowned by tiny scales, seemingly ineffective in securing transport for these fruits by air or birds, especially considering the comparatively greater weight of fruits. These scales are not only small, they do not open out into a parachute-like device as do those of *Layia*.

The Juan Fernandez Compositae also combine increased fruit size with reduced appendages. One of the tree lettuces, *Dendroseris litoralis* (9–21), illustrates this clearly. Ancestors probably had fruits much like those of the *Microseris* shown for comparison, the plumes topping the fruit longer than the body of the fruit itself. This is "aerodynamically" sound, capable of carrying the fruit for considerable distances in wind, or perhaps even catching in birds' feathers. *Dendroseris litoralis* has clearly rejected these efficient mechanisms.

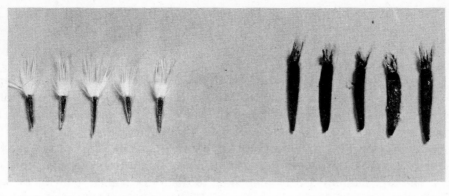

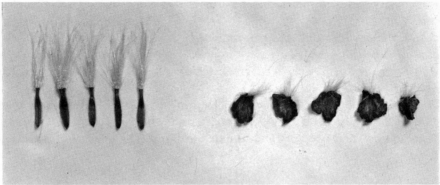

9–21. Fruits of mainland Compositae often have good dispersal mechanisms but their island representatives often have lost these devices. In each of these photographs, the mainland form is at left, the island relative at right. Above, the tarweed *Layia glandulosa* has fruits which bear a fluffy "parachute," in contrast with *Wilkesia* (see 5–6), the fruits of which are crowned by functionless scales. Below, *Microseris alpestris* has dandelion-like fruits, but the Juan Fernandez *Dendroseris litoralis* has awkward, variously shaped fruits, topped with only vestigial wisps of threads.

Fruits are greatly widened and misshapen; no two are alike. Although flattened, they could not be said to be winged. The plumes atop the fruit are only a withered wad of threads, little more than an ineffectual ornament. The fruits of *Dendroseris litoralis* are now suited to little more than dropping to the ground beneath the tree that bears them. Interestingly, the Juan Fernandez tree thistle *Centaurodendron* (8–8) has its fruit-dispersal mechanisms depreciated in exactly the same ways. The bristles topping *Centaurodendron* fruits do not open out, as do those of thistles, they merely crumble; the fruiting heads do not open out well to release fruits, they retain fruits for indefinite periods of time.

The above examples prominently represent increase in fruit size. This, however, does not occur in all cases of dispersal mechanism loss. In 9–22 are a *Pisonia* and a *Bidens* from the Hawaiian Islands. What has happened to their dispersal devices can be best appreciated by comparing them with the *Pisonia* and the *Bidens* of 2–10, which may be fairly regarded as what the ancestral types of the Hawaiian species in 9–22 looked like. In the Hawaiian *Pisonia*, the fruits lack sticky disks. The Hawaiian *Bidens* has lost the prong-like appendages on fruits. They are reduced to mere stubs, bereft of barbs, and can serve no function in dispersal at all.

Increase in seed size in autochthonous Hawaiian species can be seen in the spurges (*Euphorbia*), rues (*Evodia* and its allies, Rutaceae), and a number of others. The explanation is partly adaptation to the forest habitat, as with *Fitchia speciosa*, partly loss of dispersal mechanism for the same reasons as other island species.

In the Galápagos Islands, the tree sunflower *Scalesia* shows stages in loss of scales atop the fruits. Although most species have fruits entirely bare, a few species still retain small scales and give us hints about the appearance of fruits in ancestors of *Scalesia*.

Other ways of losing a dispersal mechanism are available to island plants. A primitive flowering plant famous to botanists is *Bubbia* (9–23). Its fruits are bright red, fleshy, and presumably attractive to birds. The genus *Bubbia* extends

9–22. The *Pisonia* and the *Bidens* shown in 2–10 have island counterparts which have lost their dispersal ability. Both island species are endemics of the Hawaiian Islands. *Pisonia sandwicensis* lacks the sticky discs which *P. aculeata* has on its fruits. *Bidens populifolia* fruits bear not the pair of barbed prongs seen in *B. pilosa*, but two ineffectual nubbins.

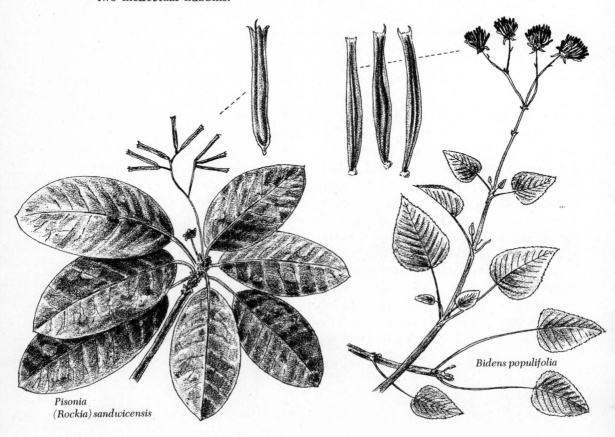

*Pisonia
(Rockia) sandwicensis*

Bidens populifolia

from New Guinea to northeastern Australia, the Solomon Islands, and New Caledonia, and may owe this distribution pattern, relatively modest though it is, to this dispersal mechanism. A close relative of *Bubbia* is a genus endemic to New Caledonia, *Zygogynum* (9–23, right). Instead of bearing several bright red fruits from a single flower, as can *Bubbia*, *Zygogynum* has all the fruits of a single flower coalesced into a single large apple-like sphere. This spherical multiple fruit is greenish at maturity, has a woody texture rather than a fleshy one, and is far too large for a bird to consume. At best, a *Zygogynum* fruit can only fall a short distance from the parent plant.

Justly famous among botanists is a palm from the Seychelles Islands, *Lodoicea maldivica* (9–24). It is better known as the coco-de-mer or double coconut. The former name derives from the fact that before the palm was discovered in its native habitats, it became known from the huge fruits, more than a foot in diameter, which floated up on faraway shores all around the periphery of the Indian Ocean. At first, these fruits were supposed to have come from the Maldive Islands, although now we know they grow only on the Seychelles. The name "double coconut" is based on the two-lobed nature of fruits—a constriction separates the fruit into two halves. Actually, the coco-de-mer is not close to coconuts, it is related to the sugar palm (*Borassus*) of southern Asia. The fruit may be the largest in the entire palm family. Although they float, sea water kills them. The huge fruits seem clearly to represent increase in size over the size of fruits in ancestors of *Lodoicea*. Natural dispersal for more than a few yards seems clearly impossible. Gigantism characterizes all parts of the plant— the leaves and flower clusters are also enormous. Moreover, the palm is very slow-living. It requires thirty years at least from seed to first flowering, and mature palms are more than a hundred years old. Interestingly, trees are either male or female, a condition unusual in palms. One would would not expect this of an island species, because at least two trees, flowering simultaneously

9–23. The fleshy, bright-red fruits of the New Guinean *Bubbia* at left (see also 13–8) might be dispersed by birds. In the same family (Winteraceae) is the New Caledonian relative *Zygogynum* (right), which has large multiple fruits capable of no dispersal other than merely falling to the ground.

9–24. Native only to the Seychelles Islands is the large palm *Lodoicea.* Its curious "double" fruits are definitely exceptional in size for the palm family, and although they float in the ocean, they do not disperse in this way, for sea water kills them. The large size of the fruits probably developed on the Seychelles. (Chicago Natural History Museum photo.)

and near each other, would be required to establish the species if ancestors also had this habit.

Many of the above examples show increase in fruit or seed size of island plants as compared with mainland relatives. Mingled with this condition, or in fruits not appreciably larger, is loss of a dispersal mechanism. The enlarged size, as suggested above, may connote adjustment to a forest habitat. What about the loss of dispersal mechanism? The explanation may be the one offered in the case of flightless birds and insects. Plants confined to small areas of land surrounded by water have a peculiar dispersal problem. The better the dissemination device, the worse the consequences for the species. If dissemination is good, seeds will be scattered over a wide area, and in the case of an island species, most of them will fall haplessly into the ocean. A poor dispersal mechanism bodes well for an island plant. Seed release in mainland plants is often timed so as to coincide with winds—the drying effect of wind triggers release of seeds or fruits, such as those of lettuces. If this happened in an island plant, discharge of seeds or fruits would occur just at the best time for them to be swept out to sea—a fatal error. Thus, a diminished dissemination device will succeed in keeping most seeds of a species on an island or in a favorable site within an island.

This course does have the proverbial effect of burning bridges behind one. Even for non-winged animals such as lizards, gigantism greatly dims the chances for further travel. Of the plant species mentioned above as having a degenerate dispersal mechanism, nearly all are confined to a single island. Thus, plants and animals forfeit their passports to travel, perhaps as a necessity, perhaps as a by-product, of their sensitive evolutionary adjustments to island life.

10 *Special Directions and Devices*

OFTEN, the products of evolution tend to run counter to, or beyond, our first expectations. Adaptive radiation provides a spread of forms, but evolution on an island may instead pursue some line of endeavor to its logical conclusion, some isolated new adaptation, habit, or mechanism. To these unique products of island life this chapter is devoted.

SITUATIONS WANTED

Even small, very recent continental islands such as those in Lake Michigan are not exempt from influencing their plants and animals. On these particular islands, spring peeper frogs and American toads, species accustomed to breedings in small, quiet ponds, are forced into beachside pools, where the waters of Lake Michigan are relatively quiet. Although the great blue heron and crows typically nest in trees, they build their nests at ground level on treeless Pismire Island in Lake Michigan. Such are the new habits forced upon island creatures, habits which can be absorbed, in some cases, into the evolutionary programs of island species.

Among Hawaiian dolichopodid flies, species which frequent wet, dripping banks have glistening metallic colors; species that have adopted streams as habitats are agile water-skaters; those living upon leaves are greenish in color; and forest floor species of this fly family tend to be dull-colored. Hawaiian species of the bug *Saldula* are tree inhabitants—but elsewhere in the world they are stream and lakeshore creatures. The Hawaiian damsel fly *Megalagrion oahuense* comes from a group which has aquatic larval stages, but this species has taken up a strictly terrestrial regime. Examples such as these suggest rapid evolution, proving that striking changes may be accelerated where conditions permit or demand them and where an adaptable group confronts these conditions. One suspects that many of these adaptations on islands, nurtured to perfection without the pressures of competition, would probably not have been tolerated on mainland areas.

NIGHT INTO DAY

With absence of predators, a nocturnal animal may be able to hunt during the day, which may be a favorable time for foraging. On the Brazilian island Queimada Grande, the snake *Bothrops insularis* is a daytime hunter. This must be a

10–1. New Zealand's kea (*Nestor notabilis*) is unusual among parrots in its carnivorous diet. In recent times, it has even taken to killing and eating sheep.

new habit for this *Bothrops*, because these island snakes still have the vertical-pupiled eyes characteristic of nocturnal animals, such as cats. Moreover, *Bothrops insularis* eats the small finch *Brachyspiza* almost exclusively. To capture this difficult prey, *Bothrops insularis* is aided by venom of exceptional toxicity. Also, the agility of this species is aided by more numerous rows of scales than its relatives have; this gives it greater flexibility, permitting it to traffic with a very rapid and evasive form of prey.

California's night lizard *Xantusia* has both mainland species and one on islands (7–2). Those on the mainland are exclusively nocturnal, but *X. riversiana* on the islands scampers about during the day as well as at night.

A SWITCH IN DIET

Diet alteration is a characteristic seen in the Australian marsupials and in flightless birds and giant reptiles—but it is accompanied by many other changes. One would expect that these changes in form would be accompanied by changes in habit. But would one expect a rather ordinary-looking parrot to (a) abandon tropic forests in favor of icy alpine regions and (b) be able to eat sheep fat?

These feats are achieved by New Zealand's kea (10–1). The long, curved upper mandible of the beak does hint at carnivorous ability—it is perhaps like a single incisor tooth. New Zealand's sheep farmers were totally unprepared for the sight of these parrots, swooping down from the mountains, quickly and fatally wounding sheep, ripping fat from them, and greedily consuming it. Reports of the kea as a compulsive carnivore are, however, exaggerations. Historically, the problem arose when pieces of sheep fat were left exposed and keas found and ate them. Pleased by this fare, a few individuals proved skillful enough to kill or wound a sheep. Keas have been alleged to be a serious problem for flocks of sheep, but the mortality of sheep has probably been relatively small. The kea may be regarded as a herbivore primarily, subsisting on fruits, young shoots, and nectar. Its natural diet, however, typically includes a variety of insects and their larvae and worms. Its liking for such animal foods doubtless made it preadapted as an eater of sheep fat, although one would not expect that a bird which normally killed relatively small insects would have sufficient boldness to wound sheep. Although the kea has not become a true carnivore, it illustrates how a change in diet might take place if conditions changed. An interesting dietary preference by an insular bird of prey is illustrated by the Philippine monkey-eating eagle, *Pithecophaga jeffreyi*. This bird, one of the largest birds of prey known, is endemic to the Philippine Islands.

A change within recent times to a new diet is represented by the leaf-rolling caterpillars belonging to the endemic Hawaiian genus *Omiodes*. Five species of this genus are restricted to feeding on bananas. Bananas were introduced by the Polynesians who colonized the Hawaiian Islands only about eight hundred years ago.

Examples like these show that swift response to new conditions on islands can be accomplished. The Hawaiian insect fauna is rich in insects with very specialized host preferences—some feed only on a single endemic plant species. These preferences and restrictions have evidently been important in diversifying the Hawaiian insects into so many species and genera.

INTO UNTRIED GROUND

How does a group of plants, accustomed to swamps and wet forests since Carboniferous time, survive in areas of Western Australia which are dry most of the year? This riddle has been solved by the club mosses, an ancient group of plants as primitive as ferns. *Phylloglossum* (10–2) is the genus which has adjusted to highly seasonal climates simply by growing only at wet seasons of the year. When rain comes, *Phylloglossum* sends up a few leaves, a spore-bearing stalk, and sends down a root and a tiny starchy tuber. As the sandy soil dries out, the leaves and roots die, the spore-bearing stalk withers, leaving only the tuber, which will last through the summer and renew the plant by performing the same cycle when wet weather returns the following year. This mechanism would not be so surprising except that it has been achieved by such an antique order of plants which have survived to the present only narrowly.

New Caledonia's conifers, living in isolation for millions of years, have been afforded the opportunity for leisurely evolutionary experiment. They have taken this opportunity, and one genus, *Podocarpus*, has achieved on one island the most extreme ecological objectives. *Podocarpus* is typically a forest tree throughout the world; most of New Caledonia's species follow this habit, too. One species, however, *P. palustris* (10–3), has moved into lakes. This is all the more surprising because lakes are in short supply on New Caledonia. *Podocarpus palustris* will exist both on soggy ground and in lakes. This feat is unique among Southern Hemisphere conifers, but in the Northern Hemisphere, the bald cypress *Taxodium* of the redwood family also has this habit in the southern United States.

Unique among conifers is the parasitism of another New Caledonia *Podocarpus, P. ustus*. The world's only parasitic conifer, it derives its nutrition from

10–2. Clubmosses are primitive plants which usually favor moist forests. This one (*Phylloglossum drummondii*) has adapted to dry conditions in Western Australia, Tasmania, and New Zealand by forming small resistant tubers.

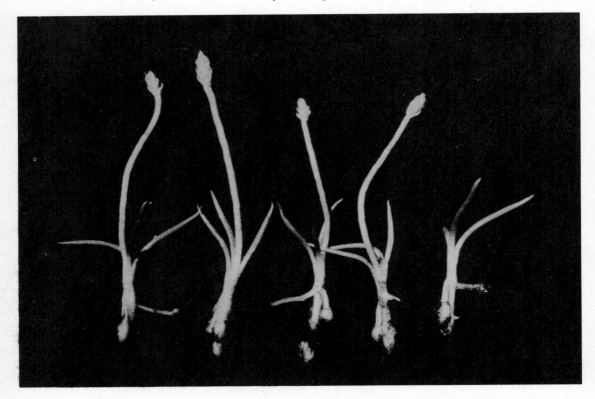

another member of its own family, *Dacrydium*, with which it makes root contact. This sort of familial infighting is not without parallel in plants—parasitic red algae parasitize members of their own families, for example. *Podocarpus ustus* is not typically greenish, but forms a reddish, almost coral-like shrub which apparently cannot survive when transplanted.

NEW WAYS OF FOOD-GETTING

Ingenuity in extracting food from the environment is certainly not the exclusive property of island animals. They seem, however, to have gone to further lengths than have continental creatures.

A definitive example of this is furnished by the Galápagos cactus finch, *Cac-*

10–3. On New Caledonia, *Podocarpus palustris* occupies an unusual site for a conifer: lake margins. It is the only Southern Hemisphere conifer to have adopted this habit. (Photograph by Robert Virot.)

10–4. The Galápagos cactus finch (*Cactospiza pallida*) has the unique custom of poking into the bark crevices with a stick or cactus thorn in search of insect larvae. Observers report it has "great intelligence" in the use of this tool.

tospiza pallida (10–4). One of two animals known to use a tool instinctively (for the other, see 11–3), *Cactospiza* performs its work with a cactus spine or stick held in its beak. The purpose of this device is to imitate the performance of a woodpecker. Woodpeckers not only excavate into wood to secure grubs and insects, they then use their tongues as probes to extract the prey. *Cactospiza* has a beak capable of peeling and tearing bark, but its tongue is no match for the woodpecker's. So, as discovered in 1919, it substitutes the stick or spine, an equally effective means of coaxing out the unlucky victim. So characteristic is this behavior that Robert I. Bowman writes, "almost every bird encountered was seen carrying a cactus spine in the bill." The adjective "intelligent" seems irresistible to those who have observed and described this bird in action. *Cactospiza* can correct mistakes—one individual was seen to try to break in two an excessively long stick it had tried to use. Another, attempting to use a forked stick, turned it around so as to use the unforked tip. These birds escaped the notice of Darwin when he was on the Galápagos, but they would have offered superb examples for his *On the Origin of Species*.

Built-in tools are employed equally well by island birds. Such tools are, of

10–5. The Samoan tooth-billed pigeon (*Didunculus strigirostris*) has a saw-toothed beak capable of grappling with larger and tougher fruits.

course, the ever-adaptable beaks. The tooth-billed pigeon of Samoa, *Didunculus strigirostris* (10–5), substitutes a notched bill for teeth. Armed with this rasp it "nibbles food in parrot fashion." The beak equips it to handle bulky, fibrous foods easily: plantains (cooking bananas), yams, and berries are ripped into morsels quickly. As yet another example of change in habits, *Didunculus,* once reported to be a ground-nesting bird, now escapes rats and man by making its nest high in trees.

New Zealand's extinct huia (10–6) differs from other birds in that males and females were differently equipped to cope with food-getting problems. Despite skepticism, observations seem to confirm that a pair of huias do, in fact, form a husband-and-wife team to secure insects and larvae in wood. According to Walter Buller:

"The males always attacked the more decayed portions of the wood, chiselling out his prey after the manner of some woodpeckers, while the female probed with her long pliant bill the other cells, when the hardness of the surrounding parts resisted the chisel of her mate. Sometimes I observed the male remove the decayed portion without being able to reach the grub, when the female would at once come to his aid and accomplish what he had failed to do. . . . however . . . the female always appropriated to her own use the morsels thus obtained."

According to J. M. Wright, "The males would tear away the outer part of a

10–6. Unique feeding habits underlie the differences in beaks between male and female huias (*Heteralocha acutirostris*). Females of this New Zealand bird have long, curved beaks; males have shorter, less curved ones.

green sapling. The female then tried to retrieve the [insect] with her long slender bill. If not successful, she would stand back while the male enlarged the hole. . . . the birds would generally succeed."

Certainly the difference in bills would be difficult to explain in any other way, and the huia represents a unique experiment.

Australia's hairy imperial spider, *Dicrostichus furcatus* (10–7), acts as an angler employing what amounts to a lure. At night the spider hangs from a horizontal web thread by its rear legs, its front legs brandishing a thread weighted by a sticky droplet. Emulating the actions of a bolo thrower or the effect of adhesive flypaper, it swings this thread, often luring a nocturnal moth, perhaps because of the motion of the droplet or because of the odor of its own body. Stuck firmly to the globule by a lucky strike, the insect is drawn up like a fish on a line. This habit is shared by a second species, *Dicrostichus magnificus*, the magnificent spider. The angling habit is only one of many at which Australian spiders excel. Australian spiders can catch birds, mice, even fish. These are not mere accidents of lucky windfalls, they are characteristically yielded by the webs certain spiders set, and are eaten by the lucky spider.

The archer fish, *Toxotes* (10–8), is mostly insular in distribution, and the five species are characteristically found around the larger islands of Indo-Malaya. These fish live in the waters of estuaries and rivers within these islands. Archer

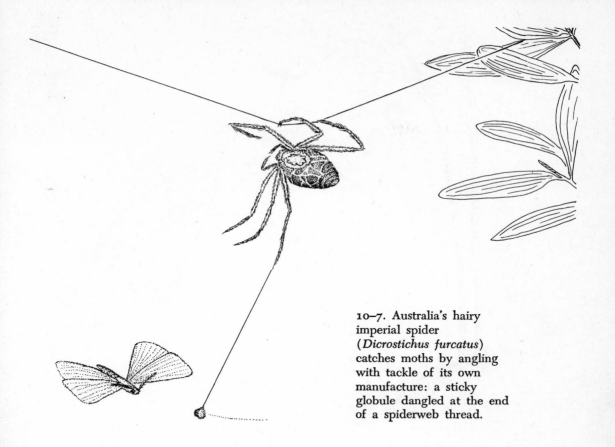

10–7. Australia's hairy imperial spider (*Dicrostichus furcatus*) catches moths by angling with tackle of its own manufacture: a sticky globule dangled at the end of a spiderweb thread.

fishes are adept beyond belief in shooting jets of water at insects above the water surface. Befuddled, the insect victims of this marksmanship are easily snapped up from the surface. Mature archer fishes can shoot accurately at distances up to six feet from their target. Special mouth modifications permit the precise ejection of water drops. These and other distinctions place the archer fishes in their own family, Toxotidae.

Changes in feeding on islands are manifold, and an interesting case is that of the wrens on St. Kilda, near Scotland. On the mainland the European wren *Troglodytes troglodytes* is sometimes polygamous. Without the aid of a male, a female can find enough food to feed her young. On bleak St. Kilda, however, scarcity of food has prompted a change in these habits. St. Kilda wrens are strictly monogamous, apparently because females alone cannot obtain enough nutrition for the young. Males aid in finding food, rearing the young, showing a fidelity evidently not mandatory on the mainland.

NOVELTIES IN LOCOMOTION

A scaleless reef fish of Pacific islands, *Antennarius* (10–9), shows how one change demands, or is concomitant with, several other changes. Sometimes known as the frogfish, *Antennarius* gropes among rocks by means of its fins: pec-

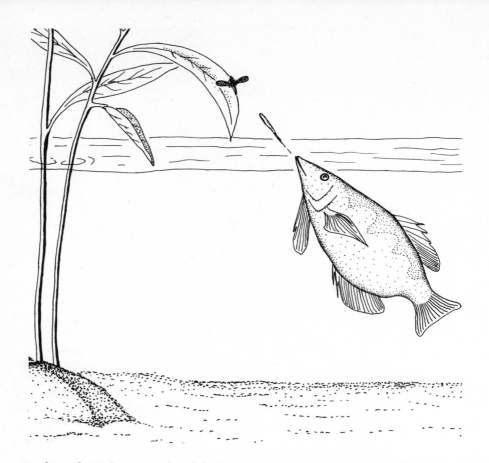

10–8. The Indo-Malaysian archer fish *Toxotes* secures insects by carefully aiming jets of water at them, snapping up the dislocated and helpless prey.

toral fins are modified into muscular arm-like appendages which permit the fish to clamber awkwardly from place to place. As shown in 10–9, *Antennarius* is poorly equipped for swimming—its fins are, to say the least, vestigial. Mostly it sits, lump-like, on the rocky bottom of reef areas. Frogfishes are subject to violent changes in color, but these seem to reflect states of activity rather than protective coloration. How does such a sluggish fish obtain food? It relies on angling, of a sort. Borne upon the nose of most species is a stalk, tipped with a variously shaped ornament, or "bait." It waves this "bait," a fleshy mobile appendage of its snout, to and fro, attracting small fish which, just short of eating the fringes of the ornaments, are consumed by the *Antennarius*.

Lack of locomotion permits the frogfish to remain in its favored pools, isolated from those of other islands by long stretches of deep water. If it had active locomotion, *Antennarius* might frequently be swept out to sea. Thus it is a "swimless" fish, perhaps for the same reasons as those of flightless moths that live among strong wind currents. *Antennarius* is known from several Pacific islands, and insular endemism is very high in this genus on account of the "swimless" habit, which means that it usually disperses only over short distances. One species, how-

10–9. Modified pectoral fins permit the walking fish *Antennarius* to clamber about on rocky bottoms of reef areas. This compensates for poor swimming ability. This specimen was collected from an inshore area of the Galápagos Islands. (Allan Hancock Foundation photo.)

ever, the "marbled angler" (*Antennarius marmoratus*), floats about in midocean on sargassum seaweed. Walking fins permit this fish to rest on the floating seaweed.

A similar restriction on locomotion has been instigated in a different way by clingfishes and suckerfishes. Belonging to various families, these inhabit both fresh and salt water. One insular species is *Gastromyzon borneensis* (10–10), the Borneo suckerfish, which lives among rocks in the torrents of mountain streams in Borneo. It has poorly developed swimming fins, but nearly the entire flattened undersurface of the fish is converted into a flat sucker. With this device it can control its motion, swimming only when calmer stream conditions permit. *Gastromyzon borneensis* may be a fresh water derivative of marine cyprinid fishes.

A MATTER OF DISSEMINATION

The palm-shaped Hawaiian tree lobeliad *Trematolobelia* has elected a dispersal mechanism entirely novel in its family (10–11). When green, fruits of this endemic genus appear like ordinary berries. But upon maturation, the fleshy parts of the fruit turn to a sort of mush and wash away in the rain, revealing a woody skeleton, perforated by holes (10–11, right). Inside the skeleton are a

10–10. The Borneo sucker fish (*Gastromyzon borneensis*) counters rushing waters of fresh water streams not with its swimming ability, which is poor, but by clinging to rocks with a broad adhesive surface on the lower side of its body.

pair of papery sacs which close whenever the fruit is wet by rains and open again when the weather dries. The seeds escape through slits in the sacs, then are shaken through the holes in the woody framework of the fruits as wind jostles the small tree. Thus, whenever weather is dry and windy, the fruit liberates seeds; rainy weather temporarily cancels the process. This shaker-type dispersal seems an adaptation to wet rain-forest conditions of the Hawaiian Islands. Because each plant, with dozens of fruits, dies after fruiting, scattering of seeds over a long period of time may be advantageous. Spread over weeks, seed dissemination may succeed in placing seeds in a larger number of favorable sites.

These porous woody fruits seemed so remarkable to botanists of half a century ago that they viewed with disbelief such a mechanism. Publications averred that the holes were merely the work of ravaging insects. Today, this is known to be false: they are preformed in young fruits, entirely free from insects.

The seeds of *Trematolobelia* go one step further toward dispersal efficiency. Unlike other members of the family Lobeliaceae, it has flat winged seeds which sail farther than rounded seeds do. Perhaps this explains why *Trematolobelia macrostachys*, the only species of that genus, is the only species of Lobeliaceae to have reached all of the major Hawaiian Islands.

10–11. When mature, the fleshy portion of fruits of the Hawaiian lobeliad *Trematolobelia macrostachys* falls away. Revealed is a woody skeleton which, in an intricate way, is a shaker for gradually releasing seeds.

EXTREMISTS AMONG THE PARASITIC PLANTS

Parasites are by no means rare on islands. Even though a host must establish before a parasite can (or at least at the same time), parasites have crossed enormous distances, as mistletoes native to the Hawaiian Islands attest. Some self-sufficient plants have, of course, switched to the parasitic habit on islands, thus increasing the roll. This is the case in *Podocarpus ustus*.

Nuytsia, Western Australia's "Christmas tree" (10–12), gives parasitism a grotesque twist. It is nothing more or less than a tree mistletoe. As a full-sized tree, it must parasitize another tree—or something smaller. In fact, studies and experiments have shown that it tends to derive its nutrition from lowly grasses which carpet the ground near its base. Each year, *Nuytsia* must establish new contacts with new victim grasses. Other plants may also be involved in its search for hosts. Like modest-sized mistletoes, *Nuytsia* has green leaves and stems and can manufacture a portion of its own food. If grown in isolation, however, tree seedlings become sickly, yellowish, and eventually die. Like many members of the mistletoe family (Loranthaceae), *Nuytsia* has colorful flowers. At Christmastime (in Australia's summer), these trees are converted to masses of yellow-orange blooms, a testament to the swarms of grasses and other plants that must pay tribute via their root connections. *Nuytsia* may have attained treehood by virtue of great success in adapting to the sandy plains near Perth where only a relatively limited number of tree species have eked out an existence.

In the same general locality as *Nuytsia* is another of the world's most excep-

10–12. Two features give Western Australia's mistletoe a wide measure of distinction: it is a full-sized tree, and it parasitizes not other trees, but grasses which grow around it. Bright golden flowers cover *Nuytsia* trees in midsummer.

tional plants: an orchid which, like a fungus, cannot manufacture its own food. Contrary to popular belief, virtually all orchids are green and self-sufficient, and though they may live upon trees, do not parasitize them. *Rhizanthella* (10–13) is thus an oddity among orchids. Topping this parasitic habit, *Rhizanthella* apparently spends its entire life underground. On account of this, the "underground orchid" has eluded plant hunters. It usually turns up during plowing, or digging out of rotten trees, around whose roots *Rhizanthella* evidently finds suitable growing conditions. Perhaps collected no more than a half dozen times, Rhizanthella's habits are almost completely unknown. How does a flower manage a completely underground existence? Do burrowing beetles aid in pollination of the dense cluster of purple flowers? Rhizanthella's habits are not only mysterious, we have no idea how or why such an orchid has evolved at all.

Equally unbelievable is another orchid which grows at the other end of Australia: *Cryptanthemis slateri* of New South Wales. It grows underground also. Although once thought to be parasitic on another orchid, *Dipodium, Chrysanthemis* is now known to grow, fungus-like, on decayed leaves and other organic matter. At the onset of flowering, stems grow upward toward the surface of the soil, apparently flowering before reaching light. Only fruiting plants have been seen exposed, and these are usually covered by fallen leaves of the trees under

10–13. *Rhizanthella gardneri* is an orchid which spends its entire life cycle under-ground. Heads of flowers form near the soil surface. The purplish flowers, shown enlarged at right, might be pollinated by small burrowing beetles. This peculiar orchid was discovered accidentally during plowing of a field. It has been found only in Western Australia.

which they grow. Although most orchids disperse their tiny seeds by wind, *Cryptanthemis* may scatter seeds by rainfall which washes them to new locations, or they may be blown along together with dust and leaves. Although similar in habits to *Rhizanthella*, *Cryptanthemis* has flowers rather different, and the two genera may not be closely related. There are many unanswered questions about both of these rare orchids.

SELF-PROTECTION

Predation is markedly lowered on islands, so fewer protective devices would be expected to have evolved. This is apparently true. On islands where we see such devices, they seem in direct proportion to the degree of danger in which the inhabitants naturally stand. Australia, which makes a closer approach to the ferocity of continental competition than do other insular areas, boasts more numerous examples. Spiny acacia trees abound, and a lizard, the moloch, is per-haps the most grotesquely spiny of all reptiles. In addition to such armor, protec-tive coloration and form characterize some animals, such as certain Australian geckos (7–3, 7–11).

To find any examples of protective mechanisms at all on islands is perhaps sur-prising. On New Zealand, however, some plants can only be explained in this way. *Aciphylla* (10–14) is a New Zealand member of the carrot family (Umbel-

10–14. Sword-like leaves and gigantic needle-like bracts on flower stalks form the formidable armor of this plant, *Aciphylla ferox*. As the fruits (right) show, this endemic New Zealand genus belongs in the carrot family (Umbelliferae).

liferae), all but unrecognizable as such, so covered with sword-like leaves are the plants. The fern-like leaf typical of most members of the carrot family has suffered a change in *Aciphylla* into a fan of stout, fibrous, pointed blades. The plant thus resembles a yucca more than any of its own true relatives. The flowering stalk does not resemble the flat-topped umbels for which carrots, dills, anise, and other members of the family are noted. Rather, the massive spike hides its fruits deep under a barricade of narrow bract leaves, leaves converted into fantastic needles. Why has such a plant evolved? The severity of New Zealand's climate could account in part for condensation of leaves, but the markedly defensive aspect must be grounded in the rapacity of some of New Zealand's animals. As one possibility, the flightless kakapo parrot (9–13) has been seen to feed on stems, fruits, even leaves of *Aciphylla*. This vegetable-loving parrot—or other animals—may well have been an inducement for *Aciphylla* to evolve its armament.

The same explanations may hold true for another New Zealand plant, *Pseudopanax ferox* (8–3). The downward-pointing, tough, saw-edged leaves may deter

10–15. Although other members of the lobelia family are not thorny, some species on the Hawaiian Islands bear a pronounced armament. *Cyanea marksii*, left, has stems and leaves covered with thorns and prickles. At right, *Cyanea aculeatiflora* has fruits and flowers densely covered with fine prickles.

an assault from below. The size of these leaves suggests that if they are useful in this regard, it is a large animal which they ward off. A small animal could easily creep through the leaves to the tender young shoots. Leaves of adult plants, quite unlike the juvenile leaves in form and armament, may represent the relative freedom of upper branches from attack by herbivores.

In the Hawaiian Islands, a similar but distinctive course has been followed by some species of the lobeliad *Cyanea* (10–15). In these, prominent prickles or thorns have evolved, inspiring names such as *"ferox"* or *"horrida"* given by botanists to certain species. Cyaneas are edible. One less spiny species, *C. tritomantha,* was eaten by early Hawaiians as a sort of spinach. Could thorns be a defense against plant-eating animals such as insect larvae or land snails? This seems the best explanation that can be offered, for the Hawaiian Islands are completely lacking in mammalian herbivores. When leaves of thorny Cyaneas are young (and therefore, perhaps more delicate and vulnerable), thorns are densely crowded. As leaves expand, thorns grow in size a little, but are spread farther apart as the leaf blade widens. These prickles or thorns are not very tough, so a more delicate animal, perhaps a soft one irritated by spiny textures, is likely to be the one against which this defense is effective.

SOMETHING CALLED MYRMECOPHILY

When plants "invite" ants to make their homes inside stems or leaves, the partnership is termed "myrmecophily," or "ant-liking." Surprisingly, this habit is a widespread one, particularly in the tropics, and various groups of plants have

10–16. Branches, flowers, and fruits of this *Myrmecodia* from New Guinea look not unlike those of coffee, to which it is related. The swollen base of the stem, however, is converted into chambers occupied by stinging ants, which protect the *Myrmecodia* plant.

succeeded in attracting ants; they even make elaborate homes for them. The basis for this partnership is alleged to be that potentially plant-eating animals are warded off by the ants, who, disturbed by the forager, run out and sting him with painful bites. As for the ants, they are offered all the conveniences of a prefabricated home, including freedom from drenching by rain and also a nest of approximately the proper size for an ant colony. Ants are, of course, capable of making their homes in various places, but when a plant builds a colony to their specifications, the temptation seems hard to resist. On balance, the advantage seems slightly more to the plants than to the ants, but ants have readily accepted these partnerships. The compulsiveness of these associations is remarkable, as many botanists who have collected plants known characteristically to harbor vicious ants will testify.

Of all ant plants, perhaps none are so bizarrely and completely adapted to myrmecophily as two genera of the Indo-Malayan islands, *Myrmecodia* (10–16) and *Hydnophytum* (10–17). Both are alike in being squat shrubs which live not on the ground, but on trees, like many orchids. This mode of life puts them out of reach of some animals, but *Hydnophytum* and *Myrmecodia* have more than one line of defense. Both agree in having a broad, round stem base. When cut open (10–16, 10–17, at right), this stem is revealed as penetrated by a complex series of galleries, spacious and lined with cork. The work of ants? No, if grown in cultivation, free from ants, both *Myrmecodia* and *Hydnophytum* develop these cavities. Ants may make a few changes, such as cutting entrances or exists to their plant home, but these genera are geared irreparably to life with

10–17. Defense and offense are combined in this New Guinean species of *Hydnophytum*, a genus which belongs to the coffee family (Rubiaceae). It lives upon (but does not parasitize) tree trunks, bears spines. The swollen stem contains galleries inhabited by stinging ants. The sticks in these plants (above) were inserted by New Guinea natives to tease the ants.

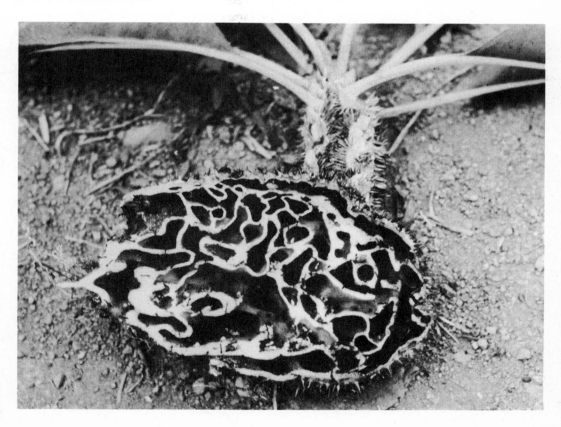

the ants. *Myrmecodia* (10–16) tops the thick stem base with long, slender branches, branches which remind one of nothing so much as a coffee plant. Indeed, white flowers and red berries complete the resemblance, for both *Myrmecodia* and *Hydnophytum* belong to the coffee family (Rubiaceae). *Hydnophytum* has a single stem and bears a rosette of large leaves. Both the upper stem and the swollen basal portion of the plant are covered with thorns. *Hydnophytum* seems one of the most thoroughly and ingeniously defended plants in the entire plant kingdom.

Hydnophytum and *Myrmecodia* are primarily island plants. Most species are native to New Guinea, Fiji, the Solomon Islands, Java, Celebes, Borneo, and Sumatra. Both genera have between twenty and thirty species apiece of which only a couple in each genus are native to a mainland area (Malaya). *Myrmecodia* and *Hydnophytum* may well have evolved in islands and spread by chance to Malaya. If their origin was a continental one, we might expect species in the forests of Burma, Indo-China, and Thailand, where they are apparently absent. In any case, the two genera have formed the majority of their species on islands and seem better attuned to or preserved by island conditions than mainland environments. Two other related genera of ant plants are entirely restricted to islands: *Myrmephytum selebicum* (Celebes) and *Myrmedoma arfakensis* (New Guinea).

THE PERILS OF POLLINATION

A change experienced by island plants unseen except by keen observers is that of pollination relationships. A plant seed may arrive on an island, grow to maturity, flower, and then find itself facing extinction because the proper insect to pollinate it, and thus insure production of more seeds, is not hovering nearby. Pollination, then, could be the weakest link in the chain of events leading to establishment and maintenance on an island. This would be true for plants which customarily require cross-pollination.

Plants which can self-pollinate without the aid of an insect would not suffer this disadvantage. A single immigrant seed could grow, flower, set seeds, and thus establish generation after generation of its kind. This seems a successful scheme for initial establishment, but viewed over long periods of time it would be a poor recipe for survival. Continual self-pollination means inbreeding, and inbreeding means the accumulation and expression of many defects, even lethal characteristics which prevent normal development. Self-pollination is a fine plan for quick spread of a species, and many have used it to advantage, but the long-term future of such a species is dim unless the species can cross-pollinate occasionally or can be "replenished" frequently from other areas. This appears to be the case with *Scaevola sericea* (2–6), a common beach shrub of the tropical Pacific. Because it occupies a constantly changing habitat, rapid production of seed of suitable plants by self-pollination is advantageous, and indeed, in Hawaii this species has been observed to self-pollinate. Because fruits of this species presumably wash up on Hawaiian shores from time to time from other islands in the Pacific, "new blood" could be added to Hawaiian populations if they "weakened" through continual self-pollination. In addition, cross-pollination may occasionally take place in Hawaiian specimens of *Scaevola sericea.*

Self-pollinated species of plants may well have established from time to time on islands, flourished, but later vanished. Most plants which have survived to the present on islands are cross-pollinated, at least occasionally. Such plants have, somehow, succeeded in attracting a pollinating insect—or else they are pollinated by wind. Both would result in cross-pollination. Although a minority of island plants appear to be wind-pollinated, the proportion is reported to be higher than on mainland areas.

Perhaps the most successful type of plant as an immigrant would be one which could self-pollinate if necessary, but which could also be cross-pollinated if any suitable insect presented itself. This is a characteristic of the sunflower family (Compositae), a family which is notable for its successes on islands. Such a plant could self-pollinate at first, with an occasional cross-pollination preventing total inbreeding. Then such a plant could, through evolutionary change, attract an insect already in residence on the island—or the insect could change its habits to include the new plant in its pollinating activities. An alternative program for an immigrant would be to change its flower structure so as to achieve pollination by wind at least now and then.

Because island populations are usually small populations, the danger of inbreeding is high, and cross-pollination becomes increasingly valuable. If variability is important, as suggested in Chapter 4, cross-pollination is highly desirable. Species or genera which survive for long periods on islands are perhaps those which maintain genetic "momentum" and which find good means for assuring cross-pollination.

The scheme which would achieve cross-pollination with the greatest certainty would be for a species to have individuals which bear either male or female flowers exclusively, a condition known as dioecism. Dioecious species usually have male flowers quite different from female ones, as shown for *Pisonia* (*Rockia*) *sandwichensis* in 10–18. If dioecious species have a successful scheme for long-term survival on islands, however, a species with this condition must immigrate to an island or the dioecious condition must be evolved from plants with bisexual flowers.

In the former case, a minimum of two seeds is required (one to yield a female plant, one to yield a male). Moreover, they must grow so as to flower simultaneously, and they must grow near enough to each other so that pollination can occur. These necessities may appear to be formidable obstacles, but they have probably been overcome a number of times. In many dioecious plants a male-plant seed and a female-plant seed are typically included together in a single fruit and are likely to be transported together. If the immigration requirements

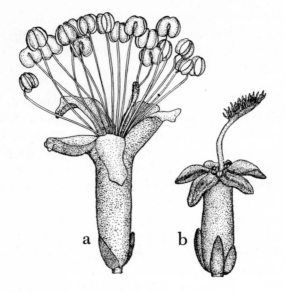

10–18. The Hawaiian
Pisonia (*Rockia*)
sandwicensis has male
(left) and female (right)
flowers much more different
from each other than are
male and female flowers of
its relatives. Development
of sexual differences in
flowers of island plants
presents an interesting
problem.

of dioecious plants seem prohibitive, one might remember that they are no more stringent than in immigrant animals, where a minimum of a mating pair (or a gravid female) is required. We have no way of knowing exactly what dispersal events have led to plants and animals now living on islands, but the likelihood seems great that dispersal units (seeds; individuals) do not arrive singly, but in groups. If events occur randomly, arrival of only a single seed of a species would occur sometimes, but more frequently several would arrive together—if any arrive at all. Most successful establishments of any plant or animal might be expected to result from simultaneous introduction of several individuals—such as part of a flock of migrating birds, blown off course.

On the other hand, a dioecious condition could evolve in a plant with bisexual flowers following its arrival on an island. Because bisexual flowers are the commonest type in flowering plants at large, one expects that this course might frequently be followed on islands, and data proves that it has. Among plant species native to New Zealand, 25 per cent are dioecious, whereas only 8 per cent are dioecious in a typical continental flora, such as that of the British Isles. Such a New Zealand genus as *Aciphylla* (10–14) is dioecious.

How can flowers formed so as to insure cross-pollination be evolved? Omitting details of genetics, one can say that a species with ordinary bisexual flowers could produce three types of individuals: (1), with flowers having style and ovary prominent and exposed, but short anthers; (2), with flowers having long anthers, short ovary and style; (3), with normal flowers. All three types of flowers could coexist in a species, as they do in New Zealand Fuchsias. These three forms of flowers could all be called bisexual, but the altered types differ from normal placement of anthers and styles enough to make self-pollination virtually impossible. In other groups of plants, the normal flowers are absent, and only long anther-short style and short anther-long style flowers are present. This condition (termed heterostyly) has evolved, for example, in Hawaiian species, of *Pittosporum, Wikstroemia, Hedyotis, Gouldia, Bobea, Labordea,* and other genera.

If anthers, rather than being short, are completely sterile on flowers of some individuals, whereas ovaries become nonfunctional on flowers of other individuals, the dioecious condition results. Normal flowers may also coexist with these in a species, producing a condition known as polygamo-dioecious. This condition obtains in the Hawaiian species of *Ilex* (holly), *Eurya, Pelea, Broussaisia, Myrsine,* and others. In other groups of flowering plants, female flowers and normal bisexual flowers but no male flowers are produced (gynodioecism). I have observed this condition in species of the endemic Hawaiian genus *Schiedea,* such as *S. globosa.* Some other Hawaiian Schiedeas have only bisexual flowers, suggesting that gynodioecism has evolved on the islands. Male and female flowers can be formed on the same individual (monoecism). Monoecious genera in the Hawaiian flora include *Euphorbia, Boehmeria, Diospyros,* and others.

Bisexual flowers which look perfectly normal may, in fact, be functionally male or female. In the Hawaiian *Gunnera mauiensis,* study by the Hawaiian botanist Dr. George Gillett revealed that flowers of some plants had anthers with sterile pollen grains exclusively. The form of a flower does not always reveal whether it is self-pollinated or cross-pollinated, and this can often be established only by special study. Studies of this sort have not been undertaken to any great degree on islands, but we may suppose that the vast majority of flowering plants on islands with normal bisexual flowers are cross-pollinated. If these could be added to the species with special mechanisms such as those described above (dioecism, polygamo-dioecism, gynodioecism, monoecism, heterostyly, wind pollination) which insure or tend to produce cross-pollination in the flora of a particular island, the proportion of cross-pollination to self-pollination would prove extremely high.

This is true not only in the New Zealand and Hawaiian floras, but in others as well. On the Juan Fernandez Islands, the endemic genera *Robinsonia, Rhetinodendron,* and *Symphyochaeta* have evolved dioecism, while *Lactoris* (13–16) is polygamo-dioecious. On St. Helena Island, the endemic genus *Petrobium* is polygamo-dioecious. On the Seychelles, the coco-de-mer (9–24) is dioecious.

If cross-pollination helps spread genetic variability throughout a species and thus is valuable to the evolution of an island species in lending it greater adaptability, another process ought to be valuable: hybridization. If a species can occasionally hybridize with another, both could be benefited by an inflow of useful new genes. Hybridization in the New Zealand flora has apparently taken place repeatedly, enabling groups of flowering plants to keep pace with such drastic changes as the spread of ice and chilling weather of the Pleistocene. In the Hawaiian flora, the purple-fruited species of *Scaevola* in mountain areas

(2–14) are now actively hybridizing, as discovered by Dr. George Gillett, and are very successful. Such hybrid swarms might eventually separate into pockets and form distinct populations, which in turn could hybridize among themselves and so on, prolonging the vigor and success of the Hawaiian Scaevolas.

IN SEARCH OF THE RIGHT POLLINATOR

Visitors to the Hawaiian Islands, the Galápagos, or New Zealand have noticed that flowers of the native floras of these islands are small and relatively colorless. Galápagos flowers are mostly small, and white or yellow. Many Hawaiian and New Zealand trees and shrubs have minute greenish or whitish flowers, lacking fragrance. Darwin's contemporary Alfred Wallace claimed that the poverty of insects was related to a similar poverty in showy flowers. There seems to be some truth in this. The larger pollinating insects, such as bumblebees and butterflies, are indeed few on distant islands. Larger insects usually do relate to larger and more colorful flowers. The Juan Fernandez Islands include in their native flora some large and colorful flowers, perhaps because their proximity to the South American mainland has permitted larger pollinating agents to reach the islands. There are three species of hummingbirds on the Juan Fernandez Islands, for example, and these are known to pollinate some of the native flowers. Insects of more distant islands are usually smaller, because dispersal problems of larger insects are so great. Consequently, Hawaiian and New Zealand flowering plants appear to have adapted, in many cases, to a world of tiny pollinators, pollinators attracted by white and green flowers in the dim light of shady rain forests. The floras of the Hawaiian Islands and New Zealand contain many exceptions to this, such as the lobeliads or *Metrosideros* (both of which may be adapted to pollination by native birds). However, the emphasis has probably shifted on such islands toward attraction of the smaller creatures by evolution of smaller flowers.

Other evolutionary roles for the pollination process on islands were claimed by Wallace. He hypothesized that the attractiveness of Compositae to a wide variety of insects has contributed to the success of this family on islands. This sounds reasonable, because securing pollination is a prime essential of any island flower. Wallace further claimed, however, that competition for pollinating insects is a selective force, coaxing herbs or shrubs into treehood. A tree, says Wallace, has a better chance for pollination by virtue of its longevity. If no pollination occurs one year, success in another year would produce enough seeds to keep the species alive. Although this situation is literally possible in trees, it may not represent an evolutionary force at all. If insects suitable for pollination are present, they should be available in relatively good numbers, year after year. Island populations of insects (and other animals) tend to be denser than mainland populations, in fact. One would expect suitable insects to be available in reasonable numbers or completely absent every year. The woody Compositae of the Juan Fernandez Islands, such as *Robinsonia* and *Phoenicoseris,* fail to flower for years, then sud-

10–19. The cone-like flower clusters of *Banksia* provide nectar for southwestern Australia's honey possum *Tarsipes* (see 6–18). The narrow nose and long tongue of *Tarsipes* are ideal for penetrating into flowers in search of this food. In the process of feeding, the possum pollinates flowers, creating a unique partnership.

denly come into a profusion of flowers. Such sudden and infrequent flowering events would demand a large stock of insects to be on hand, or the plants would set no seeds. An alternative would be wind-pollination. The Juan Fernandez genus *Rhetinodendron* shows some tendencies in this direction. Some woody Compositae, such as the Hawaiian *Wilkesia* (5–6), grow for many years, produce massive flower clusters suddenly, then die. This habit would be intolerable if insects were in short supply at the flowering time. Shortage of insects would coax such plants to extinction, not treehood.

THE UNLIKELY POLLINATORS

Outstanding in the archives of intriguing pollination devices is the story of the phalanger and the *Banksia*, for it is the only case known in which a terrestrial mammal pollinates a flower. The narrow nose of *Tarsipes* (10–19; 6–18) and its slender tongue are ideal for penetration among the narrow flowers, congested on a cob-like spike, of *Banksia* (10–19). Search for nectar leads sweet-loving *Tar-*

10–20. The orchid *Angraecum sesquipedale* lives astride tree trunks in Madagascar forests. The flowers have long spurs containing nectar. What insect has a tongue long enough to reach this nectar at the bottom of this spur and pollinate the flower? The moth *Xanthopan morgani predicta,* the "predicted" moth.

sipes to the *Banksia* flowers. Banksias are not its only nectar-provider, nor does *Banksia* rely exclusively on *Tarsipes* in the area in which the phalanger lives, southwestern Australia. However, *Tarsipes* has often been seen poking into *Banksia* flowers, and pollen grains can be found scattered among hairs on its nose, showing that unwittingly it carries pollen from one flower head to another.

An equally far-fetched partnership for the sake of pollination has developed on Madagascar. Orchid growers have been for many years familiar with *Angraecum sesquipedale,* a plant which bears large creamy-white flowers, each provided with a long spur. The name "*sesquipedale*," meaning "foot-and-a-half," denotes the fact that this spur, a long tube, can be as much as eighteen inches in length. Orchid flowers, as Darwin noted, are ingenious traps for forcing insects to pollinate them. The form of orchid flowers, he claimed, is closely keyed to the form and habits of the insects which pollinate them. Darwin was especially curious about *Angraecum sesquipedale,* the pollinator of which was not known at that time. The flowers of this orchid are white and thus conspicuous at night, and they emit a rich fragrance after sundown. Both are characteristics of a moth-pollinated flower. But what moth could account for the eighteen-inch spur? Darwin predicted that a moth with an eighteen-inch tongue would be found. Did such a "key" to this "lock" exist? Darwin was ridiculed, but such a moth was discovered—*Xanthopan morgani predicta* (10–20). The subspecies name "*predicta*" commemorates Darwin's hypothesis. The long tongue of this moth is a requisite because a shorter-tongued moth would fail to reach the nectar at the bottom of the spur tube and, frustrated, would spend little time patronizing a flower which yields it no nectar, and thereby would not pollinate the flower.

Curious pollination mechanisms are by no means the exclusive property of island plants. The two cases above, however, represent exceptionally intricate designs, designs which are distinctively the products of island isolation.

11   The Ostentatious Males

LONG familiar as a fact of life in the bird world is the tendency for males to be more colorful than females. Picking up this thread in his book *The Descent of Man,* Darwin wove it ingeniously into his theory of sexual selection. As viewed by Darwin, these birds are inexorably caught in a regime which demands more color, more display, more attractiveness from males. In securing a mate, the more successful male will be the one which excels in display, outmaneuvers his fellows. Such a species of bird often seems trapped in this race toward ostentation and is forced not only into more brilliant color patterns, but increasingly more time-consuming overtures to mating. The limits of this course are dictated by the amount of energy available for formation of decorative plumes and for performance of mating procedures on the one hand, and the tendency for brilliant birds to be easy prey on the other.

Sexual selection has operated on all continents, but nowhere have the potentialities been so thoroughly and spectacularly explored as in New Guinea and Australia. With food for birds relatively abundant, with levels of predation relatively low, evolution's experiments in sexual selection have been carried on with greater extravagance than in any other continents or islands.

The fidelity with which the cause of sexual selection has been served in Australia is demonstrated by the lyrebirds (Menuridae). The two species which comprise this family epitomize grandeur and prowess in male birds. Although females have a rather ordinary crow-like tail, males are much more elaborately endowed (11–1). In the mating season, full use is made of these plumes. Among the eucalypts and tree ferns, a male lyrebird scratches up a mound of bare dirt. This is a dance platform—a stage of sorts. Standing upon this mount, the male gives an artful performance. Tail plumes can be raised, singly or as a unit. At the height of the display, plumes are thrown forward over the head. From beneath this feather canopy, the lyrebird emits an endless variety of song. Listening to one male, an ornithologist listed a repertoire of calls mimicking no fewer than twenty other species of birds.

At this point in the procedure, a suitably impressed female may intervene. Following mating, the burden of nest-making and raising the young falls wholly on the female. The only task performed by males during this time is the offering of an occasional display and vocalization such as preceded mating. From her nest, the female is reported to look on fascinated.

The themes of courtship behavior exemplified by the lyrebird are those of "arena behavior," a sort of mating syndrome possessed by a number of different groups of birds. Arena behavior demands that males live separately from females, and that males meet females essentially only at mating time. Particular sites serve as stages, or arenas, for a male to attract a female. By means of various forms of display and attraction, females are lured to the performing male. Parting after mating, the female is left with all tasks of nesting, incubating eggs, feeding and caring for the young. She very likely will not see her mate again. This may actually be beneficial, for a resplendent male would probably be all too vulnerable to birds of prey or other predators. If a male were in close contact with the female and the chicks, the entire family would be endangered.

These themes are stated in varied and heightened form by a pair of families, the bower birds (Ptilonorhynchidae) and the birds of paradise (Paradisaeidae). This pair of closely related families represents little more than crow-like birds which have indulged in, and have been altered to an extreme degree by, arena behavior. Native to Australia, New Guinea, and nearby islands, bower birds and birds of paradise show different, but interrelated modes of expression of display tendencies.

THE BIZARRE AND THE BRILLIANT

New Guinea has been the site for most of the explosive evolutionary development of the birds of paradise. Adaptive radiation with respect to diet or ecology seems to have played little part in this evolution, however. Birds of paradise all

11–1. Males of Australia's lyrebird *Menura superba* bear attractive plumage, which can be raised and displayed somewhat in the fashion of a peacock. This display is part of a complex of habits known as arena behavior.

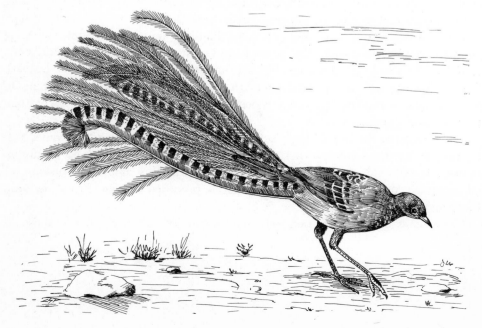

diet upon a relatively uniform selection of fruits, seeds, and insects—even frogs and lizards in a few instances. They are all forest birds. They all make cup-like nests from plant fragments, in trees. In internal anatomy, only a limited amount of difference can be noticed from genus to genus. Geographical restriction to particular portions of New Guinea has played a role in evolution of the birds of paradise, but is not the key to their diversity. Instead, they have been plunged into a progression toward all possible modes of display. Evidently, the ancestors of birds of paradise have been sufficiently plastic so that the bodies of males have been exploited for every possible means of display. From beak to tail, natural selection has left nothing unaltered in converting males into vehicles for showiness.

A full account of Paradisaeidae would require a book, but examples can show the diverse extremes within the family (Plate II).

Macgregoria pulchra (Plate II, upper left) places reliance on facial wattles for purposes of attraction. It is a bird of New Guinea's podocarp forests; it characteristically eats the olive-like fruits of these conifers. On these trees, it hops about on branch tips where it is easily seen, the orange of its wattles and leading feathers of its wings conspicuous against the crow-like black with which most of the body is clad. *Macgregoria* further advertises its presence by very noisy flight: "the wing strokes give a heavy rustling, audible for a considerable distance, and the glide a loud continued 'zing-g-g-g.'" Soft clicking and whistling noises serve to attract a female. Not a full-blown representative of arena behavior, *Macgregoria* is a genus in which males accompany females in nest-building. Males do not establish territories, however.

Lophorina superba (Plate II, extreme left, middle) is also rather crow-like in its black plumage. Its mode of display differs from that of *Macgregoria* in being less passive—erectile feathers as well as iridescence. Even in domestic crows or blackbirds one can notice, in the shiny feathers, a hint of purplish or greenish iridescence. In *Lophorina*, these qualities are exaggerated—in a localized region. *Lophorina* bears a bib of feathers which shine metallically and give off emerald or lavender glints, especially when sunlight strikes them. This aspect is caused not by colors inherent within the feathers themselves, but by microscopic sculpture of the feather barbules, which reflect light in a prismatic fashion. Both the black cape and lateral portions of the iridescent bib can be erected, forming a striking sight when seen in front view. So strong are the muscles which achieve this positioning that the bird can fly from one perch to another while these feathers are raised.

The six-plumed bird of paradise, *Parotia lawesii* (Plate II, bottom left) is closely related to *Lophorina*. Males are plump and velvety black. Tiny scale-like feathers on the throat and atop the head shimmer bronze and green, riveting the attention of a female. In addition, six feathers, with shafts bare except for the racquet-shaped tips, are fastened atop the head. During display, these six wiry feathers are thrown forward, dangling in front of the face. The shiny feathers

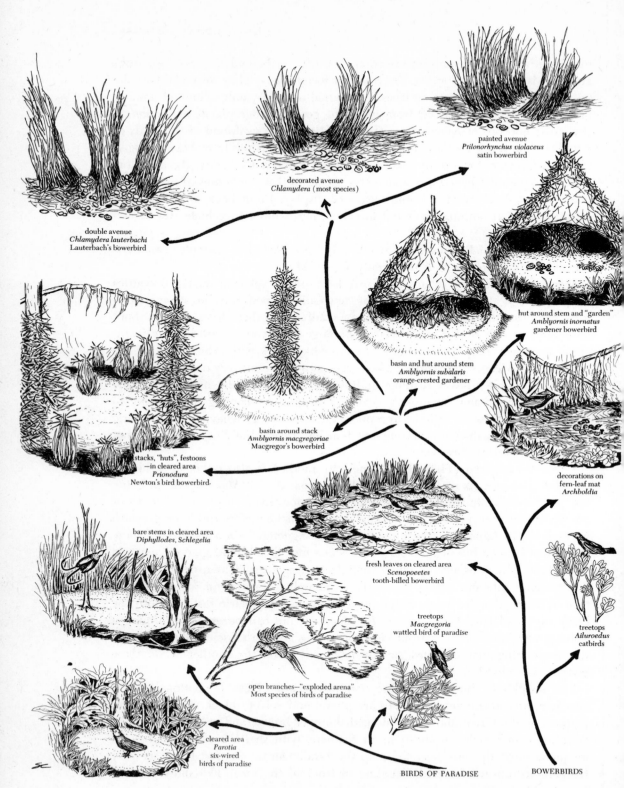

double avenue
Chlamydera lauterbachi
Lauterbach's bowerbird

decorated avenue
Chlamydera (most species)

painted avenue
Ptilonorhynchus violaceus
satin bowerbird

hut around stem and "garden"
Amblyornis inornatus
gardener bowerbird

basin and hut around stem
Amblyornis subalaris
orange-crested gardener

stacks, "huts", festoons
—in cleared area
Prionodura
Newton's bird bowerbird

basin around stack
Amblyornis macgregoriae
Macgregor's bowerbird

decorations on
fern-leaf mat
Archboldia

bare stems in cleared area
Diphyllodes, Schlegelia

fresh leaves on cleared area
Scenopoeetes
tooth-billed bowerbird

treetops
Ailuroedus
catbirds

treetops
Macgregoria
wattled bird of paradise

open branches—"exploded arena"
Most species of birds of paradise

cleared area
Parotia
six-wired
birds of paradise

BIRDS OF PARADISE   BOWERBIRDS

11–2. In the birds of paradise (Paradisaeidae) and bowerbirds (Ptilonorhynchidae), areas and devices used by males for courtship have evolved just as have brilliant feathers. Bowerbirds have become more specialized in construction of playgrounds, as this evolutionary tree indicates, and may have compensated in these elaborate arenas for their relatively uninteresting plumage.

atop the head can be erected also. A small white crest of feathers on the nose completes the equippage of *Parotia*. Capable of shrieks which may compensate for the basically dull coloration in attracting attention, it typically gives vent to a compelling "prat-prat." Parotias tend to occupy a modestly distinct arena during courtship: ". . . a round place clear of all grass and leaves . . ." This is one of the few uses of a playground among birds of paradise (11–2).

The greater sicklebill, *Epimachus fastuosus* (Plate II, center of left half) is also basically a rather dark bird—black above, brownish below. Like *Parotia* and *Lophorina*, *Epimachus* has a face well-supplied with metallic-sheened feathers. Iridescence also extends to other parts of the body as well. Metallic-tipped feathers extend down the middle of the back, and tail feathers are similarly glossy, giving a bluish or purplish appearance. More remarkable, in fact quite anomalous, are flank feathers. Looking like an extra set of wings, these shimmering groups of feathers can be raised over the head until they touch. The true wings are located above and behind these showy flanks. With its long body, strewn with arresting surfaces, this bird can quite effectively transfix the attentions of a female. Little is known about the feeding habits of the sicklebill, but the shape of the beak suggests that either its diet or its means of obtaining food differs from those of other birds of paradise.

Similar in general shape is the ribbon-tail, *Astrapia* (Plate II, left of center). Forming a ring around the beak is a prominent ruff of feathers. Head and neck bear iridescent feathers, and a modest orangeish zone of feathers crosses the breast. Most conspicuous are the two long tail plumes, white tipped with black. While perching, these feathers are almost always in motion, a feature which must make these birds quite arresting. Indeed, the apparently silent habits of this bird may be compensated by conspicuous feather movement and contrast. Ribbon-tails occur in high remote forests between 7800 and 11,000 feet.

Combining a variety of display approaches is the twelve-wired bird of paradise, *Seleucidis melanoleucus* (Plate II, center). This distinctive long-beaked bird has iridescent facial feathers, but for attractiveness it doubtless trades mostly upon an erectile fan of breast feathers, the tips especially showing sheen, and the contrast between this fan and the mass of fluffy yellow underfeathers beneath and behind the breast. In addition, twelve prominent feathers, bare to the shaft, bend under the bird and point forward. Even the greenish lining of the mouth may fascinate a watching female.

Large, conspicuous, and famous is *Paradisea apoda*, the greater bird of paradise (Plate II, right of center). In 1869, Alfred Wallace gave a fine description of this bird's courting procedure. Males "dance," he said, "in certain trees . . . which have a head of spreading branches and large but scattered leaves, giving a clear space for the birds to play and exhibit their plumes. On one of these trees a dozen or twenty full-plumaged males assemble together, raising up their wings, stretching out their necks, and elevate their exquisite plumes, keeping them in continual vibration. Between whiles they fly across from branch to branch in great excitement, so that the whole tree is filled with waving plumes in every variety of attitude and motion.

"The bird itself is nearly as large as a crow, and is of a rich coffee-brown color. The head and neck is of pure straw yellow above, and rich metallic green beneath. The long plumy tufts of golden-orange feathers spring from the side beneath each wing, and when the bird is in repose are partly concealed by them. At the time of its excitement, however, the wings are raised vertically over the back, the head is bent downward and stretched out, and the long plumes are raised up and expanded till they form two magnificent golden fans deep red at the base, and fading off into the pale brown tint of the finely divided and waving points.

"The whole bird is then overshadowed by them, the crouching body, yellow head and emerald-green throat forming but the foundation and setting to the golden glory which waves above. When seen in this attitude, the bird of paradise really deserves the name, and must be rated as one of the most beautiful and most wonderful of living things."

Wallace also noted that,

"Their loud cries, which are heard daily, show that they also are very numerous. Their note is 'wank-wank-wank-wok-wok-wok,' and is so loud and shrill as to be heard at a great distance, and to form the most prominent and characteristic sound in the Aru Islands. The mode of nidification is unknown, but the natives told me that the nest was made of leaves placed on an ants' nest or on some projecting limb of a very lofty tree, and believe that it contains only one young bird. . . . In May, when they are in full plumage, the males assemble early in the morning to exhibit themselves.

Paradisea rudolfi, the blue bird of paradise, is in color a marked departure in its genus. Wings are a light blue, underfeathers are rosy, and the head and neck are black. Acrobatics are prominently featured by this species. As shown on the chapter heading (Plate II, right), males of this species perform in an inverted position. A male "starts by sitting quietly on his perch and calling. Then, slowly and with care, he lowers himself backward. When he is hanging straight down, he shakes suddenly, throwing out his plumes on either side. As he gently rocks his body from the hips, he makes the plumes dance and flutter, and occasionally he shakes himself still harder to make the plumes stand out farther."

"All the while the bird sings in a low monotone, head tilted to one side to observe the effect, if any, of this bizarre courtship pattern."

Males of other species of the genus *Paradisea* show even more violence and frenzy in motion in their efforts to win females.

The enameled bird of paradise (Plate II, upper right), *Pteridophora alberti,* is unusual in the family. Although correctly placed in the family Paradisaeidae, it looks unlike a bird of paradise in several respects. Its two prominent plumes are often collected by natives of New Guinea. Specimens and records show that it comes from forests above five thousand feet in New Guinea. Recent motion pictures taken by the ornithologist E. Thomas Gilliard of The American Museum of Natural History show how it uses its pair of plumes. These are more like a series of enameled plates than a feather bearing soft barbs. These plates· are bluish outside, brown underneath. The contrasting black, brown, and yellow feathers of the body offer a fine array for display.

The magnificent bird of paradise, *Diphyllodes magnifica* (Plate II, center, below) is an inhabitant of lower forests which has been studied carefully. In February, March, and April, males move to display grounds. Unlike other birds of paradise, *Diphyllodes* is not satisfied by any convenient perch. He chooses. Selecting slender vertical woody stems near the ground, he defoliates them and clears away the surrounding area of debris (11–2). The area might be termed a playground, although it has also been called a bower because it seems in some ways a rudimentary version of the structures constructed by bower birds. The male climbs one of the vertical stems and, clinging to it at an angle, raises his shield of greenish breast feathers so that a broad triangle is formed and the central iridescent blue line stands out. This display is augmented when the bird assumes a horizontal position and raises the fan-like cape of yellow feathers behind its neck. At this point a female may join the male on the stem, and may respond when the male, in a pecking display, demonstrates the inside of its mouth. Mating finished, the male flies away, never to see the female again.

Cicinnurus regius, the king bird of paradise (Plate II, lower right) is both very small and very colorful. Wallace's description is still the best:

"It was a small bird, a little less than the thrush. Merely in arrangement and texture of plumage, this little bird was a gem of the first water; yet these comprised only half of its strange beauty. Springing from each side of the breast, and ordinarily lying concealed under the wings, were little tufts of greyish feathers about two inches long and each terminated by a broad band of intense emerald-green. These plumes can be raised at the will of the bird, and spread out into a pair of elegant fans when the wings are elevated. But this is not the only ornament. The two middle feathers of the tail are in the form of slender wires about five inches long and which diverge in a beautiful curve. Almost half an inch of the end of this wire is webbed on the outer side only, and colored of a fine metallic green; and being curved spirally inwards, they form a pair of elegant glittering buttons, hanging five inches below the body, and at the same distance apart. These two ornaments, the breast fans and the spiral-tipped wires, are altogether unique, combined with the most exquisite beauty of plumage, render this one of the most perfectly lovely of the many lovely productions of nature. My transports of admiration and delight quite amused my Aru hosts, who saw nothing more in 'Butong raja' than we do in the robin or goldfinch. . . . It frequents the lower trees of the less dense forest, and is very active, flying strongly with a whirring sound, and constantly hopping from branch to branch.

It eats hard stone-bearing fruits, as large as a gooseberry, and often flutters its wings after the manner of the South American manakins, at which times it elevates and expands the beautiful fans with which its breast is adorned."

The cry of *Cicinnurus* has been compared to the mewing of a kitten, the call of a quail, and the whine of a dog. Display includes, in addition to raising the flank feathers, puffing out the white silky lower feathers, emitting various warbling songs, and showing the apple-green interior of the mouth. In the final stages of display, the bird faces away from his audience and exhibits his back feathers. Occasionally the performance is concluded by swinging under the perch, walking backward and forward in the inverted position, and finally allowing his body to hang limply, swinging like an acrobat. For a small bird, its versatility seems unequaled—although perhaps other species of Paradisaeidae might rival it if they could be observed at length.

THE WHY OF HYBRIDS

Diphyllodes and *Cicinnurus* pose an interesting problem, because hybrids between them occur. Hybrids also occur between *Lophorina* and *Parotia, Lophorina* and *Paradigalla,* and *Lophorina* and *Craspedophora.* Ornithologists have been forced to this conclusion somewhat grudgingly, because natural hybrids between genera of birds—or other animals—are extremely rare. These bird of paradise hybrids are, however, valid despite the striking differences in form and color among these genera. Why is hybridization possible here, and not elsewhere among birds? Are the genera really genera in the sense that they are in other families of birds?

Birds of paradise have evolved differences among species and genera with respect to patterns of feathers and their colors, but the genetic barriers which make hybrids in other birds impossible have never evolved. Differences in pattern tend to keep species from hybridizing, in the main, so that the alternative barrier of infertility between species is unnecessary to maintain the separation between two well-adapted species. Because infertility is not the barrier between species, hybrids can form from time to time, but probably change the over-all composition of a particular species very little.

The basic explanation for hybridization in birds of paradise comes from a facet of arena behavior. The male sees the female only during courtship. Without the reinforcing of species fidelity that the constant associations of connubial habits bring—nest-building, incubating of eggs, feeding the young—the single contact at mating time can well be a chance encounter with a female of another species. Female birds of paradise are much more alike from genus to genus than are the males, and might be mistakenly identified by a male. Gratified by the approach of a female following his display routine, a male might not reject his conquest merely because it differed slightly from females of his own species. Indeed, traveling with fellow males exclusively, as most birds of paradise do, a male bird might not be familiar with the characteristics of his opposite number.

Barriers between species of birds are also enforced by strong territorial instincts in some cases. Territorial instincts are often lacking in arena-type birds.

By a strange coincidence, which seems to have been unappreciated although it may be quite significant, there is a close parallel to this in the plant world. Hybrids between genera are generally rare or impossible to make artificially in plants, but many have been created among orchids. Orchids are also among the showiest of flowers. Orchids rely for pollination upon insects, which generally form special partnerships with particular orchids. So characteristic, so constant are these associations that Darwin devoted an entire book to them. Thus, orchid species and orchid genera are kept apart by the fidelity of pollinators. Insects can easily recognize particular orchid species because of distinctive sizes, shapes, colors, patterns, and fragrances. Thus, distinctive lock-and-key relationships develop, like the *Angraecum-Xanthopan* scheme of Chapter 10. Apparently if natural selection leads primarily to forms and colors which will lead to fertilization, either in plants or animals, there is minimal selection for infertility in such a species or genus. This would operate as long as color and pattern tended, ordinarily, to keep different groups apart. The value of maintaining a pair of species (or genera) distinct is that each of them tends to be well-adjusted to particular conditions, whereas hybrids would be better in an intermediate condition. Intermediate conditions sometimes do exist, so hybrids can sometimes succeed.

THE SPECIALISTS IN RITES AND LURES

The bower birds (Ptilonorhynchidae), despite their close relationship to birds of paradise, have taken a rather different evolutionary pathway. Both Australia and New Guinea have served as theaters for evolution of bower birds. Clearly representatives of area behavior, females meet males only at the time of courtship. Both bower birds and birds of paradise are guided by sexual selection, both have similar origins. Crow-like birds are notoriously curious about bright, conspicuous objects. In the birds of paradise, this penchant is expressed in the attraction of female to male by his feather patterns, displaying, acrobatics, and a series of tricks which play on the brilliance of the male himself.

Although not as striking as birds of paradise, bower bird species do differ markedly in plumage color and pattern. Like birds of paradise, bower birds have not radiated very much with respect to diet: they take insects and fruits, the balance between the two differing somewhat from species to species. The sexual selection which has guided the development of bower birds has emphasized appreciation of colors and patterns, but this appreciation has gradually been transferred away from the body of the male to alien inanimate objects curated by the males.

The opening stages in this process find bower birds much like birds of paradise. In the catbirds, *Ailuroedus,* males evidently attract females while perched high in trees, much the same sort of place they would be found feeding (11–2)—like *Macgregoria* of the birds of paradise. In the catbirds, males have bright bluish and greenish wings, contrasting with buff underfeathers and brownish heads. This pattern probably serves for purposes of attraction well enough in the cat-birds without any special adjuncts.

Playgrounds. The much duller brown-and-buff males of the tooth-billed catbird (*Scenopoetes dentirostris*) have adopted the playground method of courtship, as the observations of Grant indicate:

"The playground of this species is formed by clearing a space, from three to five feet across, of all sticks and leaves, and placing thereon freshly gathered large green leaves of one particular kind of tree. These leaves average from forty or fifty to a hundred more in number, and on some of the playgrounds I found a great accumulation of dead leaves forming a ring around them, and in several instances over a foot in height. These 'circus rings' as we called them, were evidently made by the birds throwing or scraping the withered leaves from the frequented portion of the playground. Some are found amongst a dense undergrowth of young palms and lawyer canes; others in open parts of the scrub. . . . I have never found one except in the mountain ranges. These birds generally assemble at the playgrounds early in the morning and again in the afternoon. Usually three of four birds were seen playing about them, picking up the leaves and tossing them about or turning them over; or gamboling and chasing one another. All the while another bird perched in a bush close by was pouring out its loud and melodious notes, which are uttered very rapidly without intermission, for some considerable time. The leaves are thrown from the center to the outside of the ring, all withered ones being placed on the edge of it. Fresh leaves are picked and used for their evolutions every day. In addition to its rich and varied notes, it is also possessed of ventriloquial powers, which render it exceedingly difficult to locate, even when singing near at hand."

Archboldia papuensis sanfordi has a similar playground. A New Guinea species, its materials differ from that of the tooth-billed catbird, which is a native of northern Queensland. As observed on Mount Hagen, a male of Sanford's bower bird prepares a mat of ferns, curtained off with ferns and bamboo streamers:

"He decorates it with shells, insect skeletons, bits of resin and berries which he moves about so that streams of sunlight play on his offerings. When the female appears, the male grovels on the ground, convulsively chewing a strand of vine and uttering chirring sounds. This abject behavior apparently excites the female, who thrashes him violently with her wings. . . . After mating, the male bobs alertly in the bower, rearranging the disheveled piles of ornaments which his courtship left completely disorganized."

Basins and Huts. *Prionodura* and *Amblyornis*—sometimes collectively termed the "gardeners"—represent a departure in the direction of architecture. As A. Meston has described it, males of Newton's bower bird (*Prionodura newtoniana*) create this unusual array:

". . . the bower is usually built on the ground between trees or between a tree and a bush. It is constructed of small sticks and twigs. They are piled up almost horizontally around one of the trees in the form of a pyramid, which rises to a height varying from four to six feet; a similar pile of inferior height, about eighteen inches, is then built around the foot of the other tree; the intervening space is arched over with stems of climbing plants, the piles are decorated with white moss, and the arch with similar moss mingled with clusters of green fruit resembling wild grapes. Through and over the covered run play the birds. . . . scattered immediately around are a number of dwarf hut-like structures . . . five of them in a space of ten feet in diameter. . . . they give the spot exactly the appearance of a miniature camp. These seem to be built by bending towards each other strong stems of standing grass and capping them with a horizontal thatch of light twigs. In and out . . . and from one ['hut'] to another, the birds in their play pursue each other."

At higher elevations, bowers of *Prionodura* are reported to be made in a simpler fashion. In addition to his structural accomplishments, the male "appears to possess the marvellous imitative powers of the Australian lyre bird."

Amblyornis macgregoriae has a playground quite unlike that of any other bower bird (11–2). I have had the privilege of seeing this curious fountain-like structure on Mount Piora, New Guinea. Around a slender stem of a shrub, the earth is cleared and scratched away to form a circular depression, giving the impression of a manmade basin with a rounded curb. Around the central stick twigs are placed, almost woven into place. The stick soon bears a complicated covering of twigs, which form a spiny-looking centerpiece within the basin. The male creator of this structure will cavort in the basin around the ornament, and by his calls, actions, and the appearance of this "bower" which is his signature, will attract a female.

Building upon a central stem is the keynote which links the structure made by Macgregor's bower bird to the bower of other species of *Amblyornis*. The orange-crested bower bird, *A. subalaris*, creates a hut-like structure around the central stem, carefully described by A. P. Goodwin:

"This bower is built of twigs arranged in the shape of a hollow circular basin, about three feet in diameter, the side being some six inches higher than the center. The whole of the basin is covered with a carpet of the greenest and most delicate moss, which, as it is of a different kind to that growing around on the ground, trees, roots, etc., led me to conjecture that it had been planted by the bird itself. The surface is scrupulously cleared of all leaves, twigs, etc. In the center of the basin a small tree, without branches, about two inches in diameter, is growing. Immediately around this tree, and supported by it to a height of about two feet, is erected a light structure of small sticks and twigs, placed horizontally, and crossing one another. On the extreme outer edge of the basin a more substantial collection of twigs had been built up, which was arched above so as to join the collection around the center pole, leaving a clear space beneath for the bird to pass through in his gambols. The basin has two entrances leading into it. They are four or five inches apart, and are formed by a depression or gap in the outer rim. The bower is placed immediately to the right of the entrances. At the opposite side to the entrances, and on the highest part of the raised rim of the basin, is placed a quantity of black sticks, black beans, and the black wing-coverings of large Coleoptera. Black is evidently the most attractive colour to this bird."

Very similar in plant and sophistication is the bower of the non-crested gardener bower bird, *Amblyornis inornatus*, described in rather quaint anthropomorphic terms by O. Beccari. Around a stem about the diameter of a cane:

". . . It begins by constructing a kind of cone, chiefly of moss, of the size of a man's hand. The trunk of the tree becomes a central pillar; another whole building is supported by it. On the top of the central pillar twigs are then methodically placed in a radiating manner, resting on the ground, leaving an aperture for the entrance. Thus is obtained a conical and very regular hut. When the work is complete many other branches are placed transversely in various ways, to make the whole quite firm and impermeable. The whole is nearly three feet in diameter.

"The refined sense of the bird is not satisfied with building a hut. It is wonderful to find that it has the same ideas as a man; that is to say, what pleases the one gratifies the other. The passion for flowers and gardens is a sign of good taste and refinement.

"Before the cottage there is a meadow of moss. This is brought to the spot and kept free from grass, stones or anything which would offend the eye. On this green flowers and fruits of pretty color are placed so as to form an elegant little garden. . . . it would appear that the husband offers there his daily gifts to his wife. The objects are very various, but always of vivid color . . . rosy fruits . . . beautiful rosy flowers . . . also fungi and mottled insects placed on the turf. As soon as the objects are faded they are moved to the back of the hut. It is a clever bird, called by the inhabitants 'Buruk Gurea' (master bird) since it imitates the songs and screamings of numerous birds; also 'Tukan Kobon' which means a gardener."

The Avenues. The remainder of bower birds, belonging to the genera *Sericulus, Xanthomelus, Ptilonorhynchus,* and *Chlamydera* have switched to an avenue type of bower. In a sense, this avenue is like the tunnel of the hut of *Amblyornis*, uncovered and made straight instead of curved. All of these are much the same, except for that of *Chlamydera lauterbachi*, which is known to make a double avenue (11–2). An avenue type bower is constructed by first laying down a mat of grass and sticks. Into this mat, upright twigs are firmly inserted, interlocked with each other, until two parallel rows are formed. The two walls which form the avenue are lined with grass. A string of pebbles is placed so as to lead into the avenue. Attracted by the decorations, a female will follow the lead of the pebbles and other ornaments into the bower, and it is there that sexual union will take place.

An analysis of one double-avenue bower of Lauterbach's bower bird revealed that one thousand pebbles (total weight, ten pounds), three thousand sticks, and one thousand hair-like strands of grass had been used in its construction. Berries, shells, and colored stones are the most frequent decorations of these bowers, and are mostly placed at the entrance. Bower birds have also been known to steal human artifacts, such as buttons, spoons, nails, broken glass, cigarette packs, string, marbles, parking lot tickets, matchboxes and invitation cards.

Perhaps the most amazing decorator of the avenue building bower birds is the satin bower bird, *Ptilonorhynchus violaceus* (11–3), whose habits have been amply described by Chaffer:

"To its architectural accomplishments it adds that of an artist, for the interior of the walls of the bower are stained to a height of several inches with a pigment-like material. This unique habit of painting the bower has only been brought under notice within recent years. It has been confirmed by several observers. The first suggestion was due to the occurrence of flat circular wads of fibrous material lying between the walls of the bower (decorations and all other

11–3. Unique in his family, the male satin bowerbird *Ptilonorhynchus violaceus* paints his bower. He does this by daubing the inside of the avenue with a wad of fibers dipped in charcoal mixed with saliva.

objects are rigorously excluded from the interior of the bower). Careful watch saw the bird make use of these wads as brushes, charcoal mixed with saliva being the material used. The painted sticks when rubbed with one's fingers leave thereon a black pigment-like material."

This is one of only two known instances in which an animal habitually and instinctively uses a tool—the other is the twig or spine used by the Galápagos cactus finch (Chapters 10 and 15).

Bower birds often rearrange the decorations in the hope of better luring a female. Should one come into view, the male immediately springs into a dance. As part of this routine he often picks up a berry or other bright object and shows it to the female.

When observing the courting procedures of the fawn-breasted bower bird (*Chlamydera curviventris*), American Museum of Natural History ornithologist E. Thomas Gilliard observed a curious quirk—and thereby hangs a tale. Watching the response of a male to a female which had just entered a bower, Dr. Gilliard noticed him twitching his head toward and away from the female—just as if he were displaying a head crest. This species, however, has no crest. The male of this species, moreover, is rather dull-colored. From these and other observations, Dr. Gilliard concluded that male bower birds increase their emphasis on colorful objects in proportion to the increasing drabness of their bodies. The actions of the fawn-breasted bower bird may represent vestiges of display behavior, despite the loss of colorful feathers which would validate this habit. In *Amblyornis,* the least complicated bower is built by the brightest bird—*A. macgregoriae.* The most complicated bower, carefully decorated, is built by less showy *A. inornatus,* the name of which literally means "unadorned."

Gilliard has, logically, parlayed these facts into a theory of directions in the evolution of birds of paradise and bower birds. In his view, the colorful male birds of paradise are self-contained display units, operating in "exploded arenas" —mostly open branches of trees, but also sticks within a cleared area (*Diphyllodes*) or cleared playgrounds (*Parotia*). Unspecialized bower birds also use "exploded arenas," areas in which the theater of display is wide and relatively indefinite. However, a thread of decreasing self-display, countered by increasing object-display, runs through the more sophisticated bower birds. Thus, there is a transfer of decorative value from the body of the male to the focus of an elaborate bower and its accompanying décor. Because males of arena-type birds take no part in nesting, their nesting instincts may have been converted into bowerbuilding.

In ways such as these, the phenomenal and still incompletely known intricacy of these birds has developed. Could the cause of sexual selection have been so elaborately served on a continental area fiercely contested by a wide variety of birds—and other animals? Probably not. The remarkable panoply of these two families owes its existence, in some measure, to the less competitive trusteeship of isolated, though rich, island areas.

12   Some Stranded Beasts

A RELICT, simply, is something left behind. The biologist will read this as, "left behind with relatively little change." An animal relict would be a conservative creature, linked with very old ancestors by important features which we can still see today. Relicts are often dubbed "living fossils" or "primitive."

Whenever an animal—or plant—species becomes an island inhabitant, it has a chance of becoming a relict. After it has opted for an island existence, its mainland relatives chart new evolutionary courses and suffer different fates. Isolated from its continental fellows, an island animal also goes its own way, but in some cases seems to change less. Lowered competition on islands may favor remnants of ancient groups; if so, this is fortunate, for often antique types are unable to change, and while they calmly survive on islands, the mainland relatives often must yield to the expansion of new aggressive groups, often suffering extinction. For animals unable to maintain the competitive pace of continental life, an island is an ideal opportunity, and so it is not surprising that many islands do serve in this capacity.

One would expect old islands to be "relict areas." Many are. Relict-laden islands include Australia, New Guinea, Tasmania, New Zealand, Madagascar, Cuba, and Hispaniola, and these are all old islands. But an island need not necessarily be old to be a relict area. An animal group which has suffered extinction only recently on a continent may have survived on a relatively recent island. The islands where the tarsier (see below) survives became separated by water only recently from Southeast Asia, where tarsiers, if they once existed, no longer live.

The biological sophisticate will protest that the world's most primitive animals by no means owe their survival exclusively to islands. Primitive animals are not always unable to compete. The opossums of the Americas (Didelphidae) are structurally the most primitive of living marsupials, yet they are also among the most successful. Ironically out of key with their antiquity is the ability of opossums to spread, weed-like, into human territory and make a living from scraps and happenstance which most other animals could never convert into a livelihood. Other examples of primitive relicts on continents include among primary-division fresh water fishes some non-teleost bony fishes: the bichurs of Africa, the paddle fishes of China and east-central North America, and the bowfin of eastern North America. The lepidosirenid lungfishes of Africa and South America certainly are relicts. North America retains a primitive frog, *Ascaphus*. Among

12–1. The giant land snail *Placostylus* is an endemic of ancient lands in the southwestern Pacific. This specimen was collected in New Caledonia.

amphibians, caecilians and salamanders qualify as primitive, but survive over wide areas, mostly in the tropics and North Temperate Zone. Remarkable for their survival to the present day, but often forgotten in this regard, are crocodiles and tortoises. In a number of cases, islands may have aided their survival—both groups of these bulky reptiles are unexpectedly present on islands such as Madagascar, Cuba, and New Guinea.

Although representatives of primitive groups can be, and are often cited as, relicts, evolution habitually leaves behind genera and species which survive to the present unchanged in many ways. A family can be a relict, or even a species. An evolutionary line is always dying at its tail end as its head advances. But tail ends vanish irregularly, leaving us relict species.

Placostylus (12–1) is a giant land snail whose distribution (12–2) clearly suggests it is a relict. Some of the larger species may show some gigantism, and may be larger than ancestral *Placostylus* shells. The areas which *Placostylus* occupies stretches in an area from New Guinea through the Solomons, Fiji, New Caledonia, Lord Howe Island, the Kermadec Islands, and New Zealand. This area encompasses some of the Pacific's antique lands, suggesting that *Placostylus* might be a rather old genus of molluscs.

Another factor might operate, however, with other Pacific land snails. Some of these, like *Tornatellides* (12–3), have as peculiar distributions as one could imagine. *Tornatellides* has established on high islands around the Pacific—but it has bypassed many likely islands, such as those of Melanesia and Indo-Malaya. Remarkable in this pattern is the combination of excellent dispersal with inability

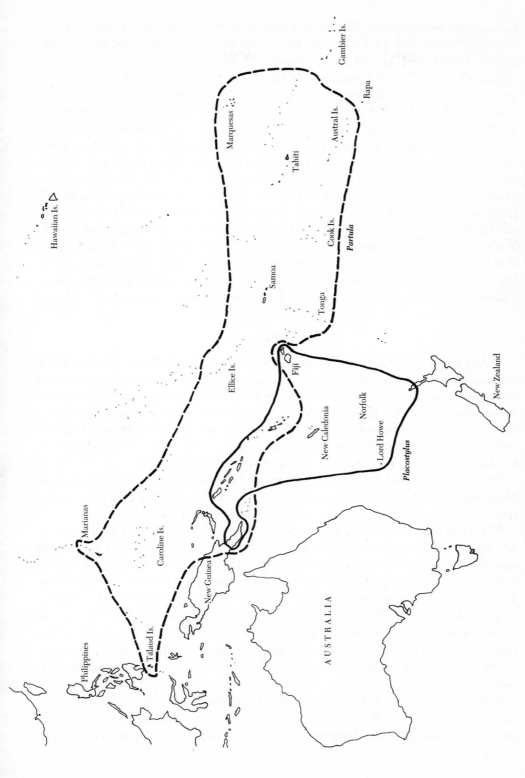

12-2. The distributions of *Placostylus* (see 12-1) and *Partula* (Chapter 4) are different, but show similar features: preference for islands, inability to invade continents. The active evolution of *Partula* described in Chapter 4 may account for its wider distribution.

Hawaiian Is.

Marianas

Caroline Is.

Talaud Is.

Philippines

New Guinea

AUSTRALIA

Ellice Is.

Fiji

New Caledonia

Norfolk

Lord Howe

Placostylus

New Zealand

Samoa

Tonga

Cook Is.

Partula

Marquesas

Tahiti

Austral Is.

Rapa

Gambier Is.

to establish on continents. The jump between Midway and the Marianas—or between Polynesia and the Galápagos Islands, or between Hawaii and the Revilla-gigedo Islands—are among the greatest transocean distances ever crossed by natural dispersal. This dispersal ability has brought the genus close to continental areas, and one inevitably supposes that some species must have, at one time or another, actually reached continents but failed to establish. Why is *Tornatellides* so strictly an island genus? Ultimately the antecedents of *Tornatellides* probably lived on continents, if we trace them back far enough. With all animal or plant groups, islands seem to serve as good receivers and fair redispersers, but no major group seems to have originated entirely on an island. If *Tornatellides* or its forebears once had a continental history, however, it certainly seems island-prone today. Adapted to high islands, *Tornatellides* faces long odds against successful dispersal and establishment, odds lessened only by good dispersal ability. We can consider this genus a "relict" at a time in its evolutionary history when it is still active. Not strictly a relict by some definitions, this designation is possible for this mollusc because relictism has overtones of a narrowed distribution—inability to compete in wider areas which its ancestors once mastered.

FISHES

Fishes relict on islands are fresh water fishes. Although some marine fishes are restricted to inshore reef areas on islands, such areas do not seem conducive to long-term preservation of ancient fishes. Fresh water fishes on oceanic islands are simply those which have been derived from marine species capable of making the transition to a non-salty way of life. Families which have succeeded in this enterprise include galaxiids, cichlids, gobies, and many others. These, however, are not true relicts, because they are relatively advanced fishes.

The important relict fishes of islands would be expected to be primary-division fresh water fishes on continental islands, fishes which secured a place on portions of continents which later lost their connection to the mainland.

The Australian lungfish *Neoceratodus forsteri* (12–4) is as ancient a relict as one could expect to find. Indeed, it is very similar to *Ceratodus,* a fish which spread over several continents in Triassic and Jurassic time. The group to which it belongs, the dipnoid fishes, has a fossil record stretching back to Carboniferous and Devonian times, when they were common. The lungfish looks rather like an amphibian. Its lateral fins are perhaps more like arms and legs than the fins of some specialized fishes. Indeed, the first scientific report of the lungfish described it as "a gigantic amphibian." It does not use its fins for walking, and even when swimming does not use them in the adept manner one associates with fish.

Today, Australia's lungfish is restricted to the Mary and Burnett river systems in southeastern Queensland. It extends from brackish water to fresh water upriver. The lungfish often frequents tidal areas, which are often muddy and

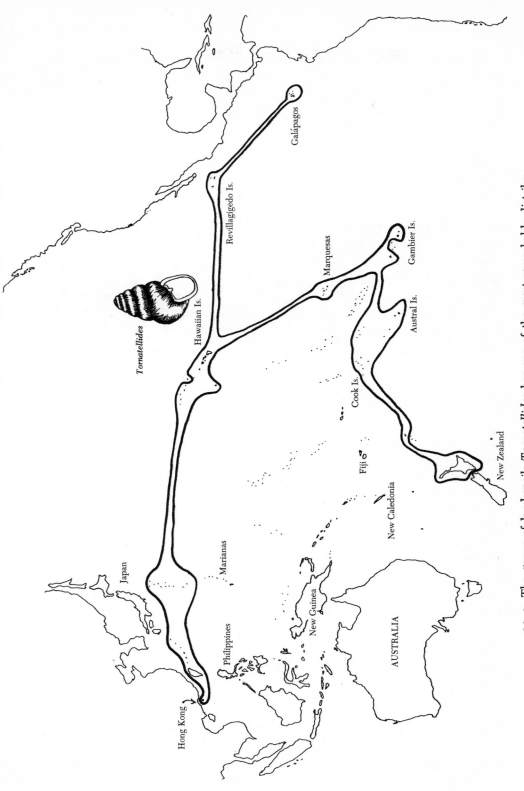

12-3. The genus of land-snails *Tornatellides* has one of the most remarkable distribution patterns to be found among plants or animals. Evidently this genus is good at dispersal, but cannot gain a foothold on continents bordering the Pacific Ocean, which it has so remarkably spanned.

12–4. Like a remnant of a vanished world, Australia's lungfish *Neoceratodus forsteri* persists in rivers of a limited region of Queensland, Australia. Swimming motions of lungfishes are inexpert, remind one more of a swimming reptile than of a fish.

fouled. Breathing by gills alone would be fatal under such conditions. The lungfish uses its lungs in an auxiliary capacity, coming to the surface to breathe when gills will not suffice. Life out of water is impossible for the lungfish, however. Curiously, the diet for this fish consists mostly of leaves of grass and eucalypts.

Not so primitive as *Neoceratodus,* but still an ancient form and a relict is *Scleropages,* the burramundi (12–5). Its history is easily traceable to the Eocene, fifty million years ago, when its antecedents inhabited North and South America and India. Today, *Scleropages leichardti* inhabits rivers of Queensland and Northern Territory in Australia and rivers of southern New Guinea. A second species reaches from Thailand, Indo-China, and Malaya into the Greater Sunda Islands west of Wallace's Line. Like the lungfish, *Scleropages* has large scales; it can attain three feet in length. Males serve as nurseries: they carry young in their mouths, and cannot eat until the hatched fishlets are old enough to swim away.

The simplest explanation of both *Neoceratodus* and *Scleropages* may be that they migrated to Australia and New Guinea when there was continuous land from Southeast Asia, and river systems positioned to permit this migration. If their present restriction to fresh water has always been compulsory, there is no other explanation. When we deal with fishes of such antiquity, however, there is

12–5. The burramundi, or barramundi (*Scleropages leichardtii*) has been preserved in rivers of northern Australia. It is very similar to fossils found over much of the world in deposits about fifty million years old.

no absolute guarantee that they have always been restricted to a fresh water regime. Uncertainties of this sort also exist along Wallace's Line. Two cyprinid fishes, *Rasbora* and *Puntius,* reach beyond Bali to Lombok, and *Rasbora* is also on Sumbawa. *Puntius* crosses Wallace's Line in the Philippines by reaching Mindanao. Are these genera, as commonly supposed, primary-division fresh water fishes? If so, has geology occasionally provided land connections across Wallace's Line? Or are they more salt-tolerant than has generally been supposed? The interpretation dictates whether such fish are exhibiting a relict pattern or an immigrant pattern. The majority of biologists today would probably favor a relict history in these particular cases.

AMPHIBIANS

Rated quite primitive among island amphibians is a frog from New Zealand, *Leiopelma* (12–6). There are perhaps three species: *L. hamiltoni* on Stephen Island, in the strait between North and South Island, and a pair of close species, *L. hochstetteri* and *L. archeyi* of northern North Island. The latter lacks webbing between the toes, and occupies hilltop sites, whereas *L. hochstetteri* prefers streams and thus puts its webbed toes to use in swimming. Considering that *Leiopelma* is an ancient frog and has probably occupied New Zealand for a very long time, it has made relatively little evolutionary progress; one would expect divergence into more numerous and more distinctive species by now. *Leiopelma* feeds on flies; unlike many frogs, it is a poor swimmer. The primitiveness of *Leiopelma* cannot be appreciated from its external appearance, which is like that of other frogs. Those versed in comparative anatomy are more impressed with such features as vestigial tail muscles which have lost their tail-wagging function.

REPTILES

A definitive example of a relict is New Zealand's tuatara, *Sphenodon punctatus* (12–7). *Sphenodon* is so distinctive in structure that although clearly a reptile, it cannot be classified with any of the four main living groups of reptiles—turtles, crocodiles, lizards, and snakes. Although superficially like a lizard, the tuatara's bone structure is quite different. Its uniqueness puts it in a group by itself, *Rhynchocephalia*. Whereas dinosaurs spread in the Jurassic (150 million years ago), reached dynastic proportions in the Cretaceous, and then suddenly died out about sixty million years ago, *Rhynchocephalia* are much older. Sphenodon's allies flourished in the Triassic, about 180 million years ago, and thinned out while dinosaurs reigned. *Rhynchocephalia* are tenuously linked with the present only by the tuatara, which now survives on—at last listing—thirteen small islands near New Zealand. Originally it also occupied the main islands, where for some time it has evidently been unable to compete. Now completely protected, the

12–6. New Zealand's primitive frog *Leiopelma hochstetteri* has its closest relatives in North America. Considered an ancient frog, it still retains tail-twitching muscles although it no longer has a tail.

tuatara is surviving well, perhaps even increasing on a few islets. Iguana-like in appearance, the tuatara bears a series of withered-appearing spines down its back. Among the obsolete features the tuatara possesses is its "third" or pineal "eye" atop its head. Although some lizards still have a "third eye" complete with retina and cornea, they lack a nerve connection to the brain; tuataras still have such a nerve trunk. The function of the "third eye" in tuataras has not been determined, but in lizards this vestigial "eye" appears to function in regulating exposure to sunlight—a feature perhaps useful, like a thermostat, in a cold-blooded animal.

Tuataras enjoy one habit which represents a peculiar adaptation to island life: they share their burrows with birds. The tolerant bird is known to New Zealanders as the mutton bird (*Puffinus carneipes*). So consistent is this association that tuataras are claimed to occupy the right side of a burrow, mutton birds the left. Tuataras are quite capable of digging their own burrows, dog-fashion, with their fat-fingered forepaws. The relationship between mutton birds and tuataras seems more one of tolerance than of mutual benefit. Advantage lies with the tuatara, possibly, because it receives a ready-made burrow and whatever leavings from a mutton bird's meal it cares to consume. Tuataras appear merely to take advantage of the accommodations provided by these good-na-

12–7. A lizard-like reptile of ancient structure, the tuatara *Sphenodon punctatus* persists only on small islands off New Zealand's coast. Its ancestors flourished long before the rise of dinosaurs. (San Diego Zoo photo).

tured birds. The characteristic food of the tuatara is beetles, although they also ingest roots and even feathers.

Unlike most lizards, *Sphenodon* enters fresh water readily, perhaps an adjustment to securing beetles in and near streams. Although salt water is a different matter, tuataras probably did reach New Zealand by sea, perhaps by rafting. Growth is slow, and they live unusually long lives for reptiles. Although they lay eight or ten eggs carefully in sand, tuataras increase in numbers only slowly even when protection is excellent. Quite able to defend themselves, they can detach their tails in moments of panic.

BIRDS

Zoologists usually decline to name relict groups of birds. In part, primitiveness in birds is difficult to demonstrate. Often considered primitive are the families of ratites—the giant flightless creatures such as rheas, ostriches, moas, emus, cassowaries, and elephant birds. If primitive, these may be regarded as relicts. In many cases they have a second criterion of relictism: restriction in geographical distribution. Some of them have only recently been extinguished (moas, elephant birds). As mentioned in Chapter 9, ratites may have been derived from more than one group of flying birds. The tinamous of South America might be like some ratite ancestors, and South America may contain more groups of primitive birds than other continents.

Very likely, flightlessness is to some degree inevitable for long-term land-bird residents of islands. Flightlessness is not a primitive feature in birds, so loss of wings, expansion of feet, increase of body size, and changes in feathers characteristic of non-fliers tend to mask or obliterate whatever primitive features these birds may have or may have had. Considering these tendencies, New Zealand's kiwi (9–14) is probably a good example of an island relict—its loss of flight appears to have been a rather ancient event.

MAMMALS

Monotremes. The platypus (12–8) and the spiny anteaters (12–9, 12–10) are among the most dramatic of Australia's ties with life of the remote past. These two groups, which together form the only monotremes the world now supports, are often more noted for their specializations than for their unspecialized features. These specializations have very likely permitted this ancient group of mammals to survive to the present. The length of their history in Australia and New Guinea has been quite long; their entry into this region may have been in the late Triassic or in the Jurassic. Foremost among the ancient habits retained by the monotremes are: (1) they lay eggs; (2) they provide milk for young, but from numerous tiny cup-like glands, not well-defined breasts. The first may be considered a vestige of reptilian modes of reproduction; the second is a rather crude early essay in the mammalian habit. Pointing to monotremes as a mid-point between reptiles and mammals would not be accurate, however: they have passed over the threshold of mammalhood, but offer more numerous reminiscences of marsupials than of reptiles.

The platypus (12–8) is essentially an aquatic modification of the monotreme line. It occupies (or occupied) rivers in Tasmania and on the Australian mainland west to the border of South Australia, east and north to Queensland. Alpine streams at six thousand feet on Mount Kosciusko suit it, as do the subtropical waters of Queensland rivers. Writings about the platypus are heavily burdened with analogy, as though it combined disparate features of various animals. The fact that those who first viewed stuffed specimens thought it was actually a taxidermist's fakery has acquired the status of legend in science.

Notably out of key for a furred animal is the bill, which has been compared with that of a duck, a spoonbill ibis, a spoonbill sturgeon, and a spoonbill dinosaur. Actually, a better comparison might be with a dog's nose, for the platypus bill is moist, fleshy, and contains many nerve endings useful for probing the river bottom in search of prey. It is also a mouthpiece suited to scooping up large quantities of molluscs and crayfish, which the platypus apparently eats ravenously. It also takes in silt, which seems to aid in digestion. The bill is thus a scoop which doubles as a sensor, substituting for whiskers, which the platypus lacks.

The front feet are webbed, reminiscent of those of otters or seals—an obvious modification for paddling. These feet, however, have strong claws useful for digging. When burrowing or walking, the platypus folds the webbing back. Thus the front feet are multipurpose tools of great versatility. The rear feet have a curious appendage: a tubular spur, which is pointed and can inject a poison, contained internally in a gland, into an enemy. A viper's fangs is the analogy often selected to describe this unique defense mechanism. Pythons and monitor lizards appear to be the chief natural enemies of the platypus. The back feet are not webbed as much as the front, and although they have a secondary use in swimming, they provide the main thrust during walking on land.

The short front shoulder bones invite comparison with those of the alligator, and indeed these animals resemble each other in their crouching stance. The platypus tail is flattened and beaver-like. It stabilizes swimming movements and aids during dives. The fur of the platypus, like that of seals and other aquatic mammals, has silky underfur beneath the longer and harsher hairs.

For homes and defense, the platypus digs long tortuous burrows. Two kinds of burrows are excavated. One is a general quarters for living, except during the breeding season, when it becomes a dormitory for the males. The other is a breeding burrow, dug by females, which is very elaborate and provided with a nest. This nest is often compared with those of birds, and might also be regarded as a substitute for a marsupial pouch. The other monotremes, the spiny anteaters, do have a marsupium-like pouch, a structure ruled out for the platypus by its

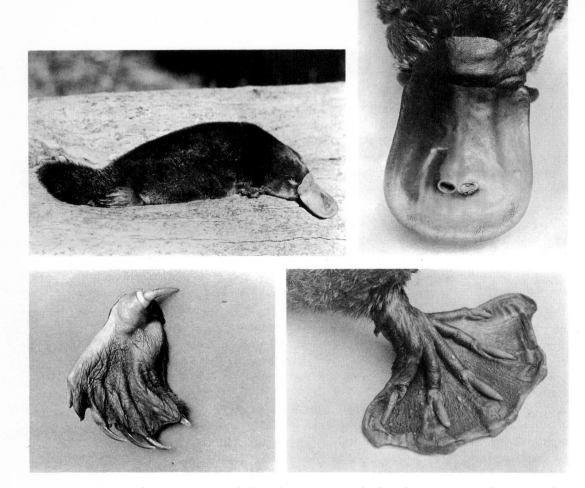

12–8. When specimens of the platypus (*Ornithorhynchus anatinus*) first arrived in Europe, they were considered the fantastic concoction of a taxidermist. The bill, feet, and form of the platypus are disparate specializations which may have permitted this representative of an ancient group to survive to the present. (New York Zoological Society photo).

aquatic mode of existence. Taking no chances when she retires to lay eggs, the female platypus constructs plugs of earth, each six or eight inches thick, at intervals in the burrow. She uses her tail both as trowel and tamper in forming these barricades. The plugs serve not only for defense, but to prevent flooding. After egg-laying, the female lies curled around the eggs, and when they hatch, close contact with the young stimulates milk flow from the pores. The infant platypuses lick it from their mother's fur.

An entirely different series of mechanisms have aided the spiny anteaters in their traverse from the dim past to the competitive present. They belong to two genera, *Tachyglossus* (12–9) and *Zaglossus* (12–10). The latter has a longer

12–9. Australia's spiny anteater *Tachyglossus aculeatus* is the closest living relative of the platypus, despite its quite different appearance. It belongs to a primitive mammal group, the monotremes. (New York Zoological Society photo).

snout and hails from New Guinea, the former is shorter-nosed and ranges from Australia's far north (Queensland) to Tasmania—an amazing range of climates. *Zaglossus* has thick fur which conceals spines—a warm covering which correlates with the cool climates of alpine New Guinea. This furriness is also characteristic of the Tasmanian *Tachyglossus*, *T. setosus*, which endures colder weather than its mainland relative, *T. aculeatus*. An additional means of withstanding cold climates shared by all of the spiny anteaters is the accumulation of thick layers of fat, which underwrites their hibernation.

Coordinated for life near the ground are claws and spines of these anteaters. Spines ward off predators, but are especially effective when the anteater literally sinks into the ground. This maneuver is performed by the rapid dredging of the claws into earth and rubble. Thus the softer belly of the anteater is safe, and only the spiny back is exposed. Attempts to dislodge an anteater submerged

12–10. New Guinea hosts the monotreme *Zaglossus bruijnii,* a long-snouted relative of Australia's spiny anteater.

in this way are futile. Curling up is an alternative means of defense, effective because when completely rolled, only spiny surfaces are exposed.

The second toe of back feet is prominently elongate in *Tachyglossus,* a device which aids in cleaning the difficult mixture of fur and spines. Claws are, however, of primary importance in food-getting. Termite nests can be ripped open, the long snout inserted, and the rasping tongue used to withdraw the insects. Dirt and sand are an article of diet for this animal, in order to achieve a gizzard-like grinding.

Tachyglossus is not a burrower, and so it does not construct nests. Eggs are laid in such a manner that they become lodged in a flap-like pouch. Thus, a close approach is made to the marsupial habit. *Zaglossus* is reported to dig burrows—perhaps for hibernation—and it lacks the elaborate routines of platypuses. Its reproduction is much like that of *Tachyglossus.*

Marsupials. The Australian marsupials may not be as primitive as the monotremes, but they also qualify as relics. The campaigns of diversification waged by the marsupials, as described in Chapter 6, may have provided a highly competitive situation, a background against which the monotremes were forced to evolve intricate and fierce mechanisms for specialized ways of life.

Insectivores. Considered a primitive group along with monotremes and marsupials, the insectivores, although more advanced, might be expected to have left many relics. They have. The hedgehogs (Erinaceidae) have been successful and occupy large areas, and on this account may not be considered relics by some. Three other families, however, have persisted in small areas. One of these, Potamogalidae, contains South Africa's otter shrew. Another, Tenrecidae, contains Madagascar's curious tenrecs, described in Chapter 16.

The third family, Solenodontidae, contains a shy and secretive creature, *So-*

12–11. A shy nocturnal animal and vestige of a group of insectivores which has largely died out, *Solenodon paradoxus* survives tenuously in the mountains of Hispaniola and Cuba. (New York Zoological Society photo.)

lenodon (12–11), from the West Indies. There are two species, S. *paradoxus* from Hispaniola and S. *cubanus* from Cuba. *Solenodon* is difficult to discover because it spends the daytime hidden in limestone caves or hollow logs. At night it emerges, sniffing sensitively with its long, bewhiskered snout, foraging for insects. Its long rat-like tail serves as a support, and using it with its two hind legs to form a tripod, it sits up while busily chewing and relishing an insect morsel. Claws designed for digging and sharp teeth aid the search for insects. The minute eyes and perceptive ears and nose seem a sensory equipment well suited to a nocturnal creature. The withdrawn habits and insular habitat of *Solenodon* may have contributed to its preservation. A closely related genus, *Nesophontes* (Solenodontidae), was once widespread in the West Indies (Cuba, Hispaniola, Puerto Rico), but is now known only as a fossil.

Primates. Primates today present a remarkable array of forms, extending from the insectivore-like tupaias to man. Along this route, a number of groups have been left behind, persisting as relicts. Among the most interesting are the lemurs, considered in Chapter 16. Another family, Tarsiidae, containing only a single genus, *Tarsius*, is an island relict.

Tarsiers (12–12) have found a refuge in the Indo-Malayan archipelago. There are three species: the Philippine tarsier (*T. syrichta*) on Samar, Leyte, Bohol, and Mindanao; the Malayan tarsier (*T. bancanus*) on Sumatra, Banka, Billiton, Borneo and Sirhassen (Natuna Islands); and the Celebesian tarsier (*T. spectrum*) on Celebes and nearby islands.

The tarsier is an admixture of specialized and unspecialized features. It is often conceded that this primate occupies a place near the base of the line leading to the greater apes. However, it has gone its own way, and the most striking elements of the tarsier's appearance reflect not so much ancestral forms as they do the adaptations of a nocturnal forest animal. The huge eyes are attuned to the night world and what it offers. Such eyes are vulnerable, and so the tarsier has the habit of squeezing them shut with each bite it takes, a habit which protects it from flying fragments of food. A flexible neck permits the head to turn 180 degrees for a backward glance. Enormous ears train on noises, carefully sifted by the tarsier's wary, nervous mind. The coarse "fingerprint" ridges and exaggerated finger pads are ideal for climbing, either defensively or in search of food. As with monkeys, the tarsier's teeth can inflict a convincing bite.

Tarsiers are extremely agile at catching and eating insects. Dexterity, larger brain size, and upright position seem interrelated, as they are in man, and these features have mutually influenced each other. Such characteristics as these have doubtless spelled success in the tarsier's fight for survival. In an evolutionary line, newer forms tend to replace those which fail to change in important respects—unless the older ones can exploit some new niche, or escape from competition. Refuged by its island habitats and bolstered by agile domination of insect-filled tropical forests at night, the tarsier is an example of the courses which relict animals often take.

And Many More. The relict program has been indulged in by many other mammals. The offshore islands of a continent offer an advantageous gambit. Survival of the marsupial wolf on Tasmania, or of another marsupial genus, *Dromiciops*, on Chile's Chiloe Island, are examples. Pygmy mammoths lingered on California's Channel Islands after they had died elsewhere. The list of more specialized mammals which have become relicts in recent time could be extended almost indefinitely.

INVERTEBRATES

The ease of distribution which invertebrates often enjoy makes them somewhat less likely to become relicts than vertebrates, because they are able to disperse to more areas which can offer them conditions fit for their survival. The pro-

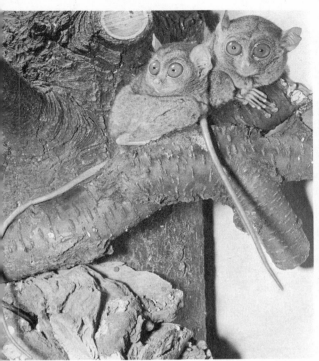 

12–12. Among primates, the tarsier (*Tarsius*) is a primitive member of the line which leads to the great apes. It seems a relict, for it is confined to the Philippines and Greater Sunda Islands. (New York Zoological Society photo).

cesses of evolution and migration of invertebrates, however, are basically the same as with vertebrates. Insects and other groups may show rapid evolution, but "lesser lights" of relictism can be found among them. *Anaspides* (12–13) is a shrimp limited to small lakes and tarns of Tasmania's mountains. *Anaspides* has many primitive features which entitle it to membership in a group of crustacea known as Syncarida. Among other living remnants of this group are *Paranaspides*, which exists in shoreline habitats of Tasmania, and *Koonunga*, from Victoria on the Australian mainland. The syncarid crustacea were prominently represented long ago, in the Carboniferous and the Permian—but have waned since then.

WAYS OF THE ENDEMICS

Endemics can be either relicts—"left behind," or they can be autochthonous— evolving their distinguishing characteristics, which place them in distinct genera or families, after arrival on islands. The two processes are not always different. Relicts may change after they have become island residents.

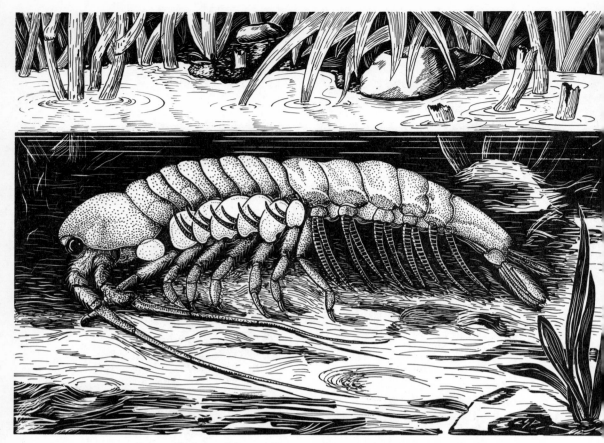

12–13. In small alpine lakes and tarns of Tasmania lives *Anaspides,* representative of a group of shrimps which flourished in the age of coal, the Carboniferous.

Where ocean barriers between an island and a mainland area separate two populations of a species, the situation is ripe for endemism. Both populations will go their own ways—and usually, one can suppose, the changes in one will be different from those in the other. The island situation brings with it many new opportunities, so *some* changes are likely, even in the case of relatively conservative relicts.

The processes of divergence and diversification described in Chapters 4 and 5 can and do continue indefinitely on islands. With incessant changes, islands might be expected to have a high proportion of endemic species. A remote but ecologically diverse island would be good for promoting formation of endemism. Lack of ecological diversity, as in the atolls of the Pacific, sharply reduces the number of endemic species. An archipelago would be better than a single island. The Hawaiian Islands ought to have a high proportion of endemic species—they do. Increased age of islands ought to magnify endemism; therefore, New Zealand should have a high rate of endemic species and genera. It does. Isolation, ecological richness, and age—perhaps in that order of importance—are the prime requisites for insular endemism. Where the magnitude of any one of these three factors drops, so does endemism. For example, endemism is greatly curtailed on offshore islands (fifty miles or less from a mainland area).

Only rough percentages of endemic species can be given for many islands, either because floras and faunas are poorly known, or because interpretations may differ on whether a species (or genus) is the same as that on an island or really distinct. There is a tendency to consider an island species endemic without exhaustive comparisons with similar specimens from mainland areas. Another problem in computing endemism is the group selected: the percentage for molluscs on an island will be different from that for ferns or that for flowering plants. Nevertheless, these figures do indicate the nature of evolution toward distinctness on islands. In the Hawaiian Islands, for example, 94.4 per cent of the flowering-plant species are endemic, and 13 per cent of the genera. As a comparison, 40.9 per cent of Galápagos flowering-plant species are endemics; about 1 per cent of the genera are restricted to the archipelago. The lower percentages on the Galápagos may reflect the fact that the Galápagos are more recent, nearer to the mainland, and drier than the Hawaiian Islands, and those interested in biological problems will enjoy estimating which factors are important in this comparison, and in what order—and in many other comparisons among islands which could be made.

Endemic island species, among either plants or animals, are so numerous that only a few find mention in this book; even endemic genera would make a formidable list. The number of endemic families of animals is surprising, but is small enough for a listing. Individual zoologists will differ in their interpretations of whether some are distinct families or only worthy of being considered as subfamilies within a family both on islands and continents.

The families below represent different phenomena: some are small relict groups, others sizable families, products of long adaptive-radiation. Australia has been included as an island in this listing. Invertebrates have been omitted. Insect families are quite numerous, and in some cases poorly known. Brief summaries of insect-family distribution can be obtained from *Classification of Insects* by C. T. Brues, A. L. Melander, and F. M. Carpenter. The families listed below do not include those which are primarily insular but also touch on continents (except Australia).

REPTILES

Sphenodontidae (tuatara): New Zealand
Carettochelydae (smooth-shelled turtles): New Guinea
Lanthanotidae (Lanthanotis lizards): Borneo
Pygopodidae (legless lizards): Australia, Tasmania, New Guinea

BIRDS

Casuariidae (cassowaries): Australia, New Guinea
Dromiceiidae (emus): Australia, Tasmania
Apterygidae (kiwis): New Zealand
Megapodiidae (megapodes): Australia, New Guinea, and many other Pacific islands
Mesoenatidae (mesites): Madagascar
Pedionomidae (collared hemipode): Australia
Rhynochetidae (kagu): New Caledonia
Chionididae (sheathbills): islands near Antarctica
Aegothelidae (owlet frogmouths): Australia, Tasmania, New Guinea, New Caledonia
Todidae (todies): Greater Antilles
Leptosomatidae (cuckoo rollers): Madagascar
Acanthisittidae (including Xenicidae) (New Zealand wrens): New Zealand
Philepittidae (asities): Madagascar
Menuridae (lyrebirds): Australia
Atrichornithidae (scrub birds): Australia
Cracticidae (bellmagpies): Australia, Tasmania, New Guinea
Grallinidae (mudnest builders): Australia, New Guinea
Ptilorhynchidae (bower birds): Australia, New Guinea
Paradisaeidae (birds of paradise): New Guinea, Moluccas, Australia
Neosittidae (Australian nuthatches): Australia, New Guinea
Hyposittidae (coral-billed nuthatches): Madagascar
Dulidae (palmchats): West Indies: Hispaniola and Gonave
Vangidae (vanga-shrikes): Madagascar
Callaeidae (wattlebirds): New Zealand
Meliphagidae (honey eaters): Australia, New Guinea, New Zealand, Bali
Drepanididae (Hawaiian honeycreepers): Hawaiian Islands

MAMMALS

MONOTREMES
Tachyglossidae (spiny anteaters): Australia, New Guinea, Tasmania
Ornithorhynchidae (platypus): Australia, Tasmania

MARSUPIALS (all listed below are from Australia, New Guinea, Tasmania, and nearby islands)
Dasyuridae (marsupial mice and cats)
Thylacinidae (marsupial wolf)
Notoryctidae (marsupial mole)
Myrmecobiidae (marsupial anteater)
Paramelidae (bandicoots)
Phalangeridae (phalangers)
Phascolarctidae (koalas)
Vombatidae (wombats)
Macropodidae (kangaroos)

INSECTIVORES
Solenodontidae (Solenodon): Greater Antilles
Tenrecidae (tenrecs): Madagascar

BATS
   Myzopodidae (sucker-footed bats): Madagascar
   Mystacinidae (short-tailed bats): New Zealand

PRIMATES
   Lemuridae (lemurs): Madagascar
   Indridae (woolly lemurs): Madagascar
   Daubentoniidae (aye-aye): Madagascar
   Tarsiidae (tarsiers): Indo-Malayan islands

FISHES

Fishes provide a special problem with regard to endemism, because endemics are usually defined by a land area. The closest counterpart among fishes is a lake—so families endemic to lakes are included below. Families of fishes endemic to fresh water streams on islands are also included. With more flexible criteria, other, rather more far-fetched cases could have been added, such as Amblyopsidae (North American cave fishes).

Ceratodontiidae (lungfish): Australia—fresh water
Retropinnatidae (retropinnatids): New Zealand and Australia—fresh and salt water
Adrianichthyidae (adrianichthyids): Celebes—two fresh water lakes
Doiichthyidae (doiichtyids): New Guinea—fresh and brackish water
Comephoridae (including Cottocomephoridae) (comephorids): Lake Baikal, Central Asia
Indostomidae (indostomids): Burma—Lake Indawygi
Chaudhuriidae (chaudhuriids): India—Lake Inlé

13 Museum-Piece Plants

JUST as antique animals take advantage of islands as refugees which prolong the tenure of their species, so do plants. Comparisons between plant and animal relicts often disclose similar patterns. In others, the disparity is remarkable. Why?

Plants and animals differ in many respects which would influence their distribution patterns. Topmost on the evolutionary tree of plants are the flowering plants; on the animal side, mammals occupy a similar position. Flowering plant species are much more numerous than mammal species. Some flowering plants have excellent dispersal mechanisms, but mammals (except bats) can cross only small sea distances. Moreover, the geological period when flowering plants exploded into dominance was not the same as the time of the rise of mammals. The primitive plants which almost seem to have crowded onto New Caledonia are not matched there by primitive animals. Among mammals, New Caledonia supports only bats. The primitive plants probably arrived when New Caledonia was easily accessible to dispersing plants. Perhaps when mammals became available, New Caledonia was shut off by too wide a gulf of water.

"PLANTS WITHOUT BACKBONES"

Plants which lack conductive tissue—fungi, mosses, liverworts, and algae—belong to ancient groups but do not appear as relicts. All of these groups disperse easily because of small spores, and almost all major groups among them are worldwide in distribution. Although old groups, many continue very active evolution. Thus, they are poor candidates as relicts in the sense of reduction of geographical range, and their rapid evolution also makes them look un-relict-like.

PSILOPHYTES

Psilophytes, the "naked plants," are ancient groups of plants, more primitive in structure than the ferns, with which they are often grouped for the sake of convenience. Psilophytes were very common in early geological periods—Silurian and Devonian—but have managed to comprise only a minute portion of the world's vegetation for the 350 million subsequent years. Psilophytes are unfamiliar because the two living genera are not common, and are usually found in tropical forests. They are almost pathetically simple plants: branched stalks, with nothing which could be called a root; the leaves are not true leaves, and are better regarded as green flaps upon the stalks. Light spores permit worldwide distribution of psilophytes, but only one of the genera, *Psilotum*, has taken advantage of this capability. Unreasonably, the other, *Tmesipteris*, stays within an ancient region. It is native to eastern Australia, New Zealand, New Caledonia, and nearby islands. Apparently it has adapted irreversibly to a very specialized way of life. *Tmesipteris tannensis* (13–1) grows only embedded within the roots of tree ferns. Tree fern stems are covered with external roots, so *T. tannensis* can be found high up these stems. A plant limited to tree fern stems, however, has only limited opportunities. It has evidently compensated for the dense shade of its fern forest haunts with the leafy flaps, which maximize the light-gathering capacity of these spindly plants. A second species, according to some, is *T. vieillardii* (13–1), endemic to New Caledonia. It demonstrates that some adaptability is left in these plants, for it has switched to the ground. It grows among decaying leaves, in rocky places. Instead of hanging pendulous as does *T. tannensis*, it is upright. Its leaf-like flaps are much smaller, more condensed. In ways such as these, *Tmesipteris* tenuously continues on the Pacific islands the programs begun by its Silurian antecedents.

FERNS

Ferns are nearly as old as the psilophytes. Like them, they are spore-bearing plants and thereby are dispersed throughout the world. Although they are a primitive group of plants, many of them are specialized in various respects, and some are even weedy. The world of two hundred million years ago was a world dominated by ferns. Today's ferns look to some people like the last of a vanishing clan. The islands of the Pacific tell another story. As though intact portions of a primitive world, islands abound in ferns, especially in their wet forested regions. If ferns as a whole can be regarded as relicts in a sense, some ferns are "more relict" than others. If we use the fossil record as a guide, one such fern turns out to be *Thyrsopteris elegans* (13–2). *Thyrsopteris* today is known only from the Juan Fernandez Islands. Its spore-bearing cupules and delicate leaves prove to be virtually indistinguishable from fossils of Jurassic time from such widely spaced places as Manchuria and Yorkshire. *Thyrsopteris* belongs to a family (Cyatheaceae) which has provided the bulk of the world's tree ferns. This family seems to lead a charmed existence on islands, and only drier islands of the Pacific are deprived of them. These circumstances hint that a "living fossil" from this family would be expected to be on an island, as *Thyrsopteris* indeed is. As islands go, the Juan Fernandez are not really very ancient, probably. *Thyrsopteris* therefore has probably been extinguished only relatively recently on continental areas.

13–1. Among the few survivors of the world's earliest land plants is *Tmesipteris* (Psilotaceae). One can find two kinds in New Caledonia: *T. tannensis*, left, grows on trunks of trees, while *T. vieillardii*, right, grows upright from rocky crevices. *Tmesipteris* is native only to the "old" lands of the southwestern Pacific.

CYCADS

Cycads were among the plant successes of the Mesozoic. Their compatriots in this era, the dinosaurs, have been swept to extinction, but the process has operated much more slowly on the cycads. These are palm-like plants which botanists today view as derived from some ancient seed-bearing ferns. Virtually all cycads are, today, located in areas which could be called relict areas. They may owe their narrow escape from extinction to their deeply penetrating taproots, their resistant leaves, generally tough structure, and tortoise-like longevity.

Islands have played a part in the survival of cycads, which are mostly scattered in small colonies around the world. Cuba has harbored one, *Microcycas*, which forms a tall tree. In Cuba, *Microcycas* seems on the decline; it is limited to a small area in the province Piñar del Rio. Seed production in *Microcycas* seems low. Like all cycad genera, *Microcycas* plants are either male or female, so only half of the individuals are seed-bearing. The colonies in Cuba seem destined for only a limited further existence, although individuals have great longevity.

Australia has become a center for preservation of cycads. *Macrozamia* (13–3) has conquered both eastern and western portions of the island-continent. Squat and palm-like, these remnants from an ancient era mingle with *Eucalyptus* and the many other recent forms which dispersal has served upon Australia, a huge target for immigrant flowering plants. *Macrozamia* species have managed to adapt to Australia's dry center, its rain forests, and intermediate habitats.

13–2. The fronds of *Thyrsopteris elegans* can be seen today only on the Juan Fernandez Islands, but millions of years ago ferns with an identical appearance were widespread.

Another genus, *Bowenia* (13–3), has mastered the deep and wet rain forest of Queensland. This mastery is suggested in the fern-like aspect of the leaves. Bowenia's leaves are much more subdivided than in other cycads, leaflets much thinner and broader. Australia and the Indo-Malayan archipelago also bear the majority of species of another genus, *Cycas*. Cycads may have reached Australia when the monotremes or marsupials did. Like tortoises, cycads have diversified slowly, perhaps because evolution is slow in an organism with very long generations. Although cycads have not diversified in a particularly spectacular manner, their achievement in surviving from a pre-mammal world is not inconsiderable.

CONIFERS

Most of the curious trees which stood side by side with ferns in the Carboniferous and Permian (two hundred million years ago) have vanished. The conifers have not. Beginning their lineage in the ages of coal formation, their steady progress to the present has witnessed the origin and disappearance of dinosaurs and many other groups. Conifers bear all the marks of a conservative group. They are saddled with inefficient and slow methods of reproduction and are rather inflexible to change, although some are still well adapted to conditions which prevail over large areas. The manifest ability of conifers to live in conditions of cold, such as northern Europe, Asia, and America, offsets disadvantages for some conifers, such as spruces. For others, such as pines, tolerance of dry conditions has been a key to survival. For a surprising number of conifer genera and species, however, the island environment has weighed heavily in their survival.

In some ways, the most primitive of the living conifers are the araucarias. These trees now are restricted to South America (three species) and the islands of the Pacific. Burdened by huge cones and crass, outsize seeds, they seem among the poorest candidates for dispersal in the plant world. The gap between South America and the nearest station for araucarias in the Pacific, New Caledonia, is formidable. Because their ability at long-distance dispersal is so very low, the distribution pattern of araucarias must have its roots in remote times when lands now vanished could have served as way stations, times when araucarias were the leading trees. The islands which stretch between South America and Antarctica and between New Zealand and Antarctica may have been greater in extent—or even a solid bridge of land. The presence of "continental" rocks on these islands enhances this possibility. Fossils show that araucarias were once widespread in North America, Europe, Asia, and South America, despite the fact that they are now limited to the Southern Hemisphere. Especially abundant in the Mesozoic, araucarias once forested even Africa and Antarctica. The handful of species we now see are the vestiges of a worldwide occupancy. Pacific islands bearing living species of araucarias include Australia (two species), Norfolk Island (one species), New Guinea (two species) and New Caledonia (eight species).

The eight species of araucarias on New Caledonia are not what one would expect, because such a small land area seems unlikely to have spawned so many species of a large tree; perhaps the island was once much larger and higher. New Caledonia's araucarias look like vestiges of some strange ancient forest. In fact, their thick, few branches, covered with tough wedge-like leaves, continue a pattern which, as fossils tell us, was common in the Mesozoic. In visiting New Caledonia's araucaria forests, we are truly visiting the past. *Araucaria* forests are not dense, they are sparse. Unlike the canopies of most forests, araucarias provide a series of isolated towers. Some cluster in spiky crystalline groves on the high moist ridges, like *A. montana* (13–14). Others form picturesque and striking elements of the coastline.

The only other genus of the araucaria family is *Agathis* (13–4). Except for a small incursion into Malaya, *Agathis* has survived wholly on islands of the South Pacific. *Agathis* extends from the Greater Sunda Islands into New Guinea,

13–3. Cycads flourished when dinosaurs roamed, but today are restricted to relatively small pockets in various parts of the world. Two genera are endemic to Australia. At left is *Macrozamia riedlei* from Western Australia and at right, a plant (with only one leaf) of *Bowenia spectabilis,* from Queensland's rain forests.

Australia, New Caledonia, Fiji, and New Zealand. *Agathis australis* (13–4) is better known as the kauri, giant trees which form forests in the far north of New Zealand. Now a small colony, kauris probably once extended much farther south in New Zealand. The kauri looks quite unlike other conifers. Trees branch irregularly, like hardwoods. Kauri leaves are also unlike the needles one expects of a conifer; they are broad and flat, with rounded tips. Only in their cones do kauris superficially recall araucarias.

Nowhere in its range is *Agathis* frequent now, and the genus has all the aspects of a vanishing group. One can imagine that araucarias and *Agathis* migrated to these lands when these trees were the undisputed dominants of forests. Separation of the islands by sea water afforded a measure of protection. During this isolation, flowering plants became rampant on other continents, began to excel at long-distance dispersal, and overcame barriers of isolation. The ancient conifers have not yet been crowded out, but we are witnessing a stage in their decline.

The fate of the araucaria family has been shared by other conifers. Island relicts among conifers are almost too numerous to mention. The redwood family, Taxodiaceae, is now exclusively found in the Northern Hemisphere—with one exception. Tasmania has become the sole preserve of *Athrotaxis* (13–5). In cooler montane Tasmania, two distinctive species (which may hybridize) form small trees—perhaps the smallest in a family which features giants such as the redwoods. Tasmania seems the farthest refuge possible for *Athrotaxis,* which seems to have parallels with the Tasmanian devil and the marsupial wolf in this regard. We know that *Athrotaxis* was once in New Zealand and South America (Cretaceous) and the Australian mainland (Oligocene).

Other islands have served redwood family relicts. Taiwan has a conifer name-

13-4. The Southern Hemisphere conifers occupy relatively limited areas and many seem to be relicts. Most primitive of these are two genera which form the araucaria family. At left, *Araucaria montana* occupies mountain tops in New Caledonia. At right, the kauri (*Agathis australis*), which forms forests of huge trees in northern New Zealand.

13–5. Sole representative of the redwood family in the Southern Hemisphere is the genus *Athrotaxis*, restricted to Tasmania. At left, a tree of *A. selaginoides;* right, the foliage and cones of the pencil pine *A. cupressoides.*

sake, *Taiwania*, which persists in a small area of mainland China as well as Taiwan; this is also true of another oriental redwood, *Cunninghamia*. Japan's capacity for maintaining redwoods is similar. Although *Cryptomeria* is reported still to exist in small colonies in China, it is the common denominator of Japanese forests; it is, in fact, Japan's chief timber tree. Another genus, *Sciadopitys* (13–6), forms huge trees which are components of Japan's oldest stable forests. Known as the Japanese umbrella pine, it grows only in these few localities. If it was once on the mainland, it has completely disappeared there. In its ecology and peculiar structure, *Sciadopitys* does look like a relict in every way.

The podocarp family ranged very widely in times past, and today is still fairly numerous. Podocarps as a whole are worldwide in distribution, but some of these conifers are limited to the ancient lands of the South Pacific. Such a genus is *Phyllocladus* (13–7), native to New Zealand, Tasmania, Fiji, New Caledonia, New Guinea, Borneo, and the Philippines. It occupies cool upland forests in all of these islands. Uniquely among conifers, its leaves are so small as to be negligible, but branchlets have become flattened and converted into sprays bearing leaf-like wings.

Other strange podocarps endemic to islands in this region include *Microstrobos*

13–6. Looking far more like a pine than the redwood relative it actually is, *Sciadopitys verticillata* is Japan's rare umbrella pine.

(*Phaerosphaera*) and *Microcachrys* on Tasmania and *Acmopyle* on New Caledonia and Fiji.

Among other families of conifers, cypresses rank the highest in number of endemic genera on islands: *Diselma* (Tasmania) *Papuacedrus* (New Guinea), *Neocallitropsis* (New Caledonia), *Thujopsis* (Japan), *Actinostrobus* (Australia), *Octoclinis* (Australia), and *Callitris* (Australia, New Caledonia, and Tasmania). The yew family (Taxaceae) is almost entirely confined to the Northern Hemisphere, but New Caledonia bears one endemic genus (*Austrotaxus*).

FLOWERING PLANTS

Count the number of mentions above for Australia, New Guinea, New Caledonia, New Zealand, and Fiji and you will suspect that these South Pacific lands have served as survival areas for aging groups of conifers. Have these islands provided refuge for flowering plants as well?

Flowering plants provide a unique problem among living organisms. Today, they outnumber all other kinds of plants, and in relatively recent fossil deposits are reasonably well represented. As we follow them backward into time, we see many groups represented over long periods of time, and then they are rather abruptly absent, giving few hints which kinds were ancestral to this history, or what they looked like. The fossil record is especially annoying because the portions of plants most essential to botanists—flowers—are very delicate and rarely preserved. Zoologists are much luckier because bones and teeth are not

13–7. To be found in the older lands of the South Pacific (except Australia) is the "celery pine," an odd conifer belonging to the podocarp family. The species shown here is *Phyllocladus glaucus* of New Zealand.

only well preserved in rocks, they are also decisive tools for interpretation of past lineages.

Lacking a good fossil history of flowering plants, botanists have had to develop concepts of the early history of this interesting group by studying what appear to be primitive flowering plants. Each of these preserves a portion of the appearance of their ancient relatives. The only problem is to select these portions and add them together—and this has proved very difficult. Nevertheless, we now have some workable ideas on what such early flowering plants must have looked like. The conclusions most generally accepted now is that the earliest flowers looked somewhat like magnolias. Today's primitive flowering plants mostly belong to a single order (*Annonales*). This order can be recognized by means of tiny cells, scattered throughout the plant, which are filled with a fragrant oil. This oil produces, for example, the scent apparent in a magnolia flower, and although the function of the oil cells is not understood, they are a universal feature of this primitive order.

As we trace the fossil record backward, magnolia-like leaves, flowers, and especially pollens can be found—along with advanced types as well. Poverty of a fossil record for the earliest flowering plants forces botanists to invent an explanation. One explanation is that they originated not in lowlands, where

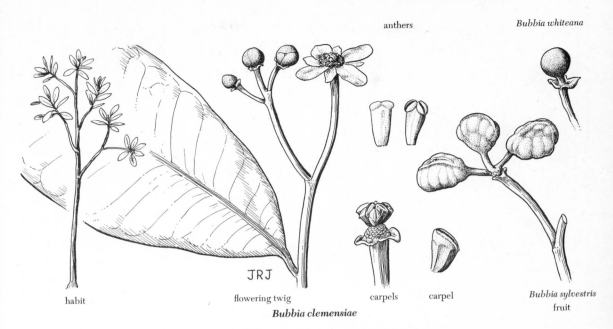

anthers

Bubbia whiteana

JRJ

habit   flowering twig   carpels   carpel   *Bubbia sylvestris*
fruit

Bubbia clemensiae

13–8. If we could see the ancestors of flowering plants, their flowers might look much like those of Winteraceae, a family mostly confined to old lands of the South Pacific. Shown here is *Bubbia,* a genus which ranges from New Caledonia to Queensland and New Guinea, is also found on Madagascar.

plants usually leave a fossil record, but in uplands, where their traces would be washed away. All facts point to the tropics as the center from which flowering plants have radiated. Thus, a tropical highland is the best hypothetical site of their origin. In the mountain-rich areas of the South Pacific are an abundance of magnolia-like plants. Are they located here because they originated there or because this area lends itself to plant relicts? Both are probably true, at least to some extent.

Of all families of flowering plants, perhaps none has retained the primitive aspect so well as the Winteraceae. *Bubbia* (13–8) is a good example. All the parts of the flower are arranged in a spiral, not condensed into successive rings or whorls as in most flowers. The sepals of *Bubbia* are like petals, but smaller. Petals are cream-colored or white, and numerous. Stamens are also quite numerous, and tend to be somewhat flattened and leaf-like, whereas those of most flowering plants are thread-like. At the center of the flower, carpels are numerous. Instead of having a brush-tipped beak to receive pollen, Bubbia's carpels have a pair of crests. These crests correspond with the margins of a leaf. If one imagines the two halves of a leaf folded together, the margins would look like this. Botanists consider the primitive carpel as nothing more than a folded leaf-like structure enclosing ovules (seeds after fertilization and maturation). *Bubbia*

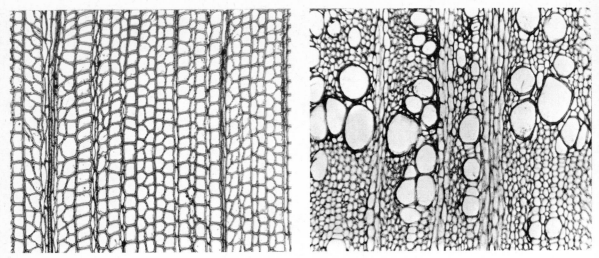

13-9. The wood of *Drimys winteri* (Winteraceae), left, shows how primitive flowering plants share the same unspecialized wood structures that ferns and conifers have. Missing in this wood are large specialized conductive cells (vessel elements), evident in the wood of a specialized flowering plant, such as *Phoenicoseris regia* at right.

is a small tree, sparsely branched, with large leaves. The fruits are usually large and reddish-colored, each a matured carpel containing several seeds. A simpler kind of fruit would be hard to imagine.

The wood of *Bubbia* and other members of the family Winteraceae (13-9, left) is unusual among flowering plants. Such wood differs from specialized types in that, like conifers, it has only one type of conducting cell (tracheid). Specialized types (13-9, right) have evolved wide tube-like cells (vessels) and narrow non-conductive cells (fibers) and may have lost tracheids altogether.

Of the family Winteraceae, only one genus has reached a continent: *Drimys*, in Central and South America. Other, more numerous species of *Drimys* occur on the Indo-Malayan islands, and on Australia. *Bubbia* ranges from northeastern Australia and Lord Howe Island to New Caledonia, the Solomon Islands, and New Guinea. Recently a species of *Bubbia* has been discovered in Madagascar. The presence of this outlying species suggests *Bubbia* once stretched from Africa across Asia into the Pacific, but has died out on the continents. *Belliolum* lives on New Caledonia and the Solomon Islands. *Zygogynum* (9-23) and *Exospermum* are New Caledonia endemics, and *Pseudowintera* is restricted to New Zealand.

A trio of families closely related to each other are Magnoliaceae, Himantandraceae, and Degeneriaceae. Magnoliaceae, the magnolia family, is abundant in the warmer regions of both the Old World and the New. The other two inhabit relict areas of the South Pacific. Himantandraceae has one genus, *Galbulimima* (13-10), with two species, one in northeastern Australia, one in New Guinea. *Galbulimima* can become an enormous tree in upland forests of these areas. The flowers have an unusual habit. Sepals are united into a cap, which

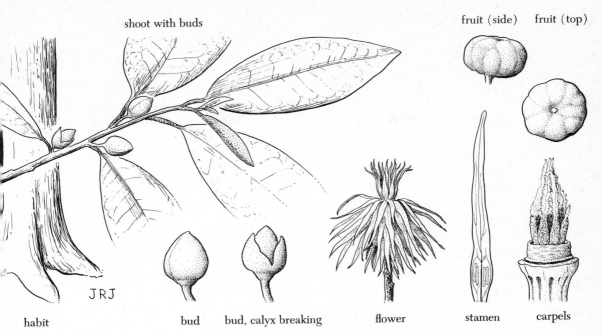

shoot with buds   fruit (side)   fruit (top)

JRJ

habit   bud   bud, calyx breaking   flower   stamen   carpels

13–10. Two species of *Galbulimima* form the family Himantandraceae, a relict flowering plant group of Australian and New Guinean rain forests. Illustrated here is *G. belgraveana.*

breaks as the flower opens. The same is true of the petals—a second cap. Fully open, the flower is a spiral of narrow blade-like stamens surrounding a spiral of narrow carpels. The stamens are very unspecialized in their leaf-like form, and in their habit of bearing anther sacs not at the tip, but embedded in the surface of the anther blades. Although narrow and elongate, the carpels have a leaf-like form botanists associate with unspecialized carpels. In fruit, all of the carpels coalesce, forming a reddish fruit (13–10, upper right). The coalescing of carpels reminds one of *Zygogynum,* the genus of Winteraceae which also has this specialization (9–23).

    Degeneria (13–11) is a distinct surprise, for it is restricted to Fiji. Fiji, however, does have many of the aspects of an antique piece of ground. Discovered only recently, *Degeneria* created quite as much excitement among botanists as a "living fossil" might have—for although no fossils of *Degeneria* are known, its flowers are exactly what one might expect in a primitive flowering plant. It is one of Fiji's large trees. Sepals and petals are like those of Winteraceae. Stamens are very broad and leaf-like, with anther sacs embedded in their surface. They form a spiral and are very numerous—the outermost stamens looking rather petal-like. Each flower of *Degeneria* has only one carpel—which one would not expect in a primitive plant—but this carpel is almost definitive in its resemblance to a folded leaf. The two margins which form the pollen-receptive stigmas of the carpel do not even close until the carpel begins to grow into a fruit—a very unspecialized feature which seems to many botanists a vestige of the days when flowering plants may have had open, not closed carpels. The fruit always bears a suture-like line where the margins have fused, much like a scar forming after a cut is healed. The bulky fruit, up to six inches in length, shows blithe disregard for dispersal. Very likely it is a gigantism, for few other primitive flowering plants have such massive fruits. It contains many large seeds. These germinate with great deliberation in Fiji's rain forest—an inefficiency common to these families of primitive plants. The habit is based upon the fact that seeds enclose a minute embryo embedded in a large amount of nutritive tissue (endosperm). This situation reminds one of marsupial embryos—born very small and pouch-nursed for long periods. Like the marsupial habit, this slow-germination process in these families of primitive flowering plants has been bettered by newer rapid-germinating seeds in advanced flowering plants—which have seeds with large embryos and little surrounding nutritive tissue.

Turning to another family, Eupomatiaceae, we find that its single genus *Eupomatia* (13–12) has evolved other variations on the primitive pattern. This relatively rare large shrub is a component of the forests of New Guinea and eastern Australia. Its sepals, like those of *Galbulimima,* are united into a cap which falls off as the flower opens. The petals, however, are separate, numerous, and spirally arranged. The stamens are petal-like in form and arrangement. Numerous spirally arranged carpels are present, but like the sepals they have

13–11. Discovered only recently and forming a family by itself is the tree *Degeneria vitiensis,* which escaped notice because it occupies remote forest areas in Fiji. Its flowers are regarded as very unspecialized.

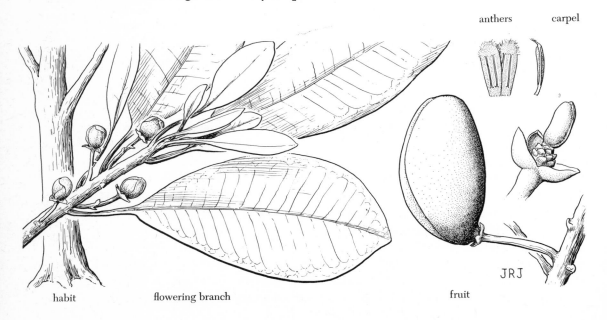

anthers   carpel

habit   flowering branch   fruit

suffered a change: they are displaced downward into a cup beneath the stamens, and they are fused to each other. As the flower matures, the fruit becomes a sort of flask containing many seeds. Like many other primitive flowering plants, *Eupomatia* proves to be beetle-pollinated. Beetles seeking pollen messily scatter pollen upon the tips of carpels during their forays. This method contrasts with the precise pollination mechanisms many advanced flowering plants have.

A recent discovery in the rain forests of northern Queensland is *Austrobaileya* (13–13). It is sparsely branched, and must be called a vining shrub or a shrubby vine. It emphatically qualifies as unspecialized in its floral structure. Instead of clearly defined sepals and petals, flowers bear a spiral series of leaf-like organs (tepals) transitional between the two categories. This condition is often thought to be less specialized than presence of clear-out sepals and petals. As a flower opens, a spiral series of stamens is revealed. These are flat and somewhat hooded. Like the stamens of *Degeneria*, those of *Austrobaileya* bear anther sacs embedded in the surface, although on the inner surface, not outer as in *Degeneria*. The center of the flower is a cluster of diminutive carpels, each like a folded leaf. Various features of this curious relict remain unknown—what pollinates it, what the fruit is like. *Austrobaileya* flowers rarely and sparsely, apparently.

13–12. *Eupomatia laurina* is a primitive flowering plant from New Guinea. Another species is found in Australia. The cup-like shape of flowers is a specialization, but the basic flower plant is what one would expect in a primitive flowering plant.

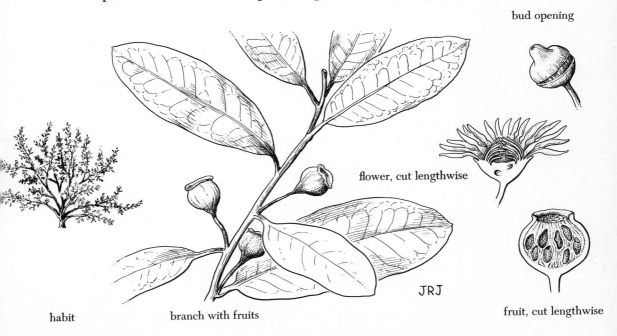

bud opening

flower, cut lengthwise

JRJ

fruit, cut lengthwise

habit   branch with fruits

Amborella (13–14), a New Caledonia endemic, has been shown to be so distinctive that it must be placed in a family by itself. It is best described as a large shrub. Nestling in shady places, it sends up large shoots from near its base, and thus has several trunks. Inspection of wood with a microscope demonstrates that it has the same conifer-like and very ancient type of wood exhibited by Winteraceae (13–9, left). This is somewhat ironic, because though one might expect unspecialized wood in plants from New Caledonia, the flowers of *Amborella* do not seem at first glance particularly primitive. The flowers are either male or female. Female flowers, however, retain a vestigial stamen apiece. The flower is clothed not with sepals and petals but with the intermediate structures (tepals). The five carpels are fairly unspecialized. Each carpel potentially can mature into a fruit, but usually only one does. The bright reddish fruit contains a single seed. Amborella's pollen grain is as unspecialized as its wood—a sphere with a single pore region for germination into a pollen tube. A simpler type is hard to imagine. Although most families of primitive flowering plants have this type of pollen grain or some modification of it, the vast bulk of flowering plants have a more sophisticated form, usually with three slits instead of the single elliptical pore.

13–13. In recent years, northern Queensland's rain forests yielded an interesting discovery: the vine-like shrub *Austrobaileya scandens*. *Austrobaileya* has very primitive flowers, and probably should be put in a family of its own.

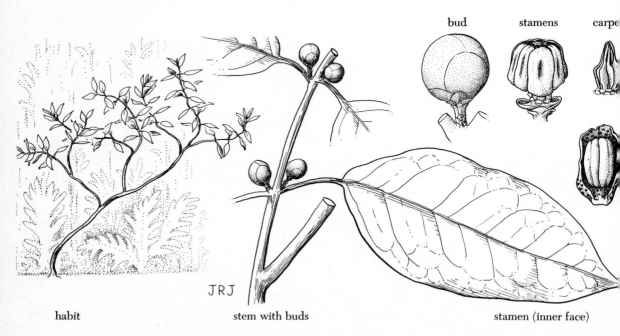

bud   stamens   carpe

JRJ

habit   stem with buds   stamen (inner face)

Trimenia (13–15), of New Guinea, Fiji and New Caledonia, shows some resemblances to *Amborella* and to other primitive flowering plants, but perhaps should be put in a family by itself, as some have done. Faced with the great diversity of ancient flowering plants, botanists must either put them into families which encompass a very heterogeneous range of forms or else separate many of the genera into families by themselves. The latter procedure does emphasize the relict nature of these plants. *Trimenia* flowers are covered, like those of *Austrobaileya* with tepals; these are brownish in color, and look more like sepals than petals, perhaps. Stamens are numerous and spirally arranged. The carpels are more modified than those of *Austrobaileya;* they are fused into a single column and topped with feathery stigmas.

Another relict of this tepal-bearing alliance is *Lactoris* (13–16). The single species is invariably assigned to a family by itself. A diminutive shrub of the misty Juan Fernandez Islands, it grows in rain forests under the shade of ferns and shrubs. Annoyingly, it combines specialized and unspecialized features in a disarming way, but the latter characteristics are more significant than the former. For example, the three separate and somewhat leaf-like carpels denote an antique character. Also, it has the oil-bearing cells which permit it to be grouped, along with the families above, in the order *Annonales.* But instead of numerous spirally arranged parts, it has, in successive levels in the flower, three

13–14. *Amborella trichopoda* lives in New Caledonia, home of many primitive plants. Although its flowers look somewhat specialized, the pollen and wood reveal that this is a primitive plant, forming the family Amborellaceae.

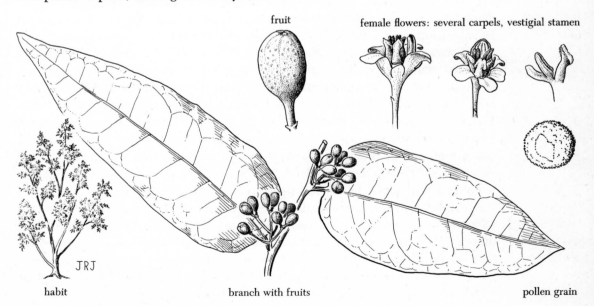

fruit

female flowers: several carpels, vestigial stamen

habit

branch with fruits

pollen grain

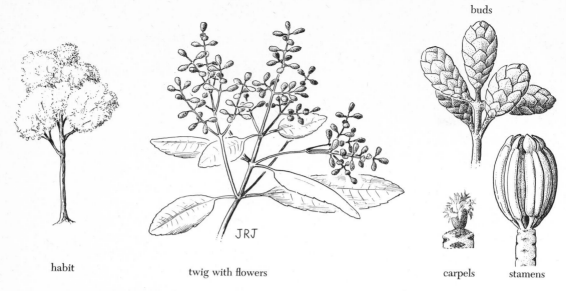

buds

habit   twig with flowers   carpels   stamens

JRJ

13–15. Forests of Fiji contain a relict flowering plant, *Trimenia weinmanniaefolia;* the nearest relatives of *Trimenia* may be *Austrobaileya* of Queensland or *Amborella* of New Caledonia.

tepals, six stamens, and three carpels. Its wood is remarkable for a high degree of specialization. Close relatives of a plant with such an incongruous combination of features cannot be designated. Unhappily, this small relict shrub may soon become extinct.

All primitive flowering plants do not belong to *Annonales.* A second order (*Hamamelidales*) which lacks the oil-bearing cells also contains some floral antiques. *Trochodendron* (13–17) is one of these. In a family by itself, *Trochodendron* is a relict confined only to islands off China: Japan (from central Honshu southward), the Ryukyu Islands, and Taiwan. It becomes a large tree in the wet upland forests of these islands. The flowers have numerous spirally arranged stamens, but the stamens are not flat or leaf-like. The carpels are numerous, but they are not arranged in a spiral. Sepals and petals? There aren't any. Even a buttercup or a rose has flowers less highly specialized than these. The wood, however, tells another story. It is of the same type as Winteraceae (13–9) and *Amborella,* and convincingly shows us that *Trochodendron* is indeed an ancient sort of plant. *Trochodendron* has a distribution which suggests it was once on the Chinese mainland, but is now extinct. Its survival on islands today is a testimonial to the relict-preserving ability of islands.

A similar instance is the kadsura tree, *Cercidiphyllum japonicum* (13–18), which belongs to a family (Cercidiphyllaceae) not too distant from Trochodendraceae. Kadsuras grow only in forests of Japan, where they are not particularly rare. In the Cretaceous, Eocene, Oligocene, and Miocene, however, these trees graced forests throughout the Northern Hemisphere. *Cercidiphyllum* is a plant which superficially hardly looks primitive. Unmasked, some decisive clues to

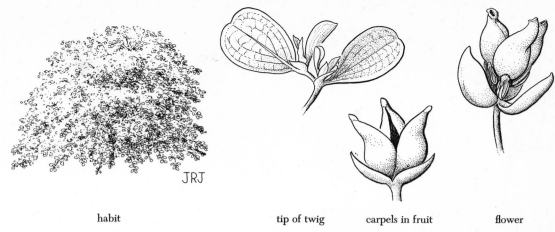

| habit | tip of twig | carpels in fruit | flower |

13–16. The diminutive shrub *Lactoris fernandeziana*, restricted to the Juan Fernandez Islands, proves to be a primitive flowering plant. This species is the lone representative of the family Lactoridaceae.

its nature appear. The wood, although not unspecialized to the degree of that of Winteraceae, represents a close approach to it in many ways. The flowers are either male or female, and appear catkin-like, reminding one of oaks or elms instead of magnolias. The altered form of Cercidiphyllum's flowers is undoubtedly an adaptation to wind-pollination, a specialization undertaken by various groups of flowering plants. The stamens, however, are numerous, as are the carpels. Fruits are of a pod-like type, and when they open to release seeds, their form resembles that of small, woody leaves.

THE ENDEMIC FLOWERS

The above genera are not the only island relicts among flowering plants. To a lesser degree, many others qualify for mention, such as the saxifrage alliance and the tea alliance. The tea family, to which camellias belong, is a relatively primitive group and has relict relatives on islands in various parts of the world. One of these is a curious small tree from New Caledonia, *Strasburgeria* (13–19), whose place is not completely clear. It is one of several New Caledonian genera which place question marks in the flora of this island. Apparently long periods of time, available for evolution of plants there, has permitted radical changes which make relationships difficult to establish. Although members of the tea family, such as camellias, have many stamens, there are only six in *Strasburgeria*. With distinctions such as these, little wonder that *Strasburgeria* has been put in a family by itself. Strasburgeria's apple-like fruits show close affinity to those of camellias, and hint that resemblances, as well as distinctions, can be found in this plant.

The same is true for a plant endemic to the Seychelles Islands, *Medusagyne oppositifolia* (13–20). It has flowers rather like those of a camellia in their

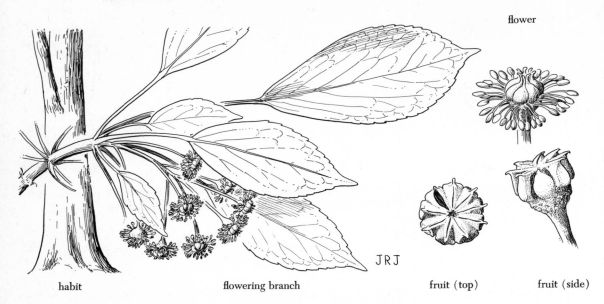

flower

habit   flowering branch   fruit (top)   fruit (side)

13–17. Botanists did not fully appreciate the primitive qualities of *Trochodendron aralioides* until they examined the wood, which looks much like that of Winteraceae (13–9). The flowers also mark this native of Japan and Taiwan as a relict.

13–18. Despite floral specializations, Japan's *Cercidiphyllum japonicum* ranks as a representative of the world's ancient flowering plants.

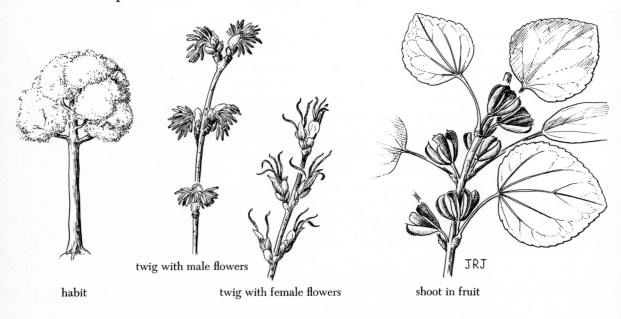

twig with male flowers

habit   twig with female flowers   shoot in fruit

13–19. Remnant of an old group of plants allied to camellias, New Caledonia's *Strasburgeria robusta* is the sole species of the family Strasburgeriaceae.

numerous stamens, but carpels are numerous, different from the single rotund pod one expects in the tea family. These carpels mature into a unique umbrella-like device, and seeds readily fall from the exposed folds of the capsule. Features such as these make *Medusagyne* a plant without close allies, so it goes in a family by itself, Medusagynaceae, although its stamens and petals suggest a distant alliance with the rose family.

The reasons why such endemics, relict and otherwise, tend to develop on islands are discussed in the preceding chapter. There are literally dozens of flowering-plant genera on the world's islands. These plants often puzzle botanists because they contain a sum of features which seem to conflict with each other, so that they do not easily slide into a particular family or into a portion within a family. Some genera are tentatively placed in the classification system, perhaps mistakenly. Plant classifiers dislike dotting their works with question marks, but they are there all the same, if one reads between the lines.

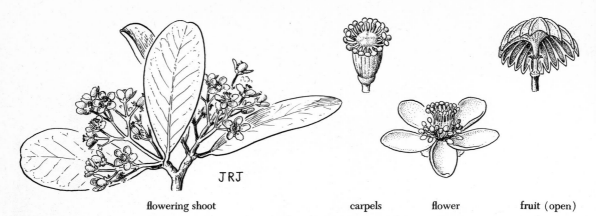

flowering shoot   carpels   flower   fruit (open)

13–20. On the Seychelles Islands botanists found *Medusagyne oppositifolia*, a plant with primitive flowers and curious fruits, features which help put *Medusagyne* in a family by itself.

Many of the families endemic to islands are in the nature of relicts, and so are described and illustrated above. Other families are endemic to Madagascar, and are covered in Chapter 16: Didiereaceae, Sarcolaenaceae, Sphaerosepalaceae, and Didmyeleaceae. The problem of *Hectorella*, which may or may not belong in a family by itself, is considered in Chapter 8. In addition to these, a listing of island endemics is given below. For these purposes, Australia is considered an island. Some families have been deliberately omitted if they are probably best included within other families which are not entirely insular (e.g., Xanthorrhoeaceae and Petermanniaceae are usually placed in Liliaceae).

Balanopsidaceae: Australia, New Caledonia, Fiji
Byblidaceae: Australia
Centrolepidaceae: Australia, Tasmania, New Guinea
Cephalotaceae: Australia
Corynocarpaceae: Australia, New Zealand
Gyrostemonaceae: Australia, Tasmania
Peripterygiaceae: Australia, New Guinea, Philippines
Picrodendraceae: West Indies
Scyphostegiaceae: Borneo
Stackhousiaceae: Australia, New Zealand
Tremandraceae: Australia

THE SMALL-SCALE RELICTS

Flowering plants offer many examples of how islands are instrumental in preserving relicts. Two are furnished by California's offshore islands (13–21). *Crossosoma*, with two species, constitutes a family related to the rose family. One, *C. bigelovii*, occurs in small pockets within the deserts of the southwestern United States. The other, *C. californicum*, occupies the islands Santa Catalina,

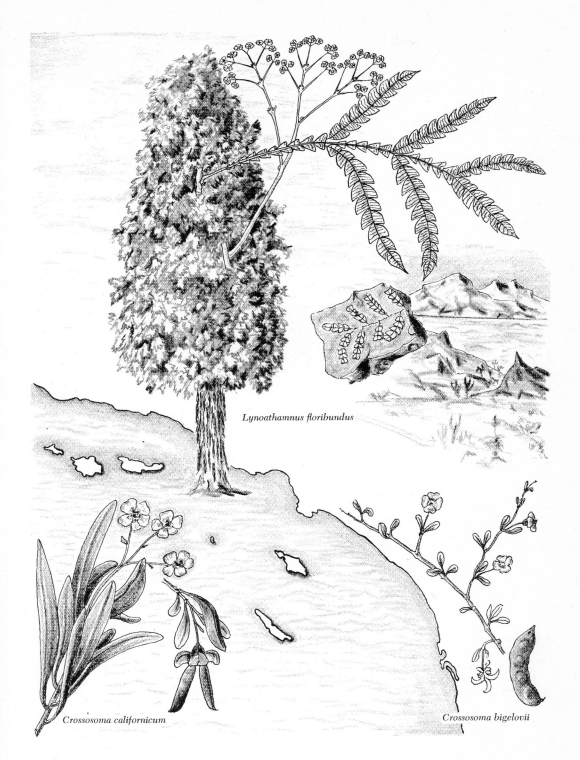

Lynoathamnus floribundus

Crossosoma californicum

Crossosoma bigelovii

13–21. Although not highly primitive plants, *Lyonothamnus* and *Crossosoma* show how islands preserve relics. *Lyonothamnus* now survives only on California's offshore islands, but fossils prove it once grew on the mainland in such places as Death Valley, a region now highly inhospitable for this tree. *Crossosoma californicum* is an insular species matched by a species, *C. Bigelovii,* which has managed to survive in western deserts. Crossosomas were probably once more widely spread, and these two species are all that is left of the family Crossosomataceae.

San Clemente, and Guadalupe. The desert regions of the Southwest were much moister in the Pliocene. At this time, *Crossosoma* may have been widespread. One species, *C. bigelovii,* has managed to adapt to desert conditions as the climate deteriorated, while the other, *C. californicum,* took advantage of the milder, moister climate of the offshore islands and perhaps has changed relatively little. The likelihood of this story is reinforced by the fact that a member of the rose family, *Lyonothamnus,* has experienced a similar fate. This large tree, with unique and easily recognized leaves, is today known only as a single species, *L. floribundus,* from Santa Cruz, Santa Catalina, and San Clemente Islands. But during the late Tertiary, it did exist on the mainland. It has been found as a fossil in such now-inhospitable places as Death Valley. *Lyonothamnus* was evidently unable to adapt to the gradual drying, but has succeeded under an island regime which includes frequent fogs and mild temperatures. These are only two of a number of examples from this region. The offshore islands have preserved other species in a relictual fashion as well. The tip of the Baja California peninsula also contains some species formerly present across broad regions of the Southwest. Thus, there are "islands in time" as well as islands in oceans. Those islands which have hosted relict plants have served as both.

14   *The Inefficient, the Unafraid, and the Obsolescent*

ADJUSTMENT to island life carries with it certain perils. The world to which an island species adapts is a limited one, curiously biased in its emphases. Continental species, steeled by competition, not only stand their ground, they are often preadapted to places far beyond the ranges they occupy. The depredations of introduced animals such as the Colorado potato beetle in Europe or the European starling in America bear adequate testimony to this. Island creatures, reared in the hothouse-like conditions of isolation, have no such reserve of rampant capabilities. Rather, they often fall victim—not only of man and the plants and animals he introduces onto islands, but often victims of the shortsighted qualities of their own evolution.

The patterns of evolution on islands usually dictate that insular organisms be overtaken. A strong atmosphere of vulnerability broods over them. The fact that island beings are not weedy, do not predominate, and are not in the grist of commerce and domestication does not mean that they are mere curiosities. They are a part of the entire pattern of life on earth, and without them, the entire pattern would be incomplete, even meaningless.

SLOW TO GROW, LATE TO MATURE

These phrases might describe a number of island animals or plants. These characteristics may be overtones of gigantism, but they are part of a wider syndrome—the entire life cycle. Longevity is often characteristic of island creatures, such as the Galápagos tortoises. The Hawaiian monk seal must be capable of becoming quite aged, for it maintains populations with an annual death rate of only 3 per cent. Among plants, cycads and conifers often live many decades. A phenomenon perhaps related—longer infancy—is suggested by various island creatures, such as the Australian marsupials. A less impressive, but illuminating example is furnished by the birds of Tristan da Cunha. The Norwegian ornithologist Yngvar Hagen says that there are "still immature birds in their second year of life, or maybe still older birds which cannot be found to have taken part in reproduction yet. They indicate *prolonged immaturity*, as a rule, among the endemic land-birds of Tristan da Cunha." Eggs of New Zealand's kiwi require an inordinately long period of incubation—seventy-five to eighty days, betokening a long period of infancy.

Unfortunately, studies of this nature are few, because prolonged observation is necessary to assess such a situation. In most cases we really have no idea of how protracted juvenile stages are, or to what age island creatures live as compared with continental relatives. Island plants in cultivation or island animals in zoos give some measures. The coco-de-mer palm of the Seychelles (9–24) must spend thirty years growing from seed before it can produce flowers.

FAMILY PLANNING

Another part of the altered-life-cycle syndrome are various types of reproductive inefficiency. The delay in breeding of the birds of Tristan da Cunha is indicative of this. An observation also made on Tristan da Cunha is the fact that among the endemic land birds as a whole, males outnumber females by a ratio of three to two. The significance and causes of this are obscure. An unbalance between the two sexes, however, would certainly reduce the breeding population, so that the lessened number of females would equal the limits of the reproductive capacity of these birds.

As a means of "birth control," however, a smaller number of offspring per parent seems the most effective. This seems clearly what has happened. Among the birds of Tristan da Cunha, according to Yngvar Hagen, "Both the Tristan thrush and the Inaccessible rail regularly lay only two eggs, sometimes three. When we remember that continental thrushes averagely lay about five, frequently twice a year, and that continental rails and gallinules produce from about six to eighteen eggs in one clutch, the difference is clear. . . . The conditions of *Atlantisea* [the Inaccessible rail] have a parallel in those of the weka rail on Macquarie Island (*Gallirallus australis*) which usually only has one young." Such examples could be multiplied many times, ranging from the single-egg habits of the emperor penguin to the single infant of which the koala is yearly capable. In many cases, reproductive habits of insular animals are still unknown.

An interesting situation has arisen on the small island Queimada Grande, off the coast of southeastern Brazil. Here lives an endemic viper, *Bothrops insularis,* a snake which subsists on the abundant sea birds, and has also managed to include four lighthouse keepers and one of their wives among its prey. A recent herpetological expedition uncovered a surprising phenomenon—a large number of hermaphrodite individuals. Such snakes appear like males, but are also capable of laying eggs, most of which are defective. A hermaphrodite individual can produce from four to six good embryos, whereas a normal female *Bothrops* on the Brazilian mainland manages twenty to twenty-four at a time. Intersex individuals are now very frequent; years ago this apparently was not true. Has *Bothrops insularis* taken a turn toward extinction, or is the lowered reproduction rate of the population containing intersexes still quite capable of maintaining the population size of this snake on a small island?

In plants, data are more difficult to obtain because fruits and seeds are so much more numerous per plant and because observers have not applied themselves to this point. One can only suspect that plants follow the same tendencies that animals do. In the Hawaiian Islands and the Juan Fernandez Islands, rarity of flowering has been noted. Examination of fruits of island plants often seems to show many shriveled seeds in proportion to the functional ones. The habit of a single flowering, just prior to death of a plant, is not the exclusive property of island plants, but it has been evolved on islands in some cases (*Wilkesia, Trematolobelia, Phoenicoseris, Centaurodendron*). This habit is a risky one, especially when coupled with poor dispersal, but it seems to have been tolerated, if not encouraged, by evolutionary forces.

A reproductive change which involves not necessarily a lowered rate of reproduction, but perhaps greater vulnerability, is that of vivipary. In the case of reptiles, this means bearing the young alive, without benefit of an egg shell or incubation. The Australian skinks are notable for this habit, and the New Zealand skinks and geckos have developed it as well.

The various reproductive changes above have the net effect of birth control, and the possibility that natural selection has induced this to prevent overstocking of islands has been suggested. If this interpretation is correct, organisms with low reproductive capacities would be at an advantage because all individuals find sufficient food, whereas individuals of prolific species would mostly be undernourished and would prove poorer competitors. This course might be operative, but it seems less likely than another explanation.

Progress toward inefficiency (as seen from the viewpoint of a continental species) on islands may result not so much from the stress of natural selection as from the relaxation of it. Such a hypothesis would say that island creatures are governed with a loose hand, allowed to slip into patterns which, although deleterious on continents, are quite acceptable on islands. Thus, a high rate of reproduction is enforced on continents by vigorous competition and predation. An animal tends to match, in its reproduction, the ferocity of the environment in which it resides. Just as with flying ability of birds, continual pressure must be applied to keep reproduction at par. Excessive *or* deficient rates would meet with "disapproval" from natural selection. Prolific reproduction where unnecessary would be disadvantageous because it is wasteful, and is just as poor a means of reproducing a species as insufficiency of offspring.

FEARLESSNESS

A disconcerting experience of expedition biologists visiting islands is the way in which island creatures react to man. Stated simply, they don't react. I enjoyed this experience one day on Clarion Island, in the Revillagigedo Islands (14–1). As a botanist, I usually tend to overlook the animals of a region. On Clarion, however, they intruded upon my awareness. Taking a burrowing owl by surprise

14–1. Fearless and thus easily caught or photographed without special equipment are these animals from the Revillagigedo Islands, Mexico. On Clarion Island are the burrowing owl (*Speotyto cunicularia rostrata*), the racer snake (*Mastacophus anthonyi*), and the iguanid lizard (*Uta clarionensis*). On San Benedicto Island, the blue-faced booby (*Sula dactylatra*).

near the beach, I photographed it easily. It bobbed up and down, blinking absently. Not far away, snakes lazily pursued their ways. They were racers—a snake noted for its rapid, evasive tactics on the mainland. The Clarion Island racer is much more docile. Reaching down, I caught one with one hand, photographing it with the other. This fat and well-fed snake objected not at all. It was quite content to wind itself around my neck or arm, and in this way accompanied me for an entire day. Also to be seen on Clarion Island were the bright blue iguanid lizards. These proved somewhat wary, but could be captured with a minimum of effort. Although mainland lizards are usually dusky in color, the brilliant blues and greens of Revillagigedo lizards flaunt their presence against the blackish and reddish tones of lava. At an opposite pole from protective coloration, these arresting colors are a sort of coloristic manifestation of fearlessness.

On San Benedicto Island, I found an equally tractable creature, the booby. Despite having been unseated the year preceding my visit by a catastrophic volcanic eruption (Chapter 2), the boobies proved as fearless as ever. Unless a close approach was made, they stayed on their nests. A mother booby (14–1) squawked a few times to apprise me that she did have a chick, upon which she sat crushingly, but she permitted me to touch her. The boobies were nesting on an open flat of volcanic ash, a site which would offer no protection whatsoever from man or other enemies.

Mexico's Guadalupe Island has proved a refuge for sea elephants (14–2), sea lions, and even fur seals. They tolerate human presence lazily, making little or no effort to shy away. Many of these enormous sea elephants will permit one to pet them or examine their fur. Mother sea elephants are understandably protective about their young, but usually react to a person by rising up and emitting enormous belching sounds. As with a dog, this is more bark than bite. In view of the bloody battles which rage among male sea elephants during the mating season, there is no reason to believe that sea elephants are incapable of dealing telling blows and bites. Humans, evidently, do not trigger danger signals for them, and if truly annoyed with a person, they will lumber off, trusting that he will go away.

So it is on island after island. On Lord Howe Island, a visitor of 1788, Surgeon Bowes, said, "On entering the woods, I was surprised to see large fat pigeons. . . . sitting on low bushes and so insensible to fear, as to be knocked down with little trouble." This pigeon (*Columba vitiensis godmanae*) is now extinct. On the Juan Fernandez Islands, the native buzzard (*Buteo erythronotus exsul*) exhibits strange behavior. Says Lönnberg, "The buzzard, formerly said to be common on Masafuera, may now only amount to about 50 pairs. During the days of the penal settlement the convicts used to hunt them, and as they are not at all shy, they were easy for destruction. Sometimes they may be killed at a distance of a few meters." The Galápagos bird fauna (Chapter 15) is notoriously fearless. So also the birds on the Mascarene Islands must have been, if we can judge from the ease with which the dodo and other flightless birds there (Chapter 9) slipped to extinction.

The giant chuckawalla *Sauromalus* (7–1) which inhabits islands of the Gulf of California is reported to be so docile that it will disregard a mild kick from a biologist's shoe. The curiosity and fearlessness evinced by emperor penguins discovering Antarctic explorers is by now a familiar sight in books and magazines.

As with the Clarion Island lizard, coloration often changes. Bright blue lizards on Mediterranean islands include *Lacerta sicula coeruleo-coerulescens* on Middle Faraglione (see 7–13) and *L. lilfordi grossae* on Ibiza. The rail (*Porphyrio porphyrio*) on Campbell Island is typically a sooty shade, but albino individuals are surprisingly frequent.

The explanation for insular fearlessness and adoption of non-protective coloration is simply the relaxation of the need for fear. On the islands where timidity has vanished, the need for defensiveness is minimal because predators are absent or not very serious. Fear is thus another feature which must constantly be maintained, or it disappears. A capability for evasive tactics is present to some degree

14–2. A pair of Guadalupe Island elephant seals (*Macrorhinus angustirostris*) doze peacefully, reacting not at all to a human presence.

with virtually all animals, but to what pitch it is raised depends on the value placed on it by the presence of predators. Excessive skitterishness is no virtue, in terms of evolution. If a bird spends much of its time flying away from false alarms, it will have that much less time for feeding and other essential activities. Thus, in a predator-free situation, a reasonably oblivious animal might be more successful than a perpetually nervous one. These equations do not include man, of course, for they were written before his presence was felt.

Allied to fearlessness is the tendencies for populations to be dense, a fact sometimes noted by island visitors. Only where predators and competitors are few could one have animals occurring thickly over a limited region. Large populations, such as that of a native of Antarctica, the Adelie penguin (14–3), are the result of such conditions. They are another aspect of vulnerability, of course. Once hunted for their fat, penguins suffered serious losses on account of their gregarious nature, as did the great auk, for the same reasons. Other factors which make for vulnerability include large size and poor locomotion, features definitively represented by a Galápagos tortoise (15–15).

IN TROUBLE, EVEN WITHOUT MAN

Not generally appreciated is the fact that long before human presence, other factors have operated to the detriment of island creatures. As mentioned in Chapters 2 and 3, isolation is never complete. The next storm might bring seeds of a far more aggressive tree, or a more predaceous insect, than now occurs on a particular island. On tomorrow's tide might come a log bearing unusually rapacious termites. Man and his domestic creatures may be the most drastic of island invaders, but they have been preceded by wave after wave of natural invasions. We know the havoc created when chestnut blight or fire ants or giant African snails are accidentally introduced by man to areas where they were absent before. Natural dispersal does the same thing, at a more gradual pace, and perhaps such havoc has occurred innumerable times on islands.

Is there any evidence that this has, in fact, happened? The question is almost impossible to answer convincingly. Indisputably, islands harbor relics, as Chapters 12 and 13 show. These relics have probably suffered pressure from more recent immigrants, but such pressure is all but invisible. Old species, such as the spiny anteaters of Australia, are sometimes remarkably lively components of floras and faunas. Others, however, seem on the verge of disappearing. Island conifers appear senescent because often they are limited in distribution to only a few mountaintops, and seem barely to be reproducing even where protected. A perceptive botanist on New Caledonia could probably list the "old" plants (many of which are mentioned in Chapter 13) and the more recent arrivals. If we examine the distribution of the former, we find they are often pocketed in a few valleys or are rare in small patches of rain forest, the most favorable and conservative habitat for aging plants. Even here, however, new plants are capable

14–3. Dense populations often make for vulnerability. Penguins formed easy prey for those who hunted the hapless birds for their fat. Shown here is a typical colony of the Adelie penguin, *Pygoscelis adeliae*, one of two penguin species which are permanent residents of the Antarctic continent. (New York Zoological Society photo.)

of entering and staying. New Caledonian species of *Scaevola* (other species are shown in 2–6 and 2–14) are probably recent upstarts on this island, but they now coexist with *Bubbia* (13–8) and other antique plants, competing successfully for space that earlier was occupied only by the primitive genera. As new immigrants halve, then quarter the ground available to the original species, they gain momentum, and the old species proportionately lose.

Climatic change, as well as recent immigrants, may force changes. New Zealand's large catalog of fossil birds is an archive, filled with creatures unable to survive the sharp changes successive geological ages brought. High in interest among these are the moas (14–4). These flightless giants, as much as twelve feet tall, have a fossil record extending back into the upper Miocene. In the Pliocene, the moas spurted forward, diverging into six genera (*Megalapteryx*, which looked like *Anomalopteryx*, is not shown in 14–4). Each of these genera contained two or more species. A recent authority groups them into two families: *Dinornis*, the giant moa, in Dinornithidae, and the remainder in Anomalopterygidae. These birds strode the grassy areas and swamps which occurred in enclaves throughout New Zealand's deep conifer forests. Relatively new and not yet fossilized remains of some moas are in such good condition that the diet (grasses and other vegetation) can be established. The Pleistocene was a disastrous period for the moas, apparently. The nature, placement, and abundance of moa remains suggest that natural causes killed many. Driven northward at least in part by the ice sheet, they may have suffered from the cold. Studies of the arrangement and quantity of moa bones found in fossil beds which must have been ancient marshes suggests that others may have become mired in swamps during the flooding of pluvial periods. Flooding may have restricted forage grounds, driving food supply below the level required to support large populations. There seems little doubt that a species or two of moas were alive when the Polynesian Maoris, whose maritime epics may have started from Tahiti or nearby islands, arrived. Perhaps by this time, the moas were "weakened" by their Pleistocene ordeals— that is, their numbers had been cut, their variability was lost, and they were unable to make rapid changes in response to new situations. A number of island creatures did not survive the Pleistocene. The "marsupial rhinoceros" of Tasmania and Australia (6–25) may have been overwhelmed by the onslaughts of the Pleistocene's violent weather.

The effect of eruption on the life of an oceanic island is difficult to estimate. We tend to imagine, instinctively, a fully formed island, which lies dormant awaiting immigrants. This is not a true picture. Volcanic islands are perpetually racked by successive eruptions. Do they extinguish species? The eruptions of Krakatau and San Benedicto show clearly that they can. The unexpected poverty of certain islands between Sumatra and Malaya with respect to plant and animal species has been alleged to have resulted from a fall of ash from a Sumatran volcano some time ago.

AND MAN INTERVENES

The moas are an instance of extinction by man. They may be among the first island creatures to have been so exterminated, in fact. Remains of most of the known species of moas have been found in kitchen middens, along with pots and other utensils left by the early Maoris. The story of this extinction is at best a speculative one; it must have taken place very early, for Maori lore and legends, although rich, contain only shadowy references to moas. Probably moas were easy victims for a crafty people like the Maoris, and suffered disadvantages in their clumsiness. Unable to progress easily through New Zealand's dense forest, moas may have been caught in thickets by hunters.

Likewise, the extinction of the dodo must be laid in large measure to its flightlessness and clumsy habits. The great auk, although a fine swimmer in water, was awkward on land, and its plentiful supply of fat, for which it was hunted, proved its undoing.

Some of New Guinea's birds of paradise are now becoming scarce—especially the more colorful ones. At celebrations—or as they are known in New Guinea,

Anomalopteryx

Pachyornis

Emeus

Dinornis

Euryapteryx

14–4. New Zealand's giant extinct moa *Dinornis* is only one of a series of mammoth flightless birds which once roamed the open spaces and grazed in grassy places.

14–5. New Guinea's birds of paradise are under heavy demand by New Guineans as decorations for ceremonial occasions. Plumes are used in headdresses and even are stuck through a hole pierced in the nasal septum. Although governmental attempts to control the traffic in bird of paradise feathers have been made, old customs are not changed easily.

"sing-sings"—bird of paradise feathers are much in evidence (14–5). Because the birds are scarce, and hunting them requires time and skill, their plumes have become symbols of wealth. Increasing scarcity of these creatures only increases their desirability, and in turn, places greater threats upon them. Although hunting of birds of paradise is officially banned in the Territory of Papua and New Guinea, the birds do not always enjoy the sanctuary which laws theoretically give them. The high value of the plumes and the fact that they can be obtained secretly insure continuation of hunting.

Expedition biologists are sometimes blamed for extirpation of island creatures by collecting them all for preservation in museums. This is probably rarely if ever true. Legend has it that more dried specimens of Galápagos tortoises now repose in the California Academy of Sciences than do living individuals in the Galápagos Islands. This is probably not true, but if it were, we could be grateful, because preserved for scientific study are races of tortoises which otherwise

14–6. On Mexico's Guadalupe Island, goats have converted the island into a grassy pasture. Some native plants are reprieved from extinction by growing on steep cliffs out of reach of goats, as exemplified by *Stephanomeria guadalupensis,* an endemic lettuce relative (right).

would only have been wantonly wiped out without ever being seen by a herpetologist.

Most extinguished island species are only indirectly victims of human activity. Some of these fatalities have been unforeseeable, the result of subtle causes. Accidental introduction of mosquitoes in Hawaii brought unexpected dangers for the honeycreepers, Drepanididae (Chapter 5). These mosquitoes carry viruses which, when transferred to the birds by biting, produce swellings on the birds' feet. These ultimately weaken and kill the bird, or avian malaria may be the cause of mortality. Thus man has unwittingly been the agent of destruction of birds deep in forest areas into which he himself has not penetrated. An example of more direct intervention was the intentional introduction of the mongoose into Hawaii. This animal, released in the hope of controlling rats, has succeeded in exterminating native ground-nesting birds.

Introduced animals are the chief plagues, where island creatures are concerned. Guadalupe Island, near Mexico, is a classic example. Goats (14–6) have converted the entire island into their private pasture. Incessant herbivores, they have reduced the vegetation to a grassland with two exceptions: branches of the

14–7. Off Guadalupe Island's south shore lies Outer Islet, a cup-shaped volcanic cone. This islet is the only known locality for *Lavatera lindsayi*, a mallow (right). This species may once have existed on Guadalupe Island proper; if so, it was doubtless extinguished there by goats. Guadalupe Island's strange tarweed *Hemizonia greeneana* (see also 5–1) may have been favored for survival on Guadalupe because its tough, hairy leaves are covered with an unpalatable resin-like varnish.

pines and cypresses above their reach, and plants growing on cliffs inaccessible to them, such as an endemic lettuce relative *Stephanomeria guadalupensis* (14–6), and many others. Seedlings of the oaks, pines, and cypresses are naturally quickly nipped, so these persist only as individuals which reached maturity before goats were introduced. Of the shrubs and herbs, some are not capable of growing on cliffs, and a few species are already extinct. A trio of offshore islets has aided in the preservation of some of Guadalupe's plant species. *Talinum guadalupense* (8–13) is rare on Guadalupe proper, but it is common on Islote Negro, only a short gap of sea water offshore. On Outer Islet, a tiny volcanic cone just south of Guadalupe, a shrubby hollyhock relative, *Lavatera lindsayi*, has its only known territory (14–7). It seems unlikely that a distinctive species (as this one is) should have evolved on the floor of this tiny crater cone, only a few acres in extent. Perhaps it was also once present on Guadalupe, and would occur there once more were goats not standing ready to munch on it. *Lavatera lindsayi* and *Talinum guadalupense* show how relicts may have occurred. Goats, of course, are not causes of ancient relict patterns elsewhere, but other causes of extinction are equally potent.

Ironically, the purpose for which the goats were introduced on Guadalupe has now vanished. They were intended for a canned goat meat enterprise which has failed, but the goats are, of course, still present. The Guadalupe caracara, an endemic bird of prey alleged by the goatherds to be a killer of kids in their flocks, was extinguished. Also gone are several other endemic land birds whose habitat has apparently been too severely altered to permit survival.

At the south end of Guadalupe Island is a small Mexican weather station. Residents kill goats nearby for fresh meat, and consequently goats have become shy of the southern part of the island. Many plants now make their appearance in open spaces where they would not survive if goats made frequent raids. In this fact lies a tempting possibility: if goats could be eliminated or greatly thinned in numbers, many of Guadalupe's threatened endemic species could return to relative abundance. Control of goats could probably be achieved by fencing off their only major source of water, a small spring at the north end of the island.

No chronicle of depredations of island native species by introduced animals would be complete without the story of the Stephen Island wren, *Xenicus* (*Traversia*) *lyalli* (14–8). The story of this bird, a native of New Zealand's Stephen Island, has been told by the ornithologist W. R. B. Oliver:

"The history of this species, so far as human contact is concerned, begins and ends with the exploits of a domestic cat. In 1894 the lighthouse keeper's cat brought in eleven specimens, which came into the hands of H. H. Travers. . . . A few more captures made and duly reported by the cat and then no more birds were brought in. It is evident, therefore, that the cat which discovered the species also immediately exterminated it."

In this case, the very small population size, governed by the small area of the island, may have contributed greatly to the extinction of this wren.

The Hawaiian flora demonstrates the subtle but effective way in which not introduced animals, but rather introduced plants, can devastate a native flora. Hawaii's moist climate, ranging from tropical in the lowlands to cool in the mountains, make it ideal for a tremendous number of plants. Domesticated and ornamental plant species escape into the wild easily. In the tropical lowlands, such notorious tropical weeds as guava and lantana are augmented by unexpected ones, such as Brazilian pepper, coffee trees, and avocados. In the uplands of Kauai, a few summer cabins with small gardens were set up. The garden plants from these are now the pests of the forest. The most serious of these is the blackberry, which is rapidly turning Kauai's higher forests into an impenetrable tangle. Joining it are such unlikely candidates for weedhood as hydrangeas, nasturtiums, and watsonias. Oriental conifers—*Cryptomeria* and *Cunninghamia*—have secured a foothold in this conducive climate, and even a tree endemic to New Zealand, *Corynocarpus laevigata*, is staging a remarkable success. At mid-elevations on Kauai, plums have gone wild. All of these are unquestionably weeds, because they are out of control. Why have they been able to spread so rapidly? They are more efficient than the native vegetation. Compared with island plants, continental plants are, in a sense, trained to be weeds. In order to survive the rigors of continental life, they have evolved an opportunism which outdistances the relatively modest ways in which native island species exploit

14–8. The Stephen Island wren, *Xenicus lyalli,* once inhabited a small island near New Zealand. Unique in the annals of island creatures, this flightless bird was both brought to light and extinguished by the lighthouse keeper's cat.

their environment. Island natives derive from such efficient ancestors, but in the process of adapting to islands, they lose these abilities—one more aspect of vulnerability. Ability to compete well, like flight or fear, must be constantly nurtured by natural selection, or it vanishes.

Disturbance of forests or even soil greatly encourages the spread of weeds. At present, Kauai's blackberries are primarily entrenched along roadsides and trails, but they are fast moving from this foothold into the forest. When trees are cut, when wild pigs root up the forest floor, weeds are literally invited. There is nothing which can be done about this now. Destroying weeds involves methods such as bulldozing or spraying, which only add to the disturbance, offering more opportunities for weeds than they had before.

Perhaps, then, conservation can only partly stem the tide of insurgent plant and animal weeds on islands. They are too numerous, too efficient, too unexpectedly devious in their paths to success. Man, even if he "protects," often unwittingly aids the destruction of native plants and animals. His prior activities, his retinue of domestic plants and animals are often quite sufficient to continue the process of extinction of island natives. Lest this story seem too grim, a reminder is necessary that extinction is the eventual fate of the island endemics, and man's incursions are only hastening the process a little.

THE ISLAND CYCLE

For centuries, a new oceanic island must await the arrival of a broad spectrum of immigrants, the waifs freighted there by the randomness of dispersal. Once arrived, the successful immigrant bursts into a flurry of inventive occupation. On continental islands, separation from the mainland sets into motion the insular tendencies of evolution. Island creatures, intricate in their adaptations, misshapen, overrefined, are victims of an inexorable process. If the ranker productions of later immigrants or of man's introductions do not overtake them, time will. As erosion levels islands, as high volcanoes are shrunken into low, rainless rocks, these creations of scattered worlds lose their places. Their tenures are limited by the existence of the island itself, and may be much shorter than it. In geology's terms, most islands last for only an instant of the world's chronology. Within those instants, however, islands exercise brief and fragile sponsorships of biological experiments we can only admire.

15 Darwin's Islands

No voice, no low, no howl is heard; the chief sound of life here is a hiss. . . . Tangled thickets of wiry bushes, without fruit and without a name, springing up among deep fissures of calcined rock, and treacherously masking them; or a parched growth of distorted cactus trees . . . clinker-bound; tumbled masses of blackish or greenish stuff like the dross of an iron-furnace, forming dark clefts and caves here and there, into which a ceaseless sea pours a fury of foam; overhanging them a swirl of gray, haggard mist, amidst which sail screaming flights of unearthly birds heightening the dismal din."

These phrases come from the dark side of a romanticist, and beneath their exaggerated volleys of Gothic evocation is a secret admiration for the fantastic Galápagos. The admirer is Herman Melville, who visited the Galápagos Islands, but wrote years later, when memory reverberated an etching more drastic than any reality. Such was the fascination of these islands, an inhospitable port of call for a long succession of buccaneers, sailors, and adventurers both before and after Melville.

Counterpointing these mariners, but more recent in time, are the scientists. On September 15, 1835, H.M.S. *Beagle* dropped anchor off Chatham Island. Aboard was Charles Darwin, a sea-weary but acute visitor. Many biologists often date Darwin's evolution theory not from its publication date in 1859 but from this landfall. Although the amazements and diversities of floras and faunas seen elsewhere on the *Beagle* voyage also had a telling effect on the young Englishman, the Galápagos plants and animals were a prime source of inspiration. Ashore on these islands, Darwin's observations and reflections on Galápagos life set into motion the hypothesizing crystallized in *On the Origin of Species*.

Galápagos plants and animals do merit attention. They offer a wide range of insular characteristics. The number of species is rather few, so biological patterns are almost definitively clear. Other island groups, such as the Hawaiian Islands, may excel the Galápagos in biological richness and complexity. The Darwinian precedent, however, has cast a long shadow. In cryptic ways, biologists are romanticists, too. They are eager to sign aboard expeditions, and are perpetually attracted by Darwin's islands. The roster of these expeditions could fill a book. In fact, they do: *The Galápagos Islands—A History of Their Exploration*, by Joseph R. Slevin. The number of forays is so great that only a brief description can be allotted to each in that volume. Many visits have been casual, of little

15–1. The dry climate of the Galápagos retards formation of vegetation, but newness of lava also accounts for bareness of these islands, as here at Cartago Bay, Albemarle Island. (Allan Hancock Foundation photo.)

scientific import. Others have been more exhaustive, like the California Academy of Sciences 1906 expedition, which spent over a year collecting and surveying in the archipelago. Undeterred by the number of previous visits, scientists always seem to see unanswered questions, for proverbially, scientific investigations appear to raise more questions than they solve.

THE LANDSCAPE

The Galápagos are a model archipelago, a swarm of islands lying on and near the equator five hundred miles west of Ecuador. They grade from seventy-five miles in length (Albemarle) to mere rocks (see map in 15–16), and some mountains reach as high as fifty-five hundred feet. All of the islands are volcanic, and look like relatively recent volcanoes. This appearance is enhanced by their bare-

15–2. Near sea level, tree cacti indelibly define the Galápagos landscape. The tall prickly pear is *Opuntia echios;* the candelabra cactus, *Cereus thouarsii.* (Photograph by E. Yale Dawson.)

ness, and by the occurrence of recent eruptions such as the one vividly described in William Beebe's *The Arcturus Adventure.* The bareness, clearly evident in the lower elevations (15–1), derives from a peculiar set of climatic conditions. Even recent lava flows become vegetated quickly in rainy locations, such as the Hawaiian Islands. The Galápagos, however, are victims of the cool Humboldt current, which inhibits rainfall not only in these islands, but in coastal northern Chile and Peru as well. Midway along its northward traverse of Ecuador, the current turns westward, so that Colombia and Panama are rainy and their coasts are richly forested.

Arid Coastal Zone. The lowlands are the parts of the islands best known to visitors. The reasons for this include not only the proximity to landing places, but the difficulty of penetrating very far inland. Anyone who has crossed bare lava flows will understand. Huge lava blocks form an obstacle course, heat discourages, and the sharpness and brittleness of the lava all make for slow progress. Thorny shrubs add further resistance. Dominating this landscape are huge cac-

15–3. The tree sunflower *Scalesia pedunculata* dominates the lower forests of the Galápagos, forming dense groves on the bare lava. (Photograph by Gunnar Harling.)

tus trees—awkward *Opuntia* and *Cereus* (15–2). In some places, very little vegetation occurs near the seacoast. Shrubs remain leafless through most of the year, suddenly leafing and flowering after the brief season of showers. Bare twigs and hairy stems give a pallid aspect to the shrubbery of the coastal region.

Transition Zone. Between one hundred and 650 feet elevation, the tree prickly pear cacti mix with the beginnings of a forest (15–8, left).

Scalesia Forest. On the larger islands, the dominant tree between 650 and one thousand feet is a tree sunflower, *Scalesia pedunculata.* The occurrence of a tree member of the sunflower family should be no surprise, for reasons suggested in Chapter 8. Scalesias form a lofty, open, generally dry forest (15–3). Where *Scalesia* reaches higher elevations, it may become involved in what can only be called a fog forest. In a fog forest, moisture is condensed from fog and clouds, although direct precipitation is rare. Such a *Scalesia* fog forest (15–4) can be recognized by the draping of liverworts, lichens, and mosses on the branches of the trees.

15–4. At higher elevations, the *Scalesia* forest enjoys frequent mists, which permit a lavish growth of lichens. (Photograph by Gunnar Harling.)

"Brown Zone." Scalesias yield at higher elevations to a forest composed of a guava (*Psidium galapageium*) and *Zanthoxylum fagara*. This zone can be found between one thousand and fifteen hundred feet.

Miconia Zone. Between fifteen hundred and nineteen hundred feet, climatic conditions induce a shrubland (15–5). The chief shrub species is *Miconia*.

Upland Zone. Above nineteen hundred feet, cooler temperatures, brisk, drying

15–5. The shrub *Miconia* takes over from *Scalesia* above two thousand feet in the Galápagos. This zone is well-marked on Indefatigable Island, where this photograph was taken. (California Academy of Sciences photo.)

winds and lessened precipitation prevent forest but encourage ferns and grasses (15–6). This almost "alpine" or "timberline" effect, well expressed at these relatively low altitudes, is responsible for the fact that the forest is best represented not at higher but at mid-altitudes, and this forest yields to shrubland and meadows above.

The above zones are based mostly on surveys of Indefatigable Island, but are quite applicable, with variations, to the other islands as well.

THE SUBTLY STARTLING PLANTS

The Galápagos have a roster of flowering plants which bulks rather large for islands often alleged to be extremely dry. The number of species and varieties totals about 550, of which about 250 are endemic. The only endemic genera are *Scalesia, Darwiniothamnus, Macraea,* and *Lecocarpus*. All of these belong to the sunflower family, Compositae, that huge and weedy family so successful at long-distance dispersal. All of these four genera are relatively close to certain mainland genera. The relatively low percentage of endemic species (compared with the Hawaiian Islands), the paucity of endemic genera, and the closeness of those genera to mainland ones all argue that the Galápagos are relatively recent.

15–6. The summits of Indefatigable Island, seen here, and the other islands of the Galápagos Archipelago are covered not with trees but with a meadow-like growth of ferns and grasses. Drying winds account for the lack of trees. (California Academy of Sciences photo.)

The nature of the flowering plants alone would show that the islands are oceanic, have never had a connection with a continent. There are a pair of underwater ridges leading to the mainland: the Cocos Ridge, stretching northeastward to Central America, and the Carnegie Ridge, pointing toward Ecuador. Both of these ridges are broken by deep valleys, and there seems little likelihood that any appreciable portion of these ridges has been above water, at least since the Galápagos began collecting plant and animal immigrants. The strong bias in favor of land bridges favored by Galápagos commentators of a generation ago has now vanished. The composition of the flora is purely that of an oceanic island. The families good at long-distance dispersal are by far the most abundant, such as Compositae. Groups with poor dispersal are absent. Moreover, the geographical affinities of Galápagos plants—the places where their closest relatives are to be found—are in exact proportion to distance. The greatest number of Galápagos species appear to have come from South America, lesser numbers from Mexico and Central America, fewer still from the West Indies. If a land bridge had ever connected the Galápagos with mainland areas, the proportions would be different.

Animals enhance this picture. Absence of mammals (except for a mouse) is clearly an oceanic island indicator.

In the main, Galápagos flowering plants are simply a collection of dry-country waifs. In a relatively brief span of time, evolution has been able to coax some interesting results from some of these, partly because of the plasticity of certain of them. The two most interesting groups are the cacti and the composites (Compositae).

Spiny Experiments. The Galápagos are the only islands—other than certain West Indian islands—on which cacti play a major role. Their presence stamps an un-

15-7. Barren lava is the habitat for *Cereus nesioticus*, which forms conspicuous yellow-green clumps along the shores of Albemarle and Narborough Islands. (Allan Hancock Foundation photo.)

usual note on the Galápagos landscape, well commemorated in the literature the islands have inspired. *Cereus thouarsii* (15-2) raises enormous candelabras along seacoasts. The prominently jointed appearance probably results from spurts of growth which occur during the short rainy season. Tall species of *Cereus* occur on the South American mainland, and one cannot state positively that *C. thouarsii*, an endemic species, is any larger than its mainland relatives.

Quite different is the second Galápagos *Cereus*, *C. nesioticus* (15-7). It favors barren sites—heaps of cinders, or flows of ropy lava, where a crevice permits a colony to begin. The stems are covered with tawny yellow spines. Eventually, colonies can form broad clumps.

These two extremes—and others—are also represented in *Opuntia*, the prickly

15–8. Two tree prickly pears have evolved on the Galápagos Islands. *Opuntia echios,* left, is taller; *O. megasperma,* right, has a more massive trunk, a rounded canopy of branches, and larger seeds. (Photograph by E. Yale Dawson.)

pear. Giant trees are formed by the endemic *O. echios* (15–8), which becomes a symbol of Galápagos coastlines to those who have seen its peculiar shape. A few mainland prickly pears attain a tree-like form, but none are quite so tall or spectacular as *O. echios.* The main trunk is relatively slender, branching high up. The tree habit is foreshadowed in young plants, which produce exceptionally long pads to form the future trunk, then branch out into the shorter, wider pads as the tree matures.

A rather different aspect is presented by *O. megasperma* (15–8). This species, less common than *O. echios,* has a massive trunk, three feet in diameter in old specimens. Branches are rather low and dense, so that a rounded head of pads is presented.

At another pole from these trees are shrubby prickly pears. *Opuntia zacana* is a sprawling shrub which has been found only on North Seymour Island. Similar in habit is *O. helleri,* of Tower Island. It presides on seaside bluffs, drooping over the edges to form odd cliffside festoons. Somewhat intermediate in habit is *O. saxicola,* of Albemarle Island. On open lava flats, it forms shrubs which occasionally hint at formation of a trunk.

Why this spread of habits among Galápagos prickly pears? All Opuntias occupy arid lowland sites, all grow amidst bare lava blocks, and this uniformity in habitat does not suggest a basis for adaptive radiation. One possibility is that different stages on the way to treehood have been preserved. The largest tree forms seem an extreme type, likely to have been evolved on the islands, so a shrubbier ancestor seems a good possibility. Another explanation would be that the present assortment of Opuntias stem from more than one ancestor, and these ancestors were varied in growth form.

Tree cacti seem appropriate to the lower elevations, ecologically. They may be the only plants among the immigrants the Galápagos have received which could form trees under these punishing conditions. Freedom from herbivorous animals may have permitted development of the tree habit, but the rugged Galápagos land iguana (15–13, 15–14) has adapted to eating Opuntias. The tree habit might minimize the ravages of the land iguanas. On North Seymour, where the low *O. zacana* exists, land iguanas are not native, nor are they on the other northern islands, where *O. helleri* is endemic. Distribution of land iguanas is probably not the only explanation for habit of the prickly pears. The island-to-island isolation within the archipelago has in all likelihood permitted formation of more *Opuntia* species than would have occurred on a single island.

Weeds Become Classics. Many entries in the Galápagos flora appear to be rather weedy plants. The islands offer definitively "disturbed" sites—unaltered lava—where weedy plants would be most likely to succeed. Soil is scarce in the Galápagos, so trees of mature forests are out of the question as immigrants. Consequently, a forest has been created out of weeds and waifs. *Scalesia* is a superb example of this. Closely related to sunflowers and their allies, *Scalesia* basically is a plant with weedy tendencies. The opportunities for treehood were present in the Galápagos, however, so from inelegant ancestors, classic endemic trees have been evolved, probably by the pathways described in Chapter 8.

The story of *Scalesia* is far more than a story of progression to treehood, however. The nature of the Galápagos archipelago has exerted several designs on this genus. Changes in growth form, race formation, and development of unexpectedly distinctive species by isolation are all plans satisfied by rapidly evolving Scalesias. The sum of these patterns is indicated in 15–11 and the habit pictures 15–3, 15–4, and 15–9.

Scalesias divide into a number of species groups. These probably represent recent derivatives from an ancestral group of species, each of which spread widely throughout the archipelago in forming those we see today. Interisland isolation has permitted divergence into distinctive populations, and accumulation of differences.

The first group of species (15–11) is represented by S. *gummifera,* S. *affinis,* S. *villosa,* and S. *crockeri.* All of these species have toothed leaves, tapered at each end. The flowering heads are rather large, and plants are shrubs.

A second group of species consists of S. *pedunculata,* S. *cordata,* and S.

15–9. *Scalesia helleri* forms low, rounded shrubs, the grayish-green color of which blends into the tone of the lava bluffs on Barrington Island, where it grows (Photograph by Gunnar Harling.)

microcephala. This trio consists of trees or near-trees with rather bare, only minutely toothed leaves. Leaves have long, thin petioles (leaf stalks). Flowering heads are relatively small.

Another group is formed by a threesome from James Island. These are all shrubs, and have narrower leaves which are rather hairy (especially so in S. *darwinii*) and tapered at both ends. The petiole is very short. Instead of a neat separation between leaves and the narrow flat structures (bracts) which enclose flower heads, there is a transition. The heads are clothed in very leaf-like bracts.

The fourth group of *Scalesia* species are those in which leaves are either deeply toothed, or complexly lobed and fern-like in their shape. From 15–11, one can easily recognize these: S. *divisa*, S. *helleri*, S. *baurii*, S. *hopkinsii*, and S. *snodgrassii*. Not shown are S. *incisa* and S. *retroflexa*, each of which have been collected only once. *Scalesia incisa* is known only from the specimen Darwin collected.

Within each of these groups, distinctions can be seen. Comparison of the species within the fourth group shows differences in leaf shape and pattern: S. *helleri* has leaves small but deeply and finely incised, S. *snodgrassii* has leaves large and coarsely cut. Despite the fact that species of *Scalesia* all probably developed on the islands from a single invader, the diversity formed within the archipelago has been remarkable.

Climatic conditions obviously do favor shrubbiness in the Galápagos Compositae, because genera other than *Scalesia* are bushy. One of these is *Darwiniothamnus* (15–10). A pair of species makes up this genus. It is probably closely related to the worldwide genus *Erigeron* (fleabanes): among these, Erigerons from central Chile look most similar. The shrubby perennial habit of *Darwiniothamnus* has probably been fostered by the uniform Galápagos climate, which has been described as a perpetual spring.

The other endemic genera of Compositae, *Macraea* and *Lecocarpus*, are also shrubs. *Macraea* has needle-like leaves well suited to resisting the excessive sun and drying heat of the islands. *Lecocarpus* looks rather like a *Scalesia*, but has peculiar appendages on the fruits.

Galápagos plants offer many interesting problems, chiefly those of species formation and relationship. Some, such as the native tomatoes, have received careful study, but many are not much better known than they were in Darwin's day. The animals seem to have attracted the majority of the attention of biologists, perhaps because the animals are so bizarre, more arresting than the plants, which are in their way equally remarkable.

THE "MESOZOIC" FAUNA

A visit to the Galápagos has been described as a visit to the Age of Reptiles. Actually, the reptilian domination of the Galápagos does not signify a remnant of a Mesozoic fauna. Rather, it is an artifact of dispersal: reptiles good, mammals poor.

Iguanas in the Surf. Every morning, along the rugged lava coasts of the Galápagos, large lizards emerge from crevices and burrows. They sun themselves, their grayish red-splotched armor-like coats absorbing sunlight, a welcome warmth along shores cooled by the Humboldt current. These are marine iguanas, *Amblyrhynchus cristatus* (15–12). As the surf laps lower and lower, they will approach their feeding grounds—slippery rocks at ebb tide. *Amblyrhynchus* is the sole proprietor of these maritime pastures, and once each day it forages on their seaweed. The brownish, slimy fronds of *Sargassum*, a brown alga, are the unlikely fodder of marine iguanas. In diet and many other ways they have departed from lizard norms.

Amblyrhynchus is the only lizard which appears truly at home in the surf. They can swim better than one might expect. Folding their legs close to their bodies, marine iguanas are propelled by swaying movements of body and tail. They can dive and feed on the bottom of a bay. The tail, although by no means fin-like, is somewhat flattened and thus a rudimentary paddle-and-rudder. When swimming, the marine iguana prefers quiet bays, for it is no match for tricky currents of the surf, into which it cannot be coaxed. *Amblyrhynchus* will sit on rocks sur-

15–10. More than one genus of the sunflower family (Compositae) has taken up the woody habit on the Galápagos Islands. Here is *Darwiniothamnus tenuifolius* subsp. *santacruzianus* from Indefatigable Island. (Photograph by Gunnar Harling.)

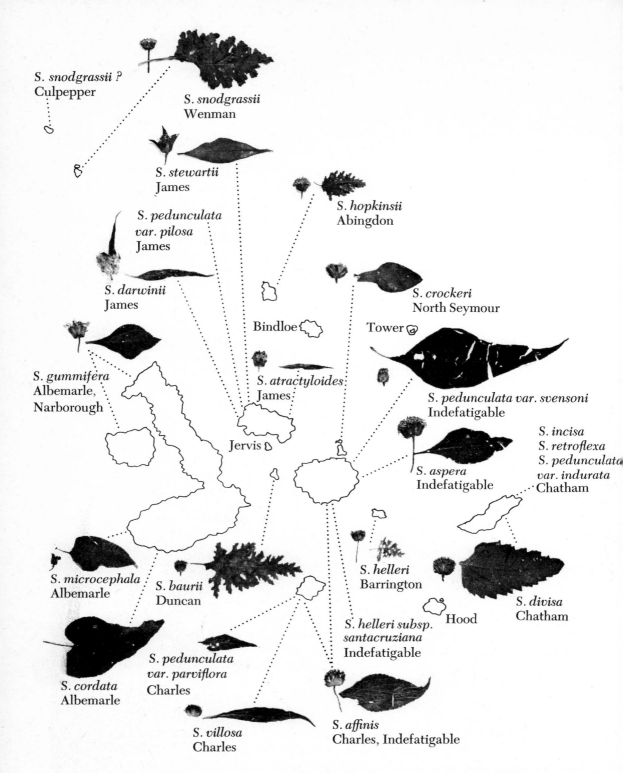

S. snodgrassii ?
Culpepper

S. snodgrassii
Wenman

S. stewartii
James

S. hopkinsii
Abingdon

S. pedunculata
var. pilosa
James

S. darwinii
James

S. crockeri
North Seymour

Bindloe

Tower

S. pedunculata var. svensoni
Indefatigable

S. gummifera
Albemarle,
Narborough

S. atractyloides
James

Jervis

S. aspera
Indefatigable

S. incisa
S. retroflexa
S. pedunculata
var. indurata
Chatham

S. microcephala
Albemarle

S. baurii
Duncan

S. helleri
Barrington

S. divisa
Chatham

Hood

S. cordata
Albemarle

S. pedunculata
var. parviflora
Charles

S. helleri subsp.
santacruziana
Indefatigable

S. villosa
Charles

S. affinis
Charles, Indefatigable

15–11. The woody sunflower of the Galápagos, *Scalesia*, has diversified not only in habit and habitat but also in leaf size and shape and in the nature of the flower heads. Most species are restricted to a single island. The questionable record from Culpepper Island is based upon the fact that the *Scalesia* there was only sighted, not collected.

15–12. The Galápagos marine
iguana *Amblyrhynchus cristatus*
lives near the shore, feeds on
seaweed at low tide. A prominent
row of spines always
characterizes the lizard, but color
is more difficult to define:
irregular blotches of red, black,
and green may decorate their
flanks. (Top, San Diego Zoo
photo; below, Allan Hancock
Foundation photo.)

rounded by swirling surf, but it is protected from being swept away by its
tenacious claws. On these rocks, it almost seems to fade into the lava, for its
skin, black when wet, and its crest of warty ornaments are like echoes of the
lava textures. Fierce when grappling with its fellows in combat, the marine
iguana never bites humans. It is quite fearless of man, in fact. William Beebe
found that *Amblyrhynchus* would tolerate tail-pulling, petting, having its initials
(*A. c.*) scratched on its skin, and even would allow itself to be caught repetitively
—evincing only tameness, perhaps curiosity, when recaptured as many as six
times.

Marine iguanas are a fine example of the island creature "syndrome": gigantism; change to a new ecological location; change of diet; melanism (blacken-
ing); and fearlessness. *Amblyrhynchus*, although an endemic genus, has been
able to develop only a single species. This exception to speciation tendencies of
other Galápagos genera is easily explained, however. The swimming habit of
these iguanas has permitted it to be distributed widely and repeatedly throughout the archipelago. True isolation, so necessary for speciation, may not exist for
colonies of *Amblyrhynchus*.

15–13. One of the world's larger lizards, the Galápagos land iguana *Conolophus subcristatus* feeds on flowers, buds, and cactus pads. In color, it varies from yellow to red. (San Diego Zoo photo, left; Allan Hancock Foundation, right.)

Iguanas under the Cacti. Inland counterpart of the marine iguana is *Conolophus* (15–13, 15–14), which is thus called the land iguana. The two genera are probably closely related. The divergence in habits and appearance has been strong, however. *Conolophus subcristatus* (15–13) is dusky or tawny in color, touches of chrome yellow around the face and yellowish brown on the flanks enlivening its body. Scales on the face are modified into horny projections. Fierce in appearance, *Conolophus* is capable of seriously damaging an opponent, particularly in battles between males at mating time. When frightened, the land iguana will head for its burrow and hide. It fights captors more vigorously than the marine iguana, but then it also is heavier, although about as long (three feet). There are two species. *Conolophus pallidus* (15–14) lives on Barrington Island only. It lacks the spines astride the back of the neck which *C. subcristatus* has. *Conolophus subcristatus* occurs on many of the larger and central islands. Both species are now relatively scarcer than the marine iguana.

Land iguanas claim notice for their diet. Despite their ferocity, they are not carnivorous—they prefer, in fact, delicate flowers, the tubular flowers of *Cordia* or the yellow petals of *Tribulus*, the puncture vine. These flowers are available only a few months every year, so land iguanas basically subsist on cactus

15–14. On Barrington Island lives a distinct species of land iguana, *Conolophus pallidus*. In the soft volcanic dust it digs squirrel-like burrows. (San Diego Zoo photo.)

fruits. As these fruits fall from the tall prickly pear trees, the iguanas pick them up and greedily munch them—seeds and spines included. Moreover, they often eat pads of the cactus as well. How their intestines can avoid puncture by masses of stout spines is difficult to understand—but they do. The spines are not digested, nor even appreciably softened.

Conolophus illustrates some of the same insular characteristics as *Amblyrhynchus,* and in addition, the conspicuous differences between the two show how a reptile group has been able to diverge into two totally unlike ways of life. The diet of *Conolophus* suggests it is a sort of reptilian goat, but the seaweed diet of the marine iguana suggests no parallel except with seaweed-nibbling fish.

Lesser Reptiles. The lizard world of the Galápagos also includes *Tropidurus,* a genus of smaller lizards which has diversified into an interesting series of species and races. The same process has been explored by the Galápagos geckos (*Phyllodactylus*). A single genus of snakes contrasts with the plurality of lizards. This illustrates the greater difficulties in dispersal experienced by snakes. This snake, a colubrid (*Leimadophis*), has undergone race and species formation in the islands. Formerly, it was considered an endemic genus.

The Namesake Reptiles. The name "Galápagos" is Spanish for "tortoises." These bulky reptiles were as famous among the early buccaneers as they are to today's scientists. Early mariners were more interested in them as sources of food, because the tortoises could be stored for long periods aboard ships without suffering ill-effects. Biologists prize them as examples of race formation (15–16).

Ironically, although hundreds of Galápagos tortoises have been collected and are available for study in the world's museums, herpetologists are not entirely in agreement about classification of these giants. Is there one species, or are there fifteen? Decisions range between these extremes, but the former view seems more likely of acceptance. The herpetologist John Van Denburgh confesses, "the various races of tortoises of the Galápagos Islands differ from one another chiefly in shape. There are no real differences in structure, such as are found in the lizards and snakes of the archipelago." Perhaps tortoises tend to evolve more slowly than short-lived reptiles. Some differences in shape described by herpetologists may be due in part to differences in age, for veteran tortoises tend to acquire more angular shapes than youngsters.

The Galápagos tortoises seem clearly derived from a single stock which landed on the archipelago. This ancestor probably was closely related to *Testudo tabulata,* a tortoise which today inhabits South America and the West Indies. Could a tortoise like *T. tabulata* cross five hundred or more miles of ocean to land successfully on the Galápagos? Various observations prove that tortoises can float in sea water. Although often alleged to be poor swimmers, tortoises have more ability than their clumsiness on land might suggest. William Beebe filmed a Galápagos tortoise which showed a good sense of direction and which was able to paddle toward several objectives. Tortoises may well have arrived on the Galápagos by rafting, however, because prolonged flotation seems somewhat damaging to these animals.

The Galápagos tortoise is a model of clumsiness (15–15). In its native habitats, it ascends lava slopes with painful slowness. Often, they have limited territories and frequent particular trails. Where they enjoy wetter conditions, as on upper Indefatigable Island, they habituate muddy water holes. Tortoises can survive without such pools, however, because they can drink large quantities of water when it is available and store it within their bodies for months. Galápagos tortoises are vegetarians, and although they have certain preferences, their diet ranges over a variety of items—grasses, seeds, leaves, even in dried conditions.

When the Galápagos tortoise lays eggs, it buries them with soil or sand in places where at least a few hours of sunlight a day will heat the nest and incubate the eggs. Recently, the San Diego Zoo hatched eggs of Galápagos tortoises for the first time outside their native habitat. Growth of the infant tortoises has proved very rapid, suggesting that the giant specimens are not as old ("four or five hundred years") as has been claimed.

THE ADAPTABLE AVIFAUNA

No group of island birds has attracted so much interest as the Darwin's finches. The number of pages in books and papers devoted to them certainly

15–15. The name "Galápagos" means tortoises, and, for early visitors, their lumbering presence became a symbol of the islands themselves. Despite their bulk and awkwardness, they probably did not require a land bridge to reach the islands; their ancestors may have been somewhat smaller. (San Diego Zoo photo.)

exceeds a thousand. They are often cited and compared in studies involving other birds—or other animals. They are small, they are not colorful, they lack spectacular qualities. But they are excellent representatives of certain stages in evolution. Their simplicity is welcome, because they demonstrate with clarity such phenomena as adaptive radiation, endemism, and race formation, to name a few.

Darwin's finches have been placed in a separate family (Geospizidae), but most ornithologists agree that the characters they all have in common are not sufficient to distinguish them very strongly from other finches (Fringillidae) except perhaps as a subfamily (Geospizinae). Only a brief outline of the many interesting patterns in the Darwin's finches can be given here, and many additional details will be found in fine books by Bowman, Lack, and Swarth.

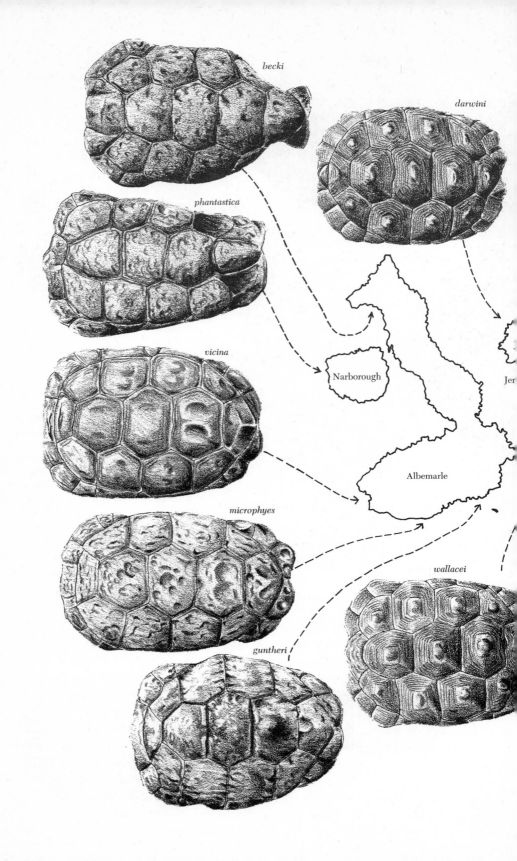

becki

darwini

phantastica

vicina

Narborough

Jer

Albemarle

microphyes

wallacei

guntheri

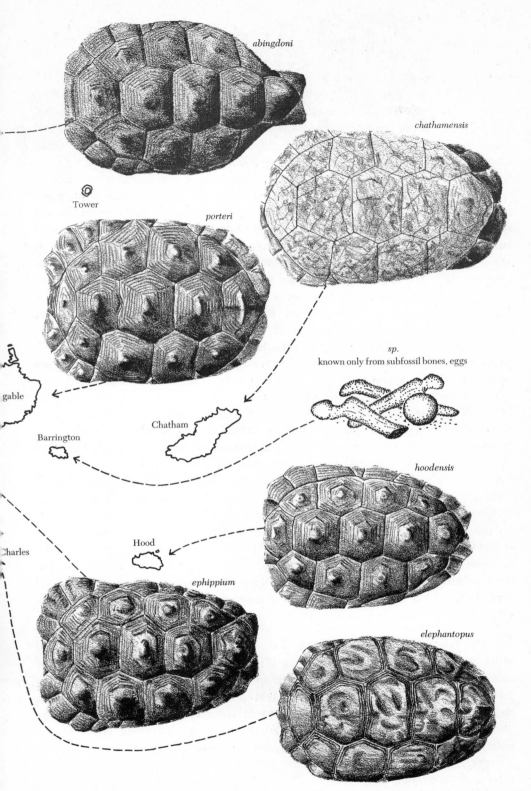

abingdoni

chathamensis

Tower

porteri

gable

sp.
known only from subfossil bones, eggs

Chatham

Barrington

hoodensis

Hood

Charles

ephippium

elephantopus

15–16. Distinctive races of tortoises inhabit the Galápagos. Although differences among them are not pronounced, there is a tendency toward a saddle-backed form on the northwestern islands, a dome-shaped contour on the central and southern islands. All should probably be regarded as subspecies of a single species, *Testudo elephantopus* (e.g., *T. elephantopus* subsp. *becki,* etc.). Classifying these tortoises is difficult because particular individuals may show differences in shape due to great age.

On the Ground. Six genera are often recognized in the Darwin's finches (Plate III, 15–17). Of these, the most conspicuous are the large blackish ground finches, *Geospiza*, with six species. *Geozpiza scandens* and *G. conirostris* are close species, but no island hosts both of them. Populations of *G. scandens* on Abingdon and Bindloe and *G. conirostris* on Tower differ from "typical" specimens of those respective species, and rather bridge the gap between the two species.

Geospiza magnirostris, G. fortis, and *G. fuliginosa* are a trio of ground finch species which form, in that order, a series from large, heavy bills to light, small ones (Plate III, right of center, top to bottom). All three occur on certain islands, such as Indefatigable. Where two or three of these species occur on the same island, they tend to "move apart." This is shown in 15–18. Bills of *G. fortis* are smaller on Chatham and Charles Islands than on Crossman Island. On the contrary, bills are larger in *G. fortis* on Chatham and Charles Islands than they are in the population on Daphne Island. The differences in bills are, of course, a clue to differences in feeding habits. The medium bills are the versatile tools to a spread of various-sized food articles. Where both species occur together, the larger-billed *G. fortis* tends to take larger items and the smaller-billed *G. fuliginosa* accepts smaller items, so the two do not compete as directly as they would if both had identical bills. *Geospiza magnirostris* has a bill capable of handling larger seeds than the other species; *Bursera* fruits are often chosen by *G. magnirostris; Cordia* berries are eaten by *G. fortis;* small seeds, such as those of grasses, suit *G. fuliginosa.* With different food sources, coexistence is possible. Moreover, the "moving apart" of three species from a single ancestral form suggests how the beginnings of adaptive radiations appear.

Geospiza difficilis suggests a remnant of the original stock of finches which originally populated the Galápagos. It occurs on the northern, outlying islands of the archipelago, but not on the southernmost. In the central islands it feeds on the ground of the humid forest. On Tower Island, however, where forest is lacking, it forages in an open habitat. On Tower, *G. difficilis* specimens tend to resemble the species *G. fuliginosa,* which is absent on Tower. Thus it has not only substituted for the small ground finch *G. fuliginosa,* it has developed similar habits and appearance. This is a case of convergent, or parallel evolution, another lesson to be learned from the Geospizinae.

Into the Trees. *Geospiza* spends half of its time foraging on the ground, but the other genera spend progressively less—*Platyspiza, Camarhynchus, Cactospiza,* and *Certhidea,* in that order. *Certhidea* spends no time at all foraging on the ground. Interestingly, two features are correlated with this trend upward from the ground: from reliance on fruits and seeds, there is a change to consumption of insects exclusively. Similarly, the sooty color of ground birds yields to the pale tan or brownish colors of tree species in this series. *Platyspiza* is exclusively a vegetarian, *Certhidea* exclusively an insectivore, and the diets of *Camarhynchus* and *Cactospiza* intermediate. These changes are, of course, involved in an adaptive radiation—reaching into new sites, new foods, new habits.

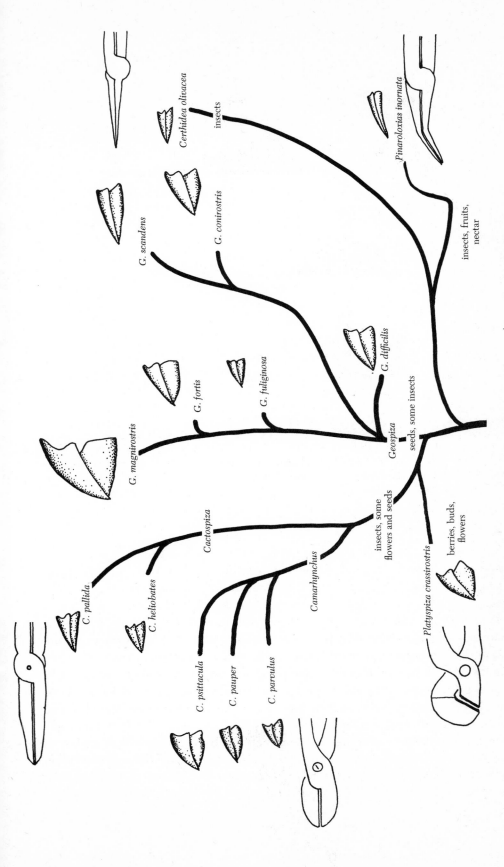

Certhidea olivacea

insects

Pinaroloxias inornata

insects, fruits, nectar

G. scandens

G. conirostris

G. magnirostris

G. fortis

G. fuliginosa

G. difficilis

Geospiza

seeds, some insects

Cactospiza

C. pallida

C. heliobates

C. psittacula

C. pauper

C. parvulus

Camarhynchus

insects, some flowers and seeds

Platyspiza crassirostris

berries, buds, flowers

15–17. Adaptive radiation is evidenced among Darwin's finches by beak features, which can be related to diet. These distinctive beaks and their associated muscles can be compared with different types of pliers, and represent "built-in" tools for dealing with food articles of different sizes and textures (based upon drawings by Lack and Bowman).

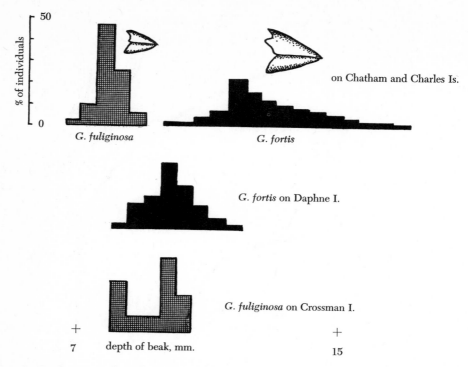

15–18. Beak size is keyed to size of prey; a medium size is most versatile. Where *Geospiza fuliginosa* and *F. fortis* coexist (Chatham and Charles Islands), they are pushed toward opposite extremes and thus avoid competing with each other in diet. Where one species or the other is absent (Daphne Island; Crossman Island), the medium-sized beak is retained. (Modified from Lack.)

Although *Platyspiza* has a smaller bill than *Geospiza magnirostris*, it can crush heavy seeds. A reminder of this ability is furnished by the analogy with parrot-head gripping pliers in 15–17. The more delicate bills of *Camarhynchus* indicate a switch to insects. The three species of *Camarhynchus* choose as food the insects and larvae which are in proportion to their respective bill and body sizes. Analysis of stomach contents shows larger larvae eaten by *C. psittacula*, smaller ones by *C. parvulus,* and intermediate ones by *C. pauper*. This trio of species is to the tree finches an exercise in spreading over a gamut of food articles much like the gamut seen in the trio of ground finches *Geospiza magnirostris, G. fortis,* and *G. fuliginosa. Camarhynchus* fills out its diet with nectar, buds, young leaves, and small seeds.

Cactospiza contains the famous tool-using finch. This custom, described in Chapter 10, represents a new departure, a feat well beyond the expectations of a plan of adaptive radiation. *Cactospiza* contains, in addition to the tool-using finch *C. pallida,* a second species, *C. heliobates,* with its own particular niche. It inhabits mangrove trees. These trees are unusual in that they grow only in shallow, muddy sea water along coasts. Because such sites are relatively few, *C. heliobates* has adapted to a specialized condition indeed. Little is known about the habits of this species, other than its habit of searching for insects by probing underneath bark. Like the cactus finch, *C. heliobates* has been reported to be a tool-using bird.

Certhidea is the "answer to a warbler" among the Darwin's finches. Mimicking warblers in food and other habits, it is a clear example of how the products of adaptive radiation on islands tend to resemble well-known continental types. *Certhidea* searches for a variety of insects, even taking them on the wing. On Hood Island, it will even eat small marine organisms at low tide. *Certhidea* has a wider range within the archipelago than the other finches, and individuals are more numerous. Its success, despite a high degree of specialization, is probably due in no small degree to its substituting for a bird virtually absent in the Galápagos—the warbler. In the terms of Chapter 4, *Certhidea* shows how a finch can "climb" an "adaptive peak." Some claim that *Certhidea* represents—in some respects—an ancestral type among the Darwin's finches.

Pinaroloxias is a unique experiment among the Darwin's finches. It occurs on an island well north of the Galápagos, Cocos. Cocos could hardly be more different from the Galápagos. Free from the rain-inhibiting effect of the Humboldt current, Cocos Island supports a luxurious rain forest. The habits of *Pinaroloxias* are not well known, so difficult is it to study in the shady recesses of these forests. Its beak, however, suggests a close approach to the habits of such nectar-feeding birds as *Loxops* or other honeycreepers (Plate I). Probably *Pinaroloxias* mixes nectar, fruit, and insects in its diet, as do species of the Hawaiian honeycreepers.

A BALANCE OF BIRDS

The Darwin's finches certainly do not have the Galápagos entirely to themselves. There are, in fact, about a hundred species of birds in the archipelago (many, to be sure, marine and shore birds). The large number of bird species may compensate in part for the absence of mammals. Both reptiles and birds on the Galápagos may have moved in on what would be the preserve of mammals on the mainland. Dogs and other mammals, when introduced on the Galápagos, have gone wild successfully. Had natural dispersal placed such mammals on the islands, the Galápagos would probably never have been able to support many of the native birds and reptiles which evolved there.

One feature common to many of the Galápagos birds is a pronounced fearlessness. Some of them are quite tame. The photograph of a booby, 15–19, shows that timidity is lacking both among marine and land birds. Such fearlessness is rather surprising, in view of the fact that a species of hawk is native to the

15–19. Fearlessness characterizes many of the more than one hundred species of birds which inhabit the Galápagos Islands. Here an expedition scientist, Dr. Edwin O. Palmer, finds that boobies unaccustomed to humans are not easily frightened. (Allan Hancock Foundation photo.)

Galápagos. Even the hawk is quite fearless: Darwin was able to knock one from its perch with the muzzle of a gun.

The richness of the archipelago in marine birds springs from a wealth of fish and other marine organisms. Small wonder that the Galápagos harbor endemic marine birds. One of these has a fame out of proportion to its small numbers—the Galápagos penguin (15–20). Unlike any other penguins, it makes its home literally on the equator. The penguin has been found chiefly on the northern is-lands—those nearest the equator, in fact. This site is occupiable by a penguin because of the cool Humboldt current. Thus, *Spheniscus mendiculus* is far from its nearest relative, the magellanic penguin *S. magellanicus* of southern Chile, the Falkland Islands, and islands near Antarctica. The Galápagos penguin also happens to be the world's smallest. These birds spend most of their time sitting upright on rocks near the shore, often in cooler lava caverns. They hop with both feet together, a clumsiness countered by their adeptness at swimming. They often quietly float in coves, but when swimming they can leap above the surface, porpoise-fashion. Much more needs to be learned about their habits.

Equally famous is the flightless cormorant (15–21), a bird which clings to a few miles of coastline on Narborough and adjacent Albemarle Island. Graceful and swan-like when sitting, the cormorant loses this grace when it waddles into the surf, swimming away to dive for prey. It is completely flightless, as indicated by the ragged, poorly feathered wings. Compensation is clearly furnished by fishing ability, for flightless cormorants succeed in catching octopus primarily, fish secondarily. Nests of the cormorant are built on bare lava, and consist merely of heaps of brown algae, into which a pair of bluish eggs is entrusted. Shreds of seaweed are also used by the cormorants as greeting tokens, brandished before a female by a male returning from the sea. The flightless cormorant is a model of vulnerability, an evolutionary happening uniquely designed and preserved by the Galápagos scene. The fact that although the Galápagos have many species of birds, but only one which has lost its flight, suggests the recentness of the archipelago; old islands, such as New Zealand, have more.

INVERTEBRATE GALAPAGIANS

Less familiar Galápagos residents, but quite as interesting in their way, are Galápagos insects. Flightlessness is frequent among them. One such case is the flightless grasshopper illustrated in 9–3. Dwarfism also appears to characterize a portion of the insects (7–8).

Not less interesting are the land shells of the Galápagos. They form complex and variable species. Among them is one, *Tornatellides*, which has managed a far reach from the west to colonize the Galápagos (12–3), apparently the only Galápagos native which has come from the west.

A MILESTONE, A MUSEUM

If biologists have a sensitivity to the history of their science, one way in which it has been manifest is their inherent interest in the Galápagos. The flora and fauna of these islands have become inseparably associated with the name of Charles Darwin and with his theories. To be found on the islands are such reminders as the Darwin Biological Station and a statue of Darwin on the spot where he first landed. The Biological Station was a result of UNESCO sponsorship, and emphasizes how much yet remains to be learned there.

Viewed as bearers of evolutionary examples, the Galápagos are unusually strategic. Islands older than these are almost "too good." The old islands support old and thoroughly tried lines of animals and plants, monuments to stress, endurance, and survival. The history of their origins, radiations, and compensations

15–20. Smallest and most northerly of penguins, *Spheniscus mendiculus* of the Galápagos is able to make its home on the equator because of the cool conditions provided by the Humboldt Current. (Allan Hancock Foundation photo.)

has been obliterated. The processes by which they descended to the present day are obscured; the main message they convey is that they have, in fact, survived. In the Galápagos, on the contrary, the ferment of recent genesis is still apparent. The Galápagos is rich not in missing links, but in "non-missing links."

Taxonomists find Galápagos creatures annoying to classify. The recentness of many Galápagos species means that they are still variable, containing a variety of individuals, extremes, and intermediates. Over longer periods of time than have been available on these islands, this variability would be thinned out, a more uniform species would be handed down. Those who must write names on specimen labels view ungraciously species as variable as those the Galápagos

15–21. Famous in biological circles as an example of a flightless island bird is the Galápagos cormorant (*Phalacrocorax harrisi*). Its weak wings, incompletely clad with feathers, attest a loss of function. (San Diego Zoo photo.)

offers. To the evolutionist, this situation means not bewilderment so much as opportunity for study. Much remains to be learned about this young and rapidly changing biota.

Biologists have already left a rich Galápagos literature. They can be expressive and sensitive scholars, as well as esoteric and term-conscious. We have reason to value Darwin's *Voyage of the Beagle* for its sense of wonder and insight. More recently, William Beebe essayed the life of these islands in *Galápagos— World's End* and *The Arcturus Adventure*. Beebe communicates the innermost feelings of an expedition biologist, patiently pondering, reacting to, the creatures which surround him. Beebe is at his best in synechdoche, converting the cove of a small island or the floor of a tiny crater into epics of life itself, unforgettable biological scenarios. More recently, Irenaus Eibl-Eibesfeldt has conveyed a sense of immediacy in his descriptions of the landscape and its creatures in a book entitled *Galápagos*.

The strangeness of the Galápagos scene, the isolation, the ironies of their animals have gained mention many times in years past both in magazines and books; they will be described many times again. But biologists have now given to an interested public, works—such as David Lack's *Darwin's Finches*—which display the full wonder which detailed knowledge of island organisms can bring. The Galápagos are no longer a deepening mystique, a "world's end." They are a model of life's unfolding.

16　Lemur Land

BIOLOGICALLY rich, a curious and remote island, Madagascar is a land unfamiliar—except to its residents and the relatively few who have visited it. Ask
a zoologist what distinctive animals inhabit Madagascar; with few exceptions,
his list will not go much beyond the lemurs, yet there are many other animals of great interest. Ask a botanist about the plants; he may have difficulty
naming more than a few. He will probably forget the Didiereas, he may not remember that one small valley in Madagascar has given to gardens throughout
the world's tropics the brilliant Flamboyant tree, also known as the Royal Poin-
ciana. Ask a geologist about Madagascar's history and he will tell you that the island is an object of some controversy, and that a number of basic facts are yet
to be learned about it. Has Madagascar ever been connected to the African
mainland? If so, how recently? We cannot answer for certain. Madagascar remains the unknown island.

THE PROBLEMATIC HISTORY

Is Madagascar a continental or an oceanic island? A basic question like this
deserves an answer. The best answer seems to be that if a connection ever existed
with the African mainland, it was at a very remote date indeed—before the
Tertiary, in all likelihood. Madagascar once did host dinosaurs, which might seem
to favor a very old land connection. Today, however, the channel between Madagascar and Africa is at least six thousand feet deep along its entire length.
Deeps around islands in Madagascar's vicinity are even more dramatic, such as
the undersea gulfs between Madagascar and the Mascarene Islands (Mauritius,
Réunion, and Rodriguez) or between Madagascar and the Seychelles. If these
islands ever served as stepping-stones for dispersal of plants or animals to Madagascar, they still must have had gaps of water of some width between them
and Madagascar, not a dry bridge of land.

About seventy species of mammals are present on Madagascar. This would
seem to argue for a former land connection with Africa. However, the mammals
present are only a very small group compared with what Africa has to offer.
Present are lemurs, civet cats, and tenrecs (a family of insectivores). Some or all
of the rodents and shrews as well as the African bush pig may well have been
introduced by man. In the Pleistocene, a pygmy hippopotamus was present. On
the other hand, Africa's wealth of mammals has never been able to make the

journey: the many cats, hyenas, giraffes, elephants, antelope-relatives, etc. have been stopped completely by the Mozambique Channel. The mammals which have reached Madagascar by natural dispersal are really remarkably few—despite a great richness of available habitats. Given enough time, could these few groups have rafted to Madagascar? Some biologists today think this is possible. Civets and primates have been able to cross Wallace's Line, so perhaps crossing a once-narrower Mozambique Channel is not impossible at all.

The fresh water fish of Madagascar include no primary-division species. Among amphibia, those most vulnerable to desiccation and poorest at long-distance dispersal—the caecilians—are absent, although they are present on the Seychelles. Other groups—reptiles and birds—can cross sea water much better than the above, so they suggest even less that Madagascar is a continental island. Even among these groups, we find a markedly attenuated condition on Madagascar. The list of African bird families which are missing on Madagascar is a shockingly large one.

On the plant side of the question, conifers would offer the best evidence of whether Madagascar were a continental island. Today, Africa south of the Sahara is remarkably poor in conifers. Of those which do occur in Africa, only the relatively easily dispersed podocarp *Podocarpus* has reached Madagascar. In the Triassic, however, a fossil conifer, *Voltziopsis,* existed both on the African mainland and on Madagascar.

Geologically, the evidence on whether Madagascar is a continental island is curious. There are sedimentary rocks of Jurassic, Cretaceous, and Tertiary ages—but the most recent rocks face the Mozambique Channel. These and other facts hint that the Channel has existed since Triassic time, an interpretation seemingly supported by the plants and animals. The easiest explanation to accept at present seems to be that Madagascar is a continental island, but that its separation from Africa dates from about Triassic time. All but a few of the plants and animals now living there could easily have crossed sea water—and even the rest may have. *Voltziopsis* and nearly all or perhaps all of the pre-channel animals, such as dinosaurs, are now extinct. Madagascar shows us how a continental island, if its time of separation from mainland is very long ago, can bear virtually the same flora and fauna as an oceanic island.

All of the world's "true" oceanic islands, or ones easily classified as oceanic, are relatively young. The life expectancy of purely volcanic islands seems relatively short. They quickly erode, leaving vestiges as atolls, reefs, or seamounts. It is possible that large islands can be semi-permanent features of the oceans. Large islands, incorporating metamorphic and sedimentary rocks, might last very long periods of time. New Zealand, Madagascar, and New Caledonia appear to be in this category, and have enjoyed land connections with mainland only long, long ago, and for a short portion of their history, very likely. If we judge dispersal ability in terms of what has arrived on relatively new islands only, we may be slighting what could happen in a much longer period of time. When a long period of time is available, as with Madagascar, can mammals cross sea water? If the Mozambique Strait once was narrower, could they have crossed it? A definite "no" would be unreasonable, and "yes" remains possible.

THE LONG LANDSCAPE

Stretching from a tropical north to a temperate south, Madagascar offers a wide variety of climates. Running the length of the island is a spine of mountains which reaches to eighty-six hundred feet. Rainfall is heavy on the northeast coast, decreasing steadily toward the southwest, which is quite arid. Thus Madagascar's vegetation runs from tropical rain forest and cool upland forest to a near-desert scrub. Much of Madagascar was an open savanna-like woodland, but this has largely been converted into farmland or burned. Within these various conditions of climate, many ecological opportunities exist. Flowering plants and birds—the usual dominants on islands—have gone farther than other groups in taking these opportunities.

SOME PERSISTENT ANCIENTS

Twenty-one species of lemurs are all that is left of a primate dynasty once spread throughout Europe, North America, and perhaps other continents as well. Lemurs are probably not on the main line of evolution in primates leading to the great apes and man; they are something of a sidetrack. The upright habit, the enlargement of a brain, the complex of characteristics which led to the higher primates are features alien to the primitive lemurs.

The Fruit Eaters. The majority of the lemurs fall into the family Lemuridae, the true lemurs. The word "lemur" comes from the Roman gods of the dead, who supposedly started out of fireplaces from behind the flames. The large, arresting eyes of the lemurs may have evoked this comparison. The greater lemurs (genus *Lemur*) are comparatively larger, and rather unlike the remainder of the lemurs. Greater lemurs have long snouts, fox-like faces, and bushy tails. In form, there is a rather interesting parallel between the greater lemurs and the tree kangaroos of New Guinea (6–21). The long grasping arms and legs, the long tail useful for balancing, are adaptations to life in the trees. Greater lemurs may do some foraging on the ground, but they always sleep in trees. They are quiet animals, and usually only grunt, but they can also shriek in alarm. The mongoose lemur (*L. mungoz,* Plate IV, above, left of center) is a woolly creature that walks with tail upright. It is native to a spot in central Madagascar, the northern tip of the island, and the Comoro Islands northwest of Madagascar. The mongoose lemur feeds by day, and likes fruits and seeds. In captivity, it proves friendly and accepts bananas, rice, even eggs.

Lemur catta (Plate IV, lower right) is the commonest of the greater lemurs. An adaptable species, it has occupied the dry regions of Madagascar's dry southwest. Better known as the ring-tail lemur, this clever, neat, and agile animal is a fine tree-climber. In its native habitat it seeks fruits, such as figs and bananas, as well as roots. A curious and quite unexplained feature is the presence of glandular sacs on the wrists and shoulder. The strong scent produced by these glands may be important in signaling the presence of an individual and keeping a tribe of ring-tail lemurs in contact with each other.

The ruffed lemur (*L. variegatus*, Plate IV, below, right of center) differs from the above in several ways. Its coloration may be black and white, or reddish and black, as shown. It dwells in treetops along both coasts of the northern end of the island. Ruffed lemurs feed at night, build nests, and are in the curious habit of sunbathing in the morning.

Close to the greater lemurs is *Hapalemur,* the snub-nosed lemur. It can be recognized by its globose head, short snout, short velvety ears, short large feet, and a tail as long as the body. *Hapalemur* will feed either at day or night; it prefers to nibble bamboo shoots.

Halfway between true lemurs and the other genera, it seems, is *Lepilemur,* a leaping animal which travels in tribes through forests. *Lepilemur* makes nests in which to rear young, and may live in these nests at other times as well. Typical of the slow reproductive habits of primitive island mammals, a *Lepilemur* female can have only a single infant each year.

The Insect Seekers. Formulas for insect-eating have been evolved by the lesser lemurs: *Microcebus, Cheirogaleus,* and *Phaner.* They also eat fruits. Their great swiftness and small size (up to a foot in length) reflects the small size of their prey. *Cheirogaleus* (Plate IV, above, right of center) and *Microcebus* (Plate IV, upper left) are nocturnal animals. This habit is clearly spelled out in their large eyes and sensitive ears. *Cheirogaleus* has the habit of storing fat in its tail. *Microcebus* is notable for its thick fur, its habit of sleeping in holes in trees, and its willingness to live in a variety of places: forest, swamp, scrub. Both of these genera of lesser lemurs may owe their survival to their nocturnal habits, because their natural enemy is a goshawk.

Phaner looks much like the other lesser lemurs, but it has the peculiar habit of sharing a cavity in a hollow tree with bees. Unharmed by them, *Phaner* apparently robs honey with impunity.

Eaters of Leaves and Buds. The family Indriidae consists of animals about the same size as the greater lemurs, but different in many technical features, such as their smaller number of teeth, long upper incisors, and larger, monkey-like brains. Like Lemuridae, Indriidae have only a single infant per season.

The sifaka, *Propithecus* (Plate IV, near center) is a tree-loving animal. In the morning and evening it feeds most actively—on leaves and bark. Sifakas also occasionally eat fruit, scraping the flesh out of the rind with their protruding teeth.

Sifakas have distinctive silky fur. When walking, they habitually go upright, arms held out in front of them or above the head, a habit one would not expect in an animal which uses arms and legs for climbing. *Propithecus* is gregarious, and individuals travel in parties of six to eight. With long, muscular legs, sifakas can make leaps of thirty feet or more.

In a neighboring genus is the woolly avahi, *Avahi laniger* (Plate IV, left). A small spherical head with large owl-like eyes is the hallmark of this animal, whose nocturnal habits contrast with other members of the family Indriidae. Exclusively a vegetarian, it lives on buds, leaves, and bark. Because it is a plant-eater, its more deliberate movements serve quite well for food-getting, whereas the lesser lemurs are rapid and agile.

The indri, *Indri brevicaudatus* (Plate IV, upper right) looks quite unlike the avahi. Indris have very short tails, very lanky limbs, and silky hairs. Their feet are more adept at gripping than are their hands. More often seen than heard, they are shy creatures of deep forest. Indris are vegetarians, but the Malagasies also claim they eat birds. This may be one of many quaint and unconfirmed legends which have grown up around this animal, often regarded as sacred by the Malagasies.

The Lemur Squirrel. Originally thought to be a squirrel, *Daubentonia* (Plate IV bottom left) is actually only a lemur mimicking such rodents. The digits are narrow, provided with long claws. The third finger is especially prominent and is used for extracting insects embedded in bark of trees—a habit like that of Australia's striped possum (6–15). Large gnawing incisors heighten the rodent resemblances of *Daubentonia,* which chews through bark in search of insects. *Daubentonia* is nocturnal, and deep in Madagascar's forests its peculiar cry "aye-aye"—which is often used as a common name for the animal—can be heard. Aye-ayes are more closely related to indris than to other lemurs, but have been placed in a family of their own (Daubentoniidae) on account of their many specializations.

A fossil species of *Daubentonia* is also known from Madagascar. It is much larger than the living species. This pattern is true of other fossil lemurs also. Apparently conditions favoring existence of giant lemurs have deteriorated.

In summary, lemurs occupy a variety of situations, corresponding to adaptive radiation. Nocturnal versus diurnal, fruit-eating versus insect-eating, large and slow versus small and agile are some of the divergences which have occurred. Maps of the distribution of lemur species show that most often they tend to exploit different areas from each other.

THE OPPORTUNIST HEDGEHOGS

Another case of adaptive radiation is furnished by Madagascar's Tenrecidae, a primitive and endemic family of insectivores commonly known (if in fact

16–1. *Echinops telfairi* is the spiny representative of Madagascar's insectivore family Tenrecidae. (New York Zoological Society photo.)

they *are* known commonly) as the tenrecs. They are not merely Madagascar hedgehogs; zoologists rate their internal structure as more primitive than that of hedgehogs, and they remind one more of the relict insectivore *Solenodon* (Chapter 12) or even shrews. Tenrecs may date their arrival in Madagascar to the same period as that of the lemurs.

The wonderfully spiny *Echinops* (16–1) is the closest approach the tenrecs have made to the hedgehog habit, but it cannot roll itself into a ball as hedgehogs can—it can only partly do this. The back and flanks of *Echinops telfairi* are covered by smoky-colored spines, blackened slightly at their tips. *Echinops* is a nocturnal animal, with a nervous, unquiet habit. It is only five or six inches long. When disturbed, it puts its nose between its forepaws, contracts somewhat, and raises its spines menacingly. The Malagasies, although they eat other tenrecs, neglect *Echinops* because its ferocity is expressed only in a defensive way, and they do not regard as fair game an animal which does not defend itself with teeth and claws. Although little is known of its habits, *Echinops* apparently digs deep burrows along rivers and likes to be near water.

The tandraka, *Tenrec ecaudatus* (16–2), is an animal which, like the spiny

16–2. *Tenrec ecaudatus* has stiff defensive bristles intermingled with its fur, virtually lacks a tail. (New York Zoological Society photo.)

16–3. *Hemicentetes nigriceps* has skunk-like fur patterns. Atop the head are bristles which can be raised and serve defensively like a porcupine's quills. (New York Zoological Society photo.)

16–4. *Oryzoctes hova* is the most mole-like of Madagascar's tenrecs.

anteater of Australia, mixes spines with hair. The compromise achieved by the tandraka is not evident at first glance, for the difference between its thicker, defensive quill bristles and the softer hairs is not an extreme one. The quill bristles, like the quills of a porcupine, can prove a painful deterrent. To their basic diet of insects, tandrakas add worms, even snakes and lizards. Prominent claws permit tandrakas to burrow. They seldom leave burrows, except at night, when feeding time comes. Indeed, they hibernate three months out of every year. Although tandrakas radiate an annoying smell of musk, they are eaten by the Malagasies.

Hemicentetes nigriceps (16–3) appears somewhat skunk-like, but its long nose immediately identifies it as an insectivore. The fur pattern is one of blackish-brown stripes on a yellowish-white background. Less completely armed than other tenrecs, it raises quill bristles on the back of the head and neck as a defensive mechanism. *Hemicentetes* is only two-thirds the size of *Tenrec,* and does not capture the larger prey tandrakas can.

Oryzoctes hova (16–4) is an experiment in the mole habit. Because the tenrecs are burrowing insectivores, they are partway toward the mole habit. *Oryzoctes* goes farther in this direction because of its weak eyes, soft mole-like fur and strong digging claws. Defensive quill bristles are absent. A tireless burrower, it finds much of its prey underground. *Oryzoctes* is frequently found in rice fields.

Miniature of the tenrecs, *Microgale* (16–5), is a tiny animal of the forest. The long tail—often twice the length of the body—is unusual among the tenrecs. Moreover, the tail is bare on the lower surface. This bare undersurface may be related to dragging on the ground, or it may be an accommodation to being used as a prop when the animal stands upright. These mouse-like animals, cov-

16–5. *Microgale cowani* is small, looks mouse-like, and engages smaller insect prey than do the larger of Madagascar's tenrecs.

ered with soft blackish fur, arouse many questions, for virtually nothing is known of their habits, despite the fact that at least eleven species have been collected and named. Likewise, little is known about genera near *Microgale*: *Geogale, Nesogale,* and *Paramicrogale.* The latter may represent transitions from the quill-bearing tenrecs.

A triumph of adaptation among the tenrecs is *Limnogale* (16–6). It is an aquatic animal, conspicuously equipped for this way of life by the webbing on its paws—particularly its rear paws. The diet of this animal seems to be aquatic plants. It has been claimed that *Limnogale* eats stems of the curious and famous river plant, *Aponogeton fenestralis.* This plant is renowned because its leaves develop spaces, like the mesh of a screen, between the veins, which thus present a lace-like appearance. *Limnogale* is now apparently extremely rare or extinct, just at a time when we would like to learn about its habits to compile a comprehensive picture of the many adaptations the tenrecs have undertaken.

A CONFUSING MAMMAL

Cryptoprocta ferox (16–7), the so-called fosa or fossa of Madagascar, confused zoologists for many years because of its cat-like habits. Like a cat, it is "plantigrade"—puts heels down first in walking. Its form, face, and hunting habits also suggest those of a cat. However, when one examines its claws, feet, skull, and teeth, it proves to be a civet (family Viverridae). This should come as no surprise, because eight other species of civets are native to Madagascar. Although fossas do not attack men, they have found his poultry a fine source of food. An excellent climber, the fossa is an enemy of the lemur.

BIRDS FOR EVERY OCCASION

Even though Madagascar's bird fauna is an impoverished one compared to that of mainland Africa, it contains a great variety, ranging from tiny forest birds to flamingos and the unique elephant bird. Even the number of endemic genera (46) is large, so that only a few can be described here, those which show a striking form of insular adaptation.

The Flightless. Forming an endemic family are the mesites (Mesoenatidae), with perhaps three species: *Mesoenas variegata* (Plate V), *M. unicolor*, and *M. benschi*. They are flightless. When picked up and dropped in midair, they open their wings but fall to the ground. Loss of flight is indicated anatomically by the

16–6. Webbed feet reveal that *Limnogale mergulus* is a tenrec adapted to living near and foraging in streams.

reduced wings and the weak sternum. Mesites are ground birds which scurry among shrubbery and trees, protected by the cover these afford. Some, however, manage to live in rather open desert brush country. Mesites nest on the ground, forming a pad of twigs or leaves. Mesites subsist on a diet of ants and other insects, caterpillars, and occasionally a little fruit. Apparently the males incubate the eggs in *mesites*. Often, only a single egg is laid annually. When a chick is stolen from the nest of *Mesoenas*, the parent will follow its abductor even into a village. The Malagasies respect this parental attachment so highly that they regard *Mesoenas* as a sacred bird.

Mesites are probably related to rails, perhaps also to herons. In view of the relationship to rails, development of the flightless habit is easy to understand. Mesites are probably descendants of a rather early rail-like immigrant to Madagascar, and time has permitted widening of their differences from rails. Appropriately, the rail family (Rallidae) is as well represented on Madagascar as on other islands. Species of the family native to Madagascar include *Canirallus kioloides, Dryolimnas cuvieri, Rallus madagascariensis, Porzana pusilla, Amaurornis olivieri, Sarothrura insularis, S. watersi, Gallinula chloropus, Porphyrula alleni, Porphyrio madagascariensis,* and *Fulica cristata*. Most of these have been captured on the ground, because they resist flight as ·a means of escape. They may be able to fly, but do so on so few occasions that functionally they are nearly flightless. Abundance of rails and their loss of flight are both salient island characteristics.

The Wattled. Almost a parallel to New Zealand's wattled crows (10–6) are Madagascar's asities (Plate VI), a group of birds which make up the endemic

16–7. *Cryptoprocta ferox* confused zoologists for many years because of its cat-like appearance. It proves to be one of several civets native to Madagascar.

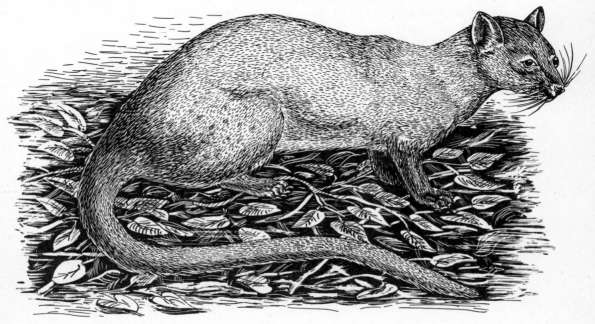

family Philepittidae. *Philepitta castanea* and *C. schlegeli* are fat, sluggish birds of the lower-elevation forests. Like the wattled crows, the asities do not fly very often or very far, and never soar above the forest canopy. They are silent birds, rarely interrupting the quiet of their forests. Philepittas are relatively fearless and can be approached closely—a familiar habit of island birds. Asities eat fruits almost exclusively, but sometimes take insects. Their nests are pendant and pear-shaped, somewhat in the fashion of an oriole nest. Male asities have various wattles around their eyes, differing from species to species and individual to individual in size and shape. The plumage of asities is brownish or yellowish. The wattles in *Philepitta castanea* is greenish; in *P. schlegeli*, blue. Thus, wattles form a contrasting color, and are allied to the color and display devices described in Chapter 11.

The difficulty taxonomists have with endemic island genera is almost one of biology's great proverbs. Evolution into new habits and form induced by island opportunities produces confusing products. Just such an example is a sickle-billed bird, *Neodrepanis* (Plate VII). A family of nectar-feeding sunbirds, Nectarinidae, lives on Madagascar and mainland Africa; *Neodrepanis* was once thought to belong to this family, on account of similar appearance and feeding habits. The position of *Neodrepanis* in the classification system has been changed several times by taxonomists. The curved beak, a criterion of the nectarinid sunbirds, has been thought not to indicate true relationship to that of *Neodrepanis*, but to be a parallelism. *Neodrepanis*, ornithologists now believe, is a nectar-feeding offshoot of Philepittidae. That it belongs in Philepittidae is suggested by the wattle, rudimentary as it may appear, around the eyes of *Neodrepanis* males and by the syrinx (vocal apparatus). *Neodrepanis* is definitely a nectar-feeder. It prefers bright, long, tubular flowers, or flowers with a tubular spur, such as *Impatiens*. It also may like insects. If *Neodrepanis* is an asity, it shows the same relationship to *Philepitta* that *Drepanis* does to *Ciridops* in the Hawaiian honey-creepers. The asities have not duplicated the full range of adaptive radiation that the honeycreepers have, but they have succeeded in part.

A Gamut of Vangas. Madagascar does, as it happens, have a close counterpart to the Hawaiian honeycreepers: the vanga-shrikes (Vangidae). The range of bill shape (16–8) is quite wide. Vanga-shrikes seem most closely related to the woodswallows of Asia (Artamidae) or the shrikes of Africa, Europe, Asia, and North America (Laniidae).

Smallest of the vanga-shrikes is *Calicalicus madagascariensis,* the red-tailed vanga. Its small beak, like that of the honeycreeper *Loxops,* suits it for taking insects: beetles, caterpillars, grasshoppers. Red-tailed vangas are abundant in low-altitude forests, mixing with many other birds.

Cyanolanius madagascarinus, the blue vanga, lives in much the same localities as *Calicalicus.* It may differ in its habits by taking somewhat larger insects, proportionate to its size.

Shetba rufa prefers the open savanna-like forests of low elevations. A fearless and rather inactive bird, it finds an ample diet among the medium-sized insects, such as locusts, which come its way in the high branches.

Xenopirostris xenopirostris is a common bird of the desert scrub in Madagascar's far south. The insect diet is like that of *Shetba,* but it differs not only in geographical location, but also in its active habits, making it conspicuous in dry regions, and in its sharp whistle.

Vanga curvirostris is the most successful of the vanga-shrikes. Spread throughout Madagascar, it occupies scrub as well as forest. *Vanga* takes insects proportionate to its large size: Orthoptera (grasshoppers, crickets, mantids) are favored, but a large and constant portion of its diet consists of vertebrates: frogs, tree lizards, and chameleons. The bill has the beginnings of a hawk-like shape, and so the taking of vertebrates is not surprising. The solitary habit of *Vanga* individuals also suggests customs of a bird of prey.

Euryceros prevostii, the helmet bird, has a curious large beak. *Euryceros* eats the diet of a bird of prey: frogs, reptiles, and insects. It is an inhabitant of the wet forests of Madagascar's northeast, and is thus much more restricted than *Vanga.*

Falculea palliata, like *Neodrepanis,* caused taxonomists some troubles on account of its sickle-shaped bill. Various families have been suggested as the correct one in which to include *Falculea,* but now it rests rather securely among the vanga-shrikes. *Falculea* captures large insects, such as locusts. It finds these among the branches of trees—but perhaps it uses different methods to secure its food than the other vangas do. The shape of the bill suggests this. Perhaps it probes in holes in tree trunks in search of insects. The loud cry ("like that of a child") is appropriate, for *Falculea* is the largest of the vanga-shrikes.

The adaptive radiation of the vanga-shrikes is perhaps not so spectacular as that of the Hawaiian honeycreepers or Darwin's finches. Both of these other groups have indulged in plant-eating as well as insect-eating. Their wider ranges of foods may be permitted by the relative paucity of other bird groups on the Hawaiian and Galápagos Islands. The large number of bird groups on Madagascar may have pre-empted some of the avenues the vanga-shrikes might otherwise have been able to take, or perhaps the vangas never had the capability of widening their food habits. Vangas are all arboreal birds, they are all carnivores; their span of diet articles, if not a triumph of adaptive radiation, is wider than many families of birds have managed.

The difficulty of placing genera of Madagascar birds in existing families, a by-product of the time Madagascar has so abundantly offered, is exhibited in other genera of this island. Families have been proposed for quite a number of them— an easy answer to a problem of classification, but sometimes the best one as well. The coral nuthatch or Madagascar creeper (*Hypositta*) has been placed in a family by itself, Hyposittidae; opinion now favors interpreting this bird as an offshoot of the vanga-shrike clan. Another Madagascar family of birds, Lepto-

Cyanolanius madagascarinus
blue vanga

Calicalicus madagascariensis
red-tailed vanga

Shetba rufa
rufous vanga

Xenopirostris xenopirostris
Lafresnaye's vanga

Euryceros prevostii
helmet bird

Vanga curvirostris
hook-billed vanga

Falculea palliata
sicklebill vanga

16–8. Madagascar's Vanga-shrikes (Vangidae) have experienced, within certain limits, adaptive radiation. Distinctive color patterns as well as differences in body size, beak shape, and diet differentiate the vangid genera.

somatidae (cuckoo rollers) is probably close to the Coracidae (rollers) of Africa and Eurasia.

The Maximal Bird. What is the largest size a bird's egg can reach? The question is not as ridiculous as it sounds, because definite structural and physical problems are involved. The larger the egg, the thicker the shell must be to prevent breakage. The thicker the shell, the greater the difficulty for the chick which must peck its way out. The limits an egg can reach and still serve its function can be roughly calculated. These limits also indirectly control the maximum size birds can reach, for the embryo and its food supply has a certain minimum size, and a bird must complete a certain portion of its growth within the egg, and not hatch too young. The maximum limits for egg size and body size in birds were reached by the elephant bird, *Aepyornis* (16–9). *Aepyornis* eggs are the shape of an American football, but somewhat larger: they have a capacity of two gallons. Their shells are thick and extremely durable. Although the elephant birds have been extinct for several centuries, eggshell fragments are common, especially in the dry parts of Madagascar, and a number of entire eggs of *Aepyornis* are in existence. *Aepyornis* was perhaps not quite as tall as the giant moa *Dinornis* (14–4), but it had coarser legs, heavier bones, and outweighed the largest of the moas, in all likelihood. Estimates of the weight of the elephant birds suggest that some individuals reached one thousand pounds.

Aepyornis may have been the victim of hunting by the Malagasies, but perhaps more particularly of the changing climate. Like the moas, *Aepyornis* may have survived the Pleistocene, but greatly "weakened" in the process. It survived into historical time, if one can believe the many legends still current in Madagascar. The elephant birds in some fashion may have given rise to the Arabian Nights legend of the roc, which was supposed, however, to have been a flying bird. A second genus of Madagascar elephant birds, *Mullerornis,* did not survive as long as *Aepyornis* did.

REPTILES IN RESIDENCE

If Madagascar's fauna is relatively poor in mammals, it is relatively rich in reptiles. These range from chameleons to crocodiles. Turtles are well represented, including an endemic genus (*Erymnochelys*).

Especially annoying to biogeographers is the presence of iguanas. Iguanas are inescapably a characteristically American family of lizards. To be sure, an iguanid (*Brachylophus*) has mysteriously reached Fiji and Tonga, on which islands the genus is endemic. But how to explain that two iguanid genera exist on Madagascar? *Chalarodon,* from the dry southwest of the island, and *Oplurus,* with six species, are living evidence that the iguanids did reach Madagascar. The best explanation seems to be that iguanas are a very ancient group of reptiles which have been extinguished on the African and Eurasian mainland, but managed,

16–9. The elephant bird *Aepyornis* is the heavyweight among the world's giant flightless birds (the scale represents one foot). *Aepyornis* became extinct only in relatively recent times.

during their tenure there, to reach what were to become refuge islands for them and other creatures, Fiji and Madagascar, before they died out on the mainland.

Geckos of Madagascar have had sufficient time to differentiate, and some zoologists have regarded the endemic genus *Uroplatus* as worthy of its own family, separate from Gekkonidae. Skinks are represented by eleven genera, five endemic. One of these (*Grandidierina*) lacks front legs and has various degrees in loss of rear legs, including absence—perhaps for the reasons suggested in Chapter 7.

Among snakes, three families (Typhlopidae, Boidae, and Colubridae) are present. Madagascar has a surprising number of native frogs; they belong to the families Ranidae, Dendrobatidae, and Brevicipitidae.

Worthy of a footnote to any account of Madagascar's land vertebrates is the very ancient walking fish, the coelocanth *Latimeria*. As a marine fish, this reptile-like "living fossil" is beyond the scope of this book, but one can note, for whatever the implication is worth, that *Latimeria* is known only from waters around northern Madagascar and the Comoro Islands.

A FOREST OF COMPLICATIONS

Add Madagascar's relative closeness to the African mainland, a closeness greater long ago, to the great dispersibility of flowering plants and the result is a very rich flora. Add a long isolation to this, and the result is a roster of endemic species (by far the majority of native ones), dozens of endemic genera, even four endemic families.

Madagascar's forests are too complicated for anyone to summarize simply. There are just too many kinds of plants. Apparently these forests cannot even be summarized in a lengthy fashion easily. Although various books tell of particular regions or particular families, no volume really leads us through the forests, nothing approaches a guide book. It is probably too soon to ask for such a thing. Discoveries are still occurring.

The Vegetable Antiques. Perhaps the most startling discovery came in 1957. Botanists had not, before that time, suspected that Madagascar harbored any members of that fabulously primitive family of flowering plants, Winteraceae. A species of *Bubbia* (see 13–8) came to light in the Madagascar forests. The nearest *Bubbia?* In New Guinea, a third of the world away. This jump in distribution is quite fantastic—unless we remember that it is paralleled by other such patterns. *Bubbia* probably once extended across mainland Africa and Asia, and is today as much a relict as the lemurs and Madagascar's iguanas.

Where one such relict occurs, many others are likely to occur also. In the case of Madagascar, the others are not so spectacularly primitive. There are a series of genera and families which could be said to center around the tea (camellia) family (Theaceae) or the linden family (Tiliaceae). These plants have numerous stamens, large bunches of them in fact. Sepals and petals in these families are in cycles, but they fold over each other, shingle-fashion, and each petal or sepal is separate, not united with its neighbors. Carpels are cyclic and united, and can be many or as few as two. The storage of food in seeds is mostly in a special tissue (endosperm), not in the embryo itself, and this condition is regarded as primitive among flowering plants by botanists. Woods of these families often look rather primitive.

Two families of these camellia-like relicts have been mentioned in Chapter 13—New Caledonia's Strasburgeriaceae and Medusagynaceae from the Seychelles Islands, not far from Madagascar. Two more families of this alliance are endemic to Madagascar: Sarcolaenaceae and Sphaerosepalaceae (also known as Rhopalocarpaceae).

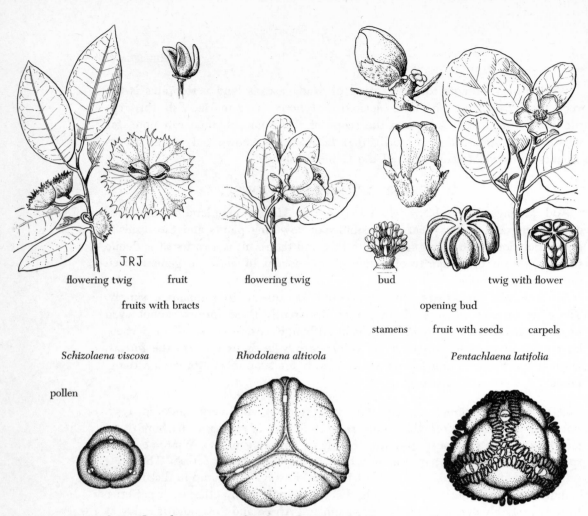

flowering twig   fruit   flowering twig   bud   twig with flower

fruits with bracts   opening bud

stamens   fruit with seeds   carpels

Schizolaena viscosa   *Rhodolaena altivola*   *Pentachlaena latifolia*

pollen

16–10. Sarcolaenaceae, a family endemic to Madagascar, offers many intricate evolutionary puzzles. Its pollen grains, formed as quartets, are probably the most elaborate in flowering plants.

The family Sarcolaenaceae (16–10) is a very distinctive member of the camellia- or linden-alliance of families. It consists of eight genera and thirty-three species. They form another case of adaptive radiation, because the family ranges from trees in coastal sand dunes (*Sarcolaena eriophora*) and a shrub in sandy plains (*Leptolaena arenaria*) to trees of moister woodlands (*Rhodolaena*). They appear particularly successful in dry forests, which cover a large portion of the island.

The family Sarcolaenaceae has many interesting series of features which are not easy to interpret. One by which most of the genera can be distinguished from each other is the nature of bracts—appendages which can form a broad leafy flange beneath the flowers, as in *Schizolaena* (16–10, left), or can be absent, as in *Rhodolaena* (center) or vestigial, as in *Pentachlaena* (16–10, right) or can even be a woody cup beneath each flower (*Xyloolaena*). Sarcolaenaceae

shoot in flower   flower cut lengthwise   flower

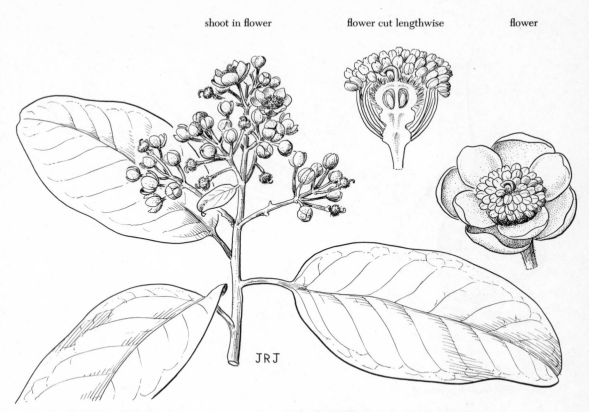

JRJ

16–11. *Rhopalocarpus madagascariensis* is a tree belonging to a family found on Madagascar exclusively. It may be a remnant of an alliance which includes camellias or lindens.

are unusual in that pollen grains are shed in groups of four. This can be seen easily in *Schizolaena* (16–10), but the foursomes become progressively more specialized in the other genera, amalgamated so that they look like a single large grain, either smooth and grooved, as in *Rhodolaena,* or knobbily ornamented, as in *Pentachlaena.*

The other family of this general alliance is Sphaerosepalaceae, formed of two genera and fourteen species. *Rhopalocarpus* (16–11) is a tree with large leaves, looking much like many other forest trees. The flowers appear quite camellia-like. The number four is the key to this family—four petals within four sepals. Another peculiar feature of the family Sphaerosepalaceae is the peculiar nature of the embryos. The pair of leaves are intricately folded into fringed and folded segments tightly folded within the seeds.

The Oversimplified. The problems posed by plants altered by evolution on islands are demonstrated by *Didymeles* (16–12). Traditionally, this genus has

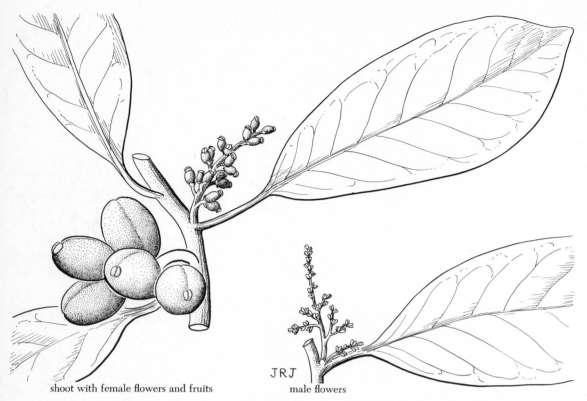

shoot with female flowers and fruits   male flowers

16–12. Simplified flower structure has made *Didymeles madagascariensis* a plant difficult to classify. Should it be put in a family by itself?

been put in a family by itself. This is the easy way to treat a problem. The more difficult, but more rewarding solution would be to find relationships for this plant. *Didymeles* gives little assistance at first glance, because it is so highly simplified. Female plants have flowers lacking petals—just a pair of united carpels, which mature into egg-shaped fruits. Male plants have flowers which amount to little more than stamens strung along twigs. This excessively reduced structure persuaded botanists that *Didymeles* belonged with plants equally simple in flower structure, like the pepper of commerce (*Piper*). Actually, the pollen grains put an end to this illusion. Pollen grains of *Didymeles* have the same peculiarities as those of *Breynia*, a genus of the spurge family, Euphorbiaceae. This family often has highly simplified flowers like those of *Didymeles*. The relationships clearly lie in this direction, and the only question which remains is whether *Didymeles* is worthy of remaining in a separate family or whether it should join Euphorbiaceae. As with so many other plants, a great deal more must be learned about *Didymeles* and about its relatives.

16–13. The "traveler's palm," *Ravenala madagascariensis,* is actually not a palm but is more closely related to the banana. The perfectly symmetrical fan of leaves has become a common sight throughout the tropics because this tree, endemic to Madagascar, has been cultivated widely as an ornamental. (Chicago Natural History Museum photo.)

Also in the Forest. Does Madagascar resemble other islands in having tree members of the sunflower family (Compositae)? Yes, and this is interesting because both Africa and Asia are relatively poor in trees belonging to this family. Madagascar offers other riches, such as a multitude of orchids. Among these is the curious "foot-and-a-half" flowered orchid *Angraecum* (10–20). Near streams in eastern Madagascar is the unusual "travelers' palm" *Ravenala* (16–13). Not a palm, but a relative of the African "bird of paradise" flower *Strelitzia,* this tree bears a single flat spray of leaves. The tubular leaf bases collect water during rains; this water remains trapped and can, according to legend, be tapped for drinking water by a desperate traveler.

Deserts Available. With one minor exception, cacti are entirely restricted to the New World. Dry regions of Africa are rich in plants belonging to various families which look like cacti in form and succulence. Some of them are remarkable mimics. The same desert conditions which have inspired evolution

 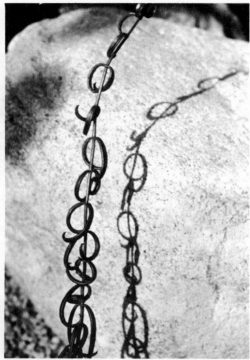

16–14. *Kalanchoë beharensis* (left) is a "miniature tree" with large, hairy leaves. Representing another extreme among Madagascar kalanchoes is *K. beauverdii* (right), a climbing succulent in which curled leaves serve like tendrils, catching on leaves and stems of other plants as it grows upward.

of cacti in the dry regions of the Americas have driven other families into these endeavors in Africa and Madagascar. One group which has an interesting array of succulent forms in drier Madagascar is *Kalanchoë*. One of these is *K. beharensis* (16–14), which has leaves up to two feet long. The leaves are wavy in form and are covered with grayish or rusty-colored hairs which form a felt. *Kalanchoë beharensis* becomes a small tree, one which probably would be ill-suited to the African mainland, where herbivorous animals would surely find it suitable fare. Other Kalanchoes on Madagascar include shrubby, herbaceous, and even one vining species, *K. beauverdii* (16–14).

The real evolutionary achievement within the desert-like regions of Madagascar, however, is the family Didiereaceae. The relationships of this family, long misunderstood, now prove to be with portulacas, mesembryanthemums, and, more distantly, the cacti. Didiereaceae (16–15 to 16–18) superficially look like cacti, but have evolved entirely independently of that great group.

Illustrating some of the ways in which Didiereaceae may have begun are

16–15. *Alluaudiopsis marnieriana*, left, has flowers which reveal that the family to which it belongs, Didiereaceae, may be related to portulacas. *Decaryia madagascariensis* at right is a shrubby representative of this family and has zigzag branches. (Photograph by Werner Rauh.)

16–16. Weird growth forms have evolved in the family Didiereaceae to suit the desert conditions of southwestern Madagascar: *Alluaudia procera*, left, bears fascicles or huge branches, whereas *A. montagnacii*, right, is little branched. Bunches of flowers at the tips of branches look like moss at a distance. The photos of branch tips of the two species, below, indicate the small, thick leaves in longitudinal rows between rows of spines. (Photograph by Werner Rauh.)

16–17. *Didierea madagascariensis* is a fountain-shaped desert shrub. According to the season, leaves are present or absent (below). Plants bear either male flowers (above, right) or female flowers (center, right). (Photograph by Werner Rauh.)

16–18. *Didierea trollii* has different growth forms in different localities, as two of these photographs indicate. Narrow leaves form rosettes on the spiny stems. (Photograph by Werner Rauh.)

Alluaudiopsis and *Decaryia* (16–15). The flowers of *Alluaudiopsis* look like those of portulacas. Like all other members of this family, this genus has both male and female plants. This feature proved confusing to botanists, who have tended to compare Didiereaceae to other families in which sexes are separated, but Didiereaceae have evolved this condition independently of those other families.

Decaryia is a shrub, reaching eighteen feet in height. It is, at first glance, not particularly different from thorny shrubs to be found in deserts all over the world. *Decaryia* has, however, distinctive zigzag branches. On either side of each leaf is a short spine. Flowers emerge from shoots above the leaf and between the spine, as seen also in *Alluaudiopsis*.

Alluaudia (16–16) shows a world of difference in form. Like tall, limp candles, the sparingly branched stalks of *Alluaudia* rise above the desert scrub. Branches are very thick and although succulent, tough as well. Spines are formed not in pairs, but singly. The large spine is formed above a tiny leaf. This leaf soon wilts, yielding to a tiny shoot which usually bears a pair of leaves. These leaf-blades are usually oriented vertically, forming lines up the stem, counterpointing the thorns. Species of *Alluaudia* can be recognized by leaf shape: *A. montagnacii* has heart-shaped leaves, *A. procera* oval ones. These two species also differ in growth form: *A. montagnacii* branches very little, *A. procera* forms a narrow fountain of stems. *Alluaudia* flowers are borne on small shoots at the summit of the tree, looking like some sort of mistletoe.

Didierea (16–17, 16–18) has a maximal spininess. The broad spray of thick branches can form small trees. On each stem, short-lived leaves are found, and above each, a spine. This spine is the first one to be borne on a short lateral spiny shoot. On young plants, these spiny offshoots are seated on a long base. During the wet season, leaves form on the short shoots, disappearing when the ground dries.

When adult, *Didierea* plants can flower. Flowers form in tight clusters instead of leaves on the spiny lateral shoots. On female plants, the flowers are larger and egg-shaped. Male flowers are smaller and funnel-shaped.

Plants of *Didierea* take varied and fantastic shapes. *Didierea trollii* (16–18) can form spreading trees with long branches, bent as though windswept. In other localities, the same species becomes cactus-like, branched at the base, with some branches erect, others sprawling. The varied growth forms of the Didiereaceae suggest a press toward treehood, however devious or seemingly awkward. Ancestors of Didiereaceae—like the ancestors of *Kalanchoë beharensis* —were undoubtedly much smaller plants, probably herbs. Development of large woody plants in these groups is to some degree a participation in the phenomenon of gigantism which has overtaken so many island creatures.

THE ALL-INCLUSIVE ISLAND

That this chapter should begin with ancient creatures of wet forests, the lemurs, and end with bizarre cactus-like desert plants is appropriate. Madagascar is a varied world in itself. Time and isolation in generous measure have produced a flora and a fauna with a full gamut of form and habit. Mingled into Madagascar life are all of the phenomena of island life: adaptive radiation, flightlessness, gigantism and dwarfism, peculiar mechanisms, relictism, endemism, vulnerability, and extinction.

Madagascar remains the unknown island, full of biological riches. The Galápagos remind one of a textbook in evolution, showing us with simplicity and clarity the equations and principles that organisms follow in their relentless diversification. Madagascar reminds one of a large and lengthy history book, filled with hundreds of characters, from which many of the earlier pages are missing. In just such a fashion have some of the stories of Madagascar's ancient and strange animals and plants been long lost, deep in forests, forests themselves changed by evolution's perpetual turnover.

References

THESE books and papers are those which were used in the preparation of this book. Some are unpretentious, delightful works which anyone would enjoy; others are highly technical. Some contain much more information worth reading than could be summarized in this book. To make this further reading easier for you, the following symbols are for your convenience:

G = of general interest, as easily understood by lay readers as by scientists; may contain some detailed information, but offers much to a reader of unspecialized background. Books and papers in this category are often available in public libraries or through bookstores.

T = technical, contains formal descriptions *but* many of these are lucidly and well written and contain much interesting and readable information on habits, etc. Books and papers in this category are not in general circulation but can be obtained in university and museum libraries. Some of these are museum publications which are still in print and can be purchased directly from the publishing institution.

I = illustrated by good photographs or drawings of animals or plants. This symbol is used for books and papers which contain habit pictures, not anatomical details only.

Chapter 1

G, I   Beebe, William L. *Galápagos— World's End.* New York: G. P. Putnam's Sons (1924).

G, I   ————*The Arcturus Adventure.* New York: G. P. Putnam's Sons (1926).

T   Briggs, John C. "The East Pacific Barrier and the Distribution of shore fishes." *Evolution* 15: 545–54 (1961).

T   Constance, L., Heckard, L., Chambers, K. L., Ornduff, R., and Raven, P. H. "Amphitropical Relations in the Herbaceous Flora of the Pacific Coast of North and South America": a symposium. *Quarterly Review of Biology* 38: 109–77 (1963).

T   Darlington, Philip J., Jr. "Carabidae of Mountains and Islands: Data on the Evolution of Isolated Faunas, and on Atrophy of Wings." *Ecological Monographs* 13: 37–61 (1943).

G   Darwin, Charles. *On the Origin of Species* (1859). Various editions available.

T   Gulick, Addison. "Biological Peculiarities of Oceanic Islands." *Quarterly Review of Biology* 7: 405–27 (1932).

T   Hedberg, Olov. "Afroalpine Vascular Plants." *Symbolae Botanicae Upsalienses* 15(1): 1–411 (1957).

T, I   May, Brenda M. "New Zealand Cave Fauna. II—The Limestone Caves between Port Waikato and Piopio Districts." *Trans. Roy. Soc. New Zealand,* Zoology 3: 181–204 (1963).

G   Wallace, Alfred R. *Island Life.* London: The Macmillan Company (1880).

REFERENCES

Chapter 2

T Brattstrom, Bayard H. "Bárcena Volcano, 1952. Its Effect on the Flora and Fauna of San Benedicto I., Mexico." In J. L. Gressitt, ed., *Pacific Basin Biogeography*, pp. 499–524. Honolulu: Bishop Museum Press (1963).

T Brown, W. H., Merrill, E. D., and Yates, H. S. "The Revegetation of Volcano Island, Luzon, Philippine Islands, since the Eruption of Taal Volcano in 1911." *Philippine Journal of Science*, Sect. C, Vol. 12 (1919).

T Dammermann, K. W. "The Fauna of Krakatau, 1883–1933." *Koninklijke Nederlandsche Akademie Wetenschappen Verhandelingen* 44: 1–594 (1948).

G Darlington, Philip J. *Zoogeography*. New York: John Wiley & Sons (1957).

T Docters van Leeuwen, W. M. "Krakatau, 1883–1933." *Annales Jardin Botanique Buitenzorg* 46–47; 1–506 (1936).

T Falla, R. A. "Oceanic Birds as Dispersal Agents." *Proceedings of the Royal Society*, Ser. B, Biology 152: 655–59 (1960).

T Fosberg, F. Raymond. "Plant Dispersal in the Pacific." In J. L. Gressitt, ed., *Pacific Basin Biogeography*, pp. 273–82. Honolulu: Bishop Museum Press (1963).

T, I Gressitt, J. Linsey. "Problems in the Zoogeography of Pacific and Antarctic Insects." *Pacific Insects Monograph* 2. Honolulu: Bishop Museum Press (1961).

G Guppy, H. B. "Observations of a Naturalist in the Pacific between 1891 and 1899." Vol. 2, *Plant, Dispersal*. London: The Macmillan Company (1906).

T Matthew, W. D. "Climate and Evolution." *Annals of the New York Academy of Sciences* 24: 171–318 (1915); reprinted (1939) as Special Publication of the New York Academy of Sciences No. 1.

G, I Munro, George C. *Birds of Hawaii*, 2nd ed. Ridgeway Press (1960).

T Rand, Austin L. "The Origin of the Land Birds of Tristan da Cunha." *Fieldiana* (Zoology) 37: 139–66 (1955).

T Rick, Charles M., and Bowman, Robert I. "Galápagos Tomatoes and Tortoises." *Evolution* 15; 407–17 (1961).

T, I Ridley, Henry N. *The Dispersal of Plants throughout the World*. Ashford, England: L. Reeve & Co. (1930).

T Simpson, George G. "Probabilities of Dispersal in Geologic Time." *Amer. Mus. Nat. Hist. Bull.* 99: 163–76 (1952).

T Skottsberg, Carl. "Plant Succession on Recent Lava Flows in the Island of Hawaii." *Göteborgs Vetensk.-o-Vitt.-Samh. Handl.*, Ser. B, 1(8): 1–32 (1941).

T Stephens, S. G. "Factors Affecting Seed Dispersal in *Gossypium*." *North Carolina Agric. Exper. Stat. Tech. Bull.* 131: 1–32 (1958).

T Yoshimoto, C. M., and Gressitt, J. L. "Trapping of Air-borne Insects on the Pacific." *Pacific Insects* 3(4): 556–58 (1961).

G, I Zimmerman, Elwood C. *Insects of Hawaii. Introduction.* Honolulu: University of Hawaii Press (1948).

Chapter 3

T, I Allorge, P., and collaborators. *Histoire du Peuplement de la Corse.* (a collection of papers comprising Vol. 1 of Memoires de la Société de Biogéographie). Paris. Paul Lechevalier. 1926.

T, I Allorge, P., and collaborators. *Contribution à l'Étude du Peuplement des Iles Atlantides* (a collection of papers comprising Vol. 8 of Memoires de la Société de Biogéographie). Paris. Paul Lechevalier. 1946.

T Axelrod, Daniel. "The Evolution of Flowering Plants." In S. Tax, ed., *Evolution after Darwin*. Chicago: University of Chicago Press (1960).

T Barbour, Thomas. "A Contribution to the Zoogeography of the West Indies, with Especial Reference to Amphibians and Reptiles." *Mus. Compar. Zool. (Harvard) Mem.* 44: 209–359 (1914).

T, I Berland, L. and collaborators. *Contribution à l'Étude du Peuplement Zoologique et Botanique des Iles du Pacifique*. (a collection of papers comprising Vol. 4 of Memoires de la Société de Biogéographie). Paris. Paul Lechevalier. 1934.

G, I Blackwall, William. *How to Know the Western Australian Wildflowers*. Pts. 1 and 2 (edited and revised by B. J. Grieve). Perth: University of Western Australia Press (1954, 1956).

T Blake, S. F., and Atwood, Alice C. "Geographical Guide to Floras of the World, Part I." *U. S. Dept. Agric. Misc. Publ.* 401 (1942).

T, I Chilton, Charles, and collaborators. *The Subantarctic Islands of New Zealand*. Wellington: New Zealand Government Printer (1909).

T Chubb, Lawrence J. "Geology of Galápagos, Cocos and Easter Islands." *Bishop Museum Bull.* 110: 1–67 (1933).

T, I Colom, G. *Biogeographica de las Baleares*. Palma de Mallorca. Estudio General Luliano. (1958).

T Amadon, Dean. "Avian Systematics and Evolution in the Gulf of Guinea." *Amer. Mus. Nat. Hist. Bull.* 100: 399–451 (1953).

T Andrews, Charles W., et al. *A Monograph of Christmas Island*. London: British Museum (1900).

G Darlington, Philip J. *Zoogeography*. New York: John Wiley & Sons (1957).

G Dickerson, Roy E., and collaborators. "Distribution of Life in the Philippines." *Philippine Bureau of Sciences Monograph* 21 (1928).

T Durham, J. Wyatt. "Paleogeographical Conclusions in Light of Biological Data." In J. L. Gressitt, ed., *Pacific Basin Biogeography*, pp. 355–65. Honolulu: Bishop Museum Press (1963).

G, I Elton, Charles S. *The Ecology of Invasions by Animals and Plants*. New York: John Wiley & Sons (1958).

T Exell, Arthur W. *Catalogue of the Vascular Plants of S. Tomé*. London: British Museum (1944).

T Falla, R. A. "Oceanic Birds as Dispersal Agents." *Proceedings of the Royal Society*, Ser. B, Biology 152: 655–59 (1960).

T, I Fosberg, F. Raymond. "The Vegetation of Micronesia." *Amer. Mus. Nat. Hist. Bull.* 119: 1–75 (1960).

T Gressitt, J. Linsey. *Insects of Micronesia. Introduction*. Honolulu: Bishop Museum Press (1954).

T Hamilton, Terrell, and Ira Rubinoff. "Isolation, Endemism and Multiplication of Species in the Darwin Finches." *Evolution* 17: 388–403 (1963).

T Hamilton, Terrell, et al. "Species Abundance: Natural Regulation of Insular Variation." *Science* 142: 1575–77 (1963).

T Inger, Robert F. "Systematics and Zoogeography of Philippine Amphibia." *Fieldiana (Zoology)* 33: 185–531 (1954).

G, I Keast, Allen. *Some Bush Birds of Australia*. Brisbane: The Jacaranda Press (1960).

T ———, et al., eds. *Biogeography and Ecology in Australia*. The Hague: W. Junk (1959).

G, I Leach, J. A. *An Australian Bird Book*. Melbourne: Whitcombe & Tombs Pty. Ltd. (1958).

T Lindroth, Carl H. "The Aleutian Islands as a Route for Dispersal across the North Pacific." In J. L. Gressitt, ed., *Pacific Basin Biogeography*, pp. 121–31. Honolulu: Bishop Museum Press (1963).

T   MacArthur, Robert H., and Wilson, Edward O. "An Equilibrium Theory of Insular Zoogeography." *Evolution* 17: 373–87 (1963).

G, I   McKeown, Keith C. *Australian Spiders*, 2nd ed. Sydney: Angus & Robertson (1952).

G, I   McPhee, David R. *Some Common Snakes and Lizards of Australia*, 2nd ed. Brisbane: The Jacaranda Press (1963).

G, I   Marlow, Basil J. *Marsupials of Australia*. Brisbane: The Jacaranda Press (1962).

T   Mayr, Ernst, ed. "The Problem of Land Connections across the South Atlantic, with Special Reference to the Mesozoic." *Amer. Mus. Nat. Hist. Bull.* 99: 85–258 (1952).

G, I   Melliss, John C. *St. Helena.* London: L. Reeve & Co. (1875).

T   Merrill, Elmer D. "A Discussion and Enumeration of Philippine Flowering Plants." *Philippine Bureau of Science Popular Bulletin* 2 (1926).

T   ———. "A Botanical Bibliography of the Islands of the Pacific." *Contrib. U. S. Nat. Herbarium* 30(1): 1–404 (1947).

T, I   Paramonov, S. J. "Lord Howe Island, a Riddle of the Pacific." *Pacific Science* 12: 83–91; 14: 75–85; 17: 361–73 (1958, 1960, 1963).

T   Raven, Henry C. "Wallace's Line and the Distribution of Indo-Australian Mammals." *Amer. Mus. Nat. Hist. Bull.* 68: 179–283 (1935).

T, I   Skottsberg, Carl, ed. *The Natural History of Juan Fernandez and Easter Island.* Stockholm: Almqvist & Wiksell (1953).

T   Smith, A. C. "Phanerogam Genera with Distributions Terminating in Fiji." *Jour. Arnold Arboretum* 36: 273–92 (1955).

T   Tatewaki, Misao. "Phytogeography of the Islands of the North Pacific." In J. L. Gressit, ed., *Pacific Basin Biogeography*, pp. 23–28. Honolulu: Bishop Museum Press (1963).

T   Taylor, E. H. "Philippine Land Mammals." *Philippine Bureau of Science Monograph* 30 (1934).

T   Thorne, Robert F. "Biotic Distribution Patterns in the Tropical Pacific." In J. L. Gressitt, ed., *Pacific Basin Biogeography*, pp. 311–50. Honolulu: Bishop Museum Press (1963).

G, I   Troughton, Ellis. *Furred Animals of Australia.* New York: Charles Scribner's Sons (1947).

G   Wallace, Alfred R. *Island Life.* London: The Macmillan Company (1880).

G   ———. *The Malay Archipelago.* New York: Harper Brothers (1885).

G, I   Whitley, Gilbert P. *Native Freshwater Fishes of Australia.* Brisbane: The Jacaranda Press (1960).

G, I   Zimmerman, Elwood C. *Insects of Hawaii. Introduction.* Honolulu: University of Hawaii Press (1948).

Chapter 4

T   Bailey, Donald W. "Re-examination of the Diversity in *Partula taeniata*." *Evolution* 10: 360–366. 1956.

T   Berry, R. J. "The Evolution of an Island Population of the House Mouse." *Evolution* 18: 468–483. 1964.

T, I   Crampton, H. E. "Studies on the Variation, Distribution and Evolution of the Genus *Partula*." *Carnegie Institution of Washington Publication* 228 (1916).

T, I   ———. "Contemporaneous Differentiation in the Species of *Partula* Living on Moorea, Society Islands." *American Naturalist* 59: 5–35 (1925).

T, I   ———. "Studies on the Variation, Distribution and Evolution of the Genus *Partula*, the Species Inhabiting Moorea." *Carnegie Institution of Washington Publication* 410 (1932).

G, I Grant, Verne. *The Origin of Adaptations*. New York: Columbia University Press (1963).

T Lowe, Charles H., Jr. "An Evolutionary Study of Island Faunas in the Gulf of California, Mexico, with a Method for Comparative Analysis." *Evolution* 9: 339–344. 1955.

T Rattenbury, J. A. "Cyclic Hybridization as a Survival Mechanism in the New Zealand Forest Flora." *Evolution* 16: 348–63 (1962).

G Simpson, George G. *The Major Features of Evolution*. New York: Columbia University Press (1953).

T Wheeler, Bernice. "Comparison of the Block Island 'Species' of *Microtus* with *M. pennsylvanicus*." *Evolution* 10: 176–186 (1956).

Compar. Zool. (Harvard) Bull. 123(8): 305–495 (1961).

T, I Keck, David D. "The Hawaiian Silverswords: Systematics, Affinities and Phytogeographic Problems of the Genus *Argyroxiphium*." *Occasional Pap. Bishop Mus.* 11(19): 1–38 (1936).

T, I Rock, Joseph F. "A Monographic Study of the Hawaiian Species of the Tribe Lobelioideae, Family Campanulaceae." *Bishop Mus. Memoirs* 7(2): 1–394 (1919).

T, I ———. "Some New Hawaiian Lobelioids." *Occasional Pap. Bishop Mus.* 22(5): 35–66 (1957).

T ———. "Hawaiian Lobelioids." *Occasional Pap. Bishop Mus.* 23(5): 65–75 (1962).

T, I ——— and Neal, Marie C. "A New Variety of Silversword." *Occasional Pap. Bishop Mus.* 22(4): 32–34 (1957).

Chapter 5

T, I Amadon, Dean. "The Hawaiian honeycreepers (Aves, Drepaniidae)." *Amer. Mus. Nat. Hist. Bull.* 95: 157–62 (1950).

T Baldwin, Paul H. "Annual Cycle, Environment and Evolution in the Hawaiian Honeycreepers (Aves: Drepaniidae)." *Univ. Calif. Publ. Zool.* 52: 285–398 (1953).

T Carlquist, S. "Leaf Anatomy and Ontogeny in *Argyroxiphium* and *Wilkesia*." *Amer. Jour. Bot.* 44: 696–705 (1957).

T ———. "Vegetative Anatomy of *Dubautia*, *Argyroxiphium* and *Wilkesia*." *Pacific Science* 13: 195–210 (1959).

T, I ———. "Studies on Madinae: Anatomy, Cytology, and Evolutionary Relationships." *Aliso* 4: 171–236 (1959).

T Keast, Allen. "Bird Speciation on the Australian Continent." *Mus.*

Chapter 6

G, I Bergamini, David, et al. *The Land and Wildlife of Australia*. New York: Time, Inc. (1964).

G, I Fleay, David. "The Rare Dasyures (Native Cats)." *Victorian Naturalist* 49: 63–68 (1932).

G, I ———. "The Pygmy Flying Possum." *Victorian Naturalist* 49: 165–71 (1932).

G, I ———. "A Beautiful Phalanger." *Victorian Naturalist* 50: 35–40 (1933).

G, I ———. "The Greater Flying Phalanger." *Victorian Naturalist* 50: 135–142 (1933).

T Glaessner, M. F. "Isolation and Communication in the Geological History of the Australian Fauna." In Leeper, G. W., ed., *The Evolution of Living Organisms*. Parksville, Victoria: Melbourne University Press (1962).

G, I Harper, Francis. *Extinct and Vanishing Mammals of the Old*

World. New York: American Committee for International Wildlife Protection (1945).

G, I Le Souef, A. S., and Burrell, Harry. *The Wild Animals of Australasia.* London: G. Harrap & Co. (1926).

G, I Marlow, Basil. *Marsupials of Australia.* Brisbane: The Jacaranda Press (1962).

T Raven, Henry C., and Gregory, William K. "Adaptive Branching of the Kangaroo Family in Relation to Habitat." *Amer. Mus. Nat. Hist. Novitates* 1309: 1–33 (1946).

T Ride, W. D. L. "On the Evolution of Australian Marsupials." In G. W. Leeper, ed., *The Evolution of Living Organisms.* Parksville, Victoria: Melbourne University Press (1962).

T Simpson, George G. "Historical Zoogeography of Australian Mammals." *Evolution* 15: 431–46 (1961).

T Tate, G. H. "The Marsupial Genus *Phalanger.*" *Amer. Mus. Nat. Hist. Novitates* 1283: 1–41 (1945).

T ———. "The Marsupial Genus *Pseudocheirus* and Its Subgenera." *Amer. Mus. Nat. Hist. Novitates* 1287: 1–30 (1945).

T ———. "Notes on the Squirrel-like and Mouse-like possums (Marsupialia)." *Amer. Mus. Nat. Hist. Novitates* 1305: 1–12 (1945).

T ———. "On the Anatomy and Classification of the Dasyuridae (Marsupialia)." *Amer. Mus. Nat. Hist. Bull.* 88: 97–156 (1947).

T ———. "Studies on the Anatomy and Phylogeny of the Macropodidae (Marsupialia)." *Amer. Mus. Nat. Hist. Bull.* 91: 237–351 (1948).

T ———. "Studies in the Peramelidae (Marsupialia)." *Amer. Mus. Nat. Hist. Bull.* 92: 317–46 (1948).

T ———. "The Banded Anteater, *Myrmecobius* Waterhouse (Marsupialia)." *Amer. Mus. Nat. Hist. Novitates* 1521: 1–8 (1951).

T ———. "The Wombats (Marsupialia, Phascolomyidae)." *Amer. Mus. Nat. Hist. Novitates* 1525: 1–18 (1951).

G, I Troughton, Ellis. *Furred Animals of Australia.* New York: Charles Scribner's Sons (1947).

T ———. "The Marsupial Fauna: Its Origin and Radiation." In A. Keast, et al., eds., *Biogeography and Ecology in Australia.* The Hague: W. Junk (1959).

Chapter 7

G, I Attenborough, David. *Zoo Quest for a Dragon.* London: Lutterworth Press (1957).

T Barbour, Thomas. "A Contribution to the Zoogeography of the East Indian Islands." *Mus. Compar. Zool. (Harvard) Mem.* 44(1): 1–203 (1912).

T ———. "A Contribution to the Zoogeography of the West Indies, with Especial Reference to Amphibians and Reptiles." *Mus. Compar. Zool. (Harvard) Mem.* 44(2): 209–358 (1914).

T, I ———. "*Sphaerodactylus.*" *Mus. Compar. Zool. (Harvard) Mem.* 47(3): 217–78 (1921).

T, I ——— and Ramsden, Charles T. "The Herpetology of Cuba." *Mus. Compar. Zool. (Harvard) Mem.* 47(2): 73–213 (1918).

G, I Burden, W. Douglas. *Dragon Lizards of Komodo.* New York: G. P. Putnam's Sons (1927).

T, I Cooke, C. Montague, Jr., and Kondo, Yoshio. "Revision of Tornatellidae and Achatinellidae (Gastropoda, Pulmonata)." *Bishop Mus. Bull.* 221: 1–303 (1960).

G, I Dickerson, Roy E., et al. *Distribution of Life in the Philippines.* Manila: Bureau of Printing (1928).

T Dunn, Emmett R. "Notes on *Varanus komodoensis.*" *Amer. Mus. Nat. Hist. Novitates* 286: 1–10 (1927).

G, I Gillsäter, Sven. *We Ended in Bali.* London: George Allen & Unwin (1961).

G, I Grandidier, G., and Petit, G. *Zoologie de Madagascar*. Paris: Société d'Éditions Geographiques, Maritimes et Coloniales (1932).

T Hecht, Max K. "Natural Selection in the Lizard Genus *Aristelliger*." *Evolution* 6: 112–24 (1952).

T Kenny, Julian, et al. "The Anoles of the Eastern Caribbean (Sauria, Iguanidae)." *Mus. Compar. Zool. (Harvard) Bull.* 121: 187–226 (1959).

G, I Klingel, Gilbert C. *The Ocean Island (Inagua)*. New York: Doubleday & Company, Inc. (1961).

T, I Kramer, Gustav. "Body Proportions of Mainland and Island Lizards." *Evolution* 5: 193–206 (1951).

G Loveridge, Arthur. *Reptiles of the Pacific World*. New York: the Macmillan Company (1946).

G, I McPhee, David R. *Some Common Snakes and Lizards of Australia*, 2nd ed. Brisbane: The Jacaranda Press (1963).

T, I Mertens, Robert. "Die Insel-Reptilien, ihre Ausbreitung, Variation, und Artbildung." *Zoologica* 32(6): 1–209 (1934).

T ———. "Die Inseleidechsen des Golfes von Salerno." *Senckenbergiana Biologica* 42: 31–40 (1961).

T, I ———. "Der Eidechsenschwanz als Haftorgan." *Senckenbergiana Biologica* 45: 117–122 (1964).

T, I Rooij, Nelly de. *The Reptiles of the Indo-Australian Archipelago*. Leiden: E. J. Brill (1915, 1917).

T, I Tillyard, R. J. *The Insects of Australia and New Zealand*. Sydney: Angus & Robertson (1926).

T, I Van Denburgh, John. "The Gigantic Land Tortoises of the Galápagos Archipelago." *Proceed. Calif. Acad. Sci.*, 4th Ser., 2: 203–374 (1914).

T, I ———. *The Reptiles of Western North America*. San Francisco: California Academy of Sciences (1922).

T Williams, Ernest. "*Testudo cubensis* and the Evolution of Western Hemisphere Tortoises." *Amer. Mus. Nat. Hist. Bull.* 95: 1–36 (1950).

T ———. "A New Fossil Tortoise from Mona Island, West Indies." *Amer. Mus. Nat. Hist. Bull.* 99: 545–60 (1952).

T Zweifel, Richard G. "Notes on Reptiles and Amphibians from the Pacific Coastal Islands of Baja California." *Amer. Mus. Nat. Hist. Novitates* 1895: 1–17 (1958).

Chapter 8

T Allan, H. H. *Flora of New Zealand*, Vol. 1. Wellington: R. E. Owen, Government Printer (1961).

T Baker, J. G. *Flora of Mauritius and the Seychelles*. London: L. Reeve & Co. (1877).

T, I Børgesen, F. "Contributions to the Knowledge of the Vegetation on the Canary Islands." *Mem. Acad. Roy. Soc. Lettres Danemark*, Sci. Ser. 8, 6(3): 285–398 (1924).

T Carlquist, S. "Systematic Anatomy of *Hesperomannia*." *Pacific Science* 11: 207–15 (1957).

T, I ———. "The genus *Fitchia* (Compositae)." *Univ. Calif. Publ. Bot.* 29: 1–144 (1957).

T ———. "Anatomy and Systematic Position of *Centaurodendron* and *Yunquea*." *Brittonia* 10: 78–93 (1958).

T ———. "A Theory of Paedomorphosis in Dicotyledonous Woods." *Phytomorphology* 12: 30–45 (1962).

T, I Chastain, André. "*La Flore et la Végétation des Iles de Kerguelen*." *Mem. Mus. Nat. Hist. Nat. (Paris)*, Ser. B., Bot. 11(1): 1–136 (1958).

T Christophersen, Erlin. "Flowering Plants of Samoa," II. *Bishop Mus. Bull.* 154: 1–77 (1938).

T Curtis, Winifred M. *The Student's Flora of Tasmania*, Vol. 2. Hobart: Government Printer (1963).

T, I Harling, Gunnar. "On Some Compositae Endemic to the Galápagos

Islands." *Acta Horti Bergiani* 20(3): 63–120 (1962).

T, I Hauman, Lucien. *"Les 'Lobelia' Géants des Montagnes du Congo Belge."* Mem. Inst. Roy. Col. Belge 2: 1–50 (1933).

T, I ———. *"Les 'Senecio' Arborescents du Congo."* Rev. Zool. Bot. Afr. 28(1): 1–76 (1935).

T Hillebrand, William. *Flora of the Hawaiian Islands.* Heidelberg: privately published (1888).

T, I Lems, Kornelius. "Botanical Notes on the Canary Islands. II. The Evolution of Plant Forms in the Islands: *Aeonium.*" Ecology 41: 1–17 (1960).

T ———. "Botanical Notes on the Canary Islands. III. The Life Form Spectrum and Its Interpretation." Ecology 42: 569–72 (1961).

G, I Melliss, John C. *St. Helena.* London: L. Reeve & Co. (1875).

G, I Philipson, W. R., and Hearn, D. *Rock Garden Plants of the Southern Alps.* Christchurch, New Zealand: The Caxton Press (1962).

T, I Praeger, R. Lloyd. *An Account of the* Sempervivum *Group.* London: The Royal Horticultural Society (1932).

T Raven, Peter. "A Flora of San Clemente Island, California." *Aliso* 5: 289–347 (1963).

T, I Rock, Joseph. *The Indigenous Trees of the Hawaiian Islands.* Honolulu: privately published (1913).

T ———. "The Genus *Plantago* in Hawaii." Amer. Jour. Bot. 7: 195–210 (1920).

T, I Schenck, H. *"Vergleichende Darstellung der Pflanzengeographie der subantarktischen Inseln."* Deutsche Tiefsee Exp. 2(1): 1–224 (1905).

T, I ———. *"Beiträge zur Kenntnis der Vegetation der Canarischen Inseln."* Deutsche Tiefsee Exp. 2(1): 225–406 (1907).

T, I Skottsberg, Carl. *"Die Flora der Desventuradas-Inseln."* Göteborgs

Kungl. Vetensk.-o-Vitterh. Samh. Handl., B, 5(6): 1–88 (1927).

T ———. "Notes on Some Recent Collections Made in the Islands of Juan Fernandez." Medd. Göteborgs Trädg. 4: 155–71 (1928).

T ———. "The Arboreous Nyctaginaceae of Hawaii." Svensk Bot. Tidsk. 30: 722–43 (1936).

T ———. "On Mrs. C. Bock's Collection of Plants from Masatierra (Juan Fernandez), with Remarks on the Flowers of *Centaurodendron.*" Medd. Göteborgs Trädg. 12: 361–73 (1938).

T ———. *"Une Seconde Espèce de* Centaurodendron *Johow."* Bull. Jard. Bot. Bruxelles 27: 585–89 (1957).

T ———. *Über* Yunquea tenzii *Skottsb.* Ber. Deutsche Bot. Gesell. 71: 45–52 (1958).

T, I ———, ed. *The Natural History of Juan Fernandez and Easter Island.* Stockholm: Almqvist & Wiksell (1953).

T, I Wardle, P. "Growth Habits of New Zealand Subalpine Shrubs and Trees." New Zealand Jour. Bot. 1: 18–47 (1963).

Chapter 9

T, I Bailey, L. H. "Palms of the Seychelles." Gentes Herbarum 6: 1–48 (1942).

T Baker, Rollin H. "The Avifauna of Micronesia, Its Origin, Evolution and Distribution." Univ. Kansas Mus. Nat. Hist. Pub. 3(1): 1–359 (1951).

G, I Beebe, William. *Galápagos—World's End.* New York: G. P. Putnam's Sons (1924).

T Brinck, Per. "Coleoptera of Tristan da Cunha." *Results of the Norwegian Scientific Expedition to Tristan da Cunha* 17: 1–121 (1948).

T   Brooks, Sprague. "Notes on Some Falkland Island Birds." *Mus. Compar. Zool. (Harvard) Bull.* 61(17): 135–60 (1917).

T, I   Darlington, Philip J., Jr. "Carabidae of Mountains and Islands: Data on the Evolution of Isolated Faunas, and on Atrophy of Wings." *Ecological Monographs* 13: 37–61 (1943).

G   Darwin, Charles. "Letter to J. D. Hooker, March 7, 1855" in *Life and Letters* (Francis Darwin, ed.) (1962).

T, I   Diels, L. *"Beiträge zur Kenntnis der Vegetation und Flora der Seychellen."* *Wiss. Ergebn. Deutsch. Tiefsee Exp.* 2(1:4): 409–66 (1922).

G   Eckert, Allan W. *The Great Auk.* Boston: Little, Brown & Co. (1963).

T   Enderlein, G. *"Die Insektfauna der Insel St.-Paul . . . Insel Neu-Amsterdam."* *Wiss. Erg. Deutsche Tiefsee Exp., Zool.* 2(4): 481–85, 486–92 (1909).

G, I   Greenway, James C., Jr. *Extinct and Vanishing Birds of the World.* New York: American Committee for International Wild Life Protection (1958).

T   Gressitt, J. L., and Leech, R. E. "Insect Habitats in Antarctica." *Polar Record* 10: 501–4 (1961).

T, I   Gressitt, J. Linsey, et al. "Insects of Campbell Island." *Pacific Insects Monograph* 7: 1–663 (1964).

G, I   Hachisuka, Masauji. *The Dodo and Kindred Birds.* London: H. F. & G. Witherby (1953).

T, I   Hagen, Yngvar. "Birds of Tristan da Cunha." *Results of the Norwegian Scientific Expedition to Tristan da Cunha* 20: 1–248 (1952).

T   L'Heritier, P., Neefs, Y., and Teissier, G. *"Aptérisme des Insectes et Sélection Naturelle."* *Comptes Rendus Acad. Sci. Paris* 204: 907–9 (1937).

T   Holdgate, M. W. "The Fauna of the Mid-Atlantic Islands." *Proc. Royal Soc. London,* Ser. B, 152: 550–67 (1960).

T, I   Holloway, Beverley A. "Wing Development and Evolution of New Zealand Lucanidae (Insecta: Coleoptera)." *Trans. Roy. Soc. New Zealand Zoology* 3: 99–116 (1963).

T   Jeannel, R. *"L'aptérisme chez les Insectes Insulaires."* *Comptes Rendus Acad. Sci. Paris* 180: 1222–24 (1925).

T   Lowe, Percy R. "A Description of *Atlantisea rogersi,* the Diminutive and Flightless Rail of Inaccessible Island (Southern Atlantic) with Some Notes on Flightless Rails." *Ibis* 1928: 99–131 (1928).

T   ———. "On the Evidence for the Existence of Two Species of Steamer Duck *(Tachyeres),* and Some Primary and Secondary Flightlessness in Birds." *Ibis* 1934: 467–95 (1934).

T   Mackintosh, N. A. "The Pattern of Distribution of the Antarctic Fauna." *Proc. Royal Soc.,* Ser. B, 152: 624–31 (1960).

G   Mayr, Ernst. *Birds of the Southwest Pacific.* New York: The Macmillan Company (1945).

G, I   Munro, George C. *Birds of Hawaii,* 2nd ed. Rutland, Vermont: The Ridgeway Press (1960).

T   Oldroyd, H. "A Wingless Dolichopodid (Diptera) from Campbell Island." *Records of the Dominion Museum (N.Z.)* 2: 243–46 (1956).

T, I   Oliver, W. R. B. *New Zealand Birds,* 2nd ed. Wellington: A. H. & A. W. Reed (1955).

T, I   Paramonov, S. J. "Lord Howe Island, A Riddle of the Pacific." *Pacific Science* 14: 75–85 (1960).

T   Rand, Austin L. "The Distribution and Habits of Madagascar Birds." *Amer. Mus. Nat. Hist. Bull.* 72: 142–499 (1936).

T   ———. "The Origin of the Land Birds of Tristan da Cunha." *Fieldiana (Zoology)* 37: 139–66 (1955).

G, I Rivolier, Jean. *Emperor Penguins.* New York: Robert Speller & Sons (1958).

T, I Salmon, J. T., and Bradley, J. D. "Lepidoptera from the Cape Expedition and Antipodes Islands." *Records of the Dominion Museum* (N.Z.) 3: 61–81 (1956).

G, I Shirland, Michael. *Tasmanian Birds,* 3rd ed. Sydney: Angus & Robertson (1958).

T Simpson, George G. "Fossil Penguins." *Amer. Mus. Nat. Hist. Bull.* 87: 7–99 (1946).

T, I Skottsberg, Carl, ed. *The Natural History of Juan Fernandez and Easter Island.* Stockholm: Almqvist & Wiksell (1953).

T Stonor, C. R. "Anatomical Notes on the New Zealand Wattled Crow (*Callaeas*) with Especial Reference to Its Powers of Flight." *Ibis* 1942: 1–18 (1942).

T, I Tillyard, R. J. *The Insects of Australia and New Zealand.* Sydney: Angus & Robertson (1926).

G, I Van Tyne, Josselyn, and Berger, Andrew J. *Fundamentals of Ornithology.* New York: John Wiley & Sons (1959).

T Viette, P. "*Croisière du Bougainville aux Iles Australes Françaises. 20. Lepidoptera.*" *Mem. Mus. Nat. Hist. Nat.* (Paris) 27(1): 1–28 (1948).

T, I ——. "Lepidoptera." *Results of the Norwegian Scientific Expedition to Tristan da Cunha* 23: 1–19 (1952).

T, I ——. "*Lépidoptères de l'île d'Amsterdam (Récoltes de Patrice Paulian, 1955–1956).*" *Bull Soc. Entomol. France* 64: 22–29 (1959).

G Zimmerman, Elwood C. "Report," in "Director's Report for 1934." *Bishop Mus. Bull.* 133: 68–71 (1935).

G, I ——. *Insects of Hawaii. Introduction.* Honolulu: University of Hawaii Press (1948).

T, I ——. *Insects of Hawaii,* Vol. 6. "Ephemeroptera — Neuroptera — Trichoptera." Honolulu: University of Hawaii Press (1957).

Chapter 10

T Allan, H. H. *Flora of New Zealand,* Vol. 1. Wellington: R. E. Owen, Government Printer (1961).

T Baker, Herbert G. "Self-Compatibility and Establishment after 'Long-Distance' Dispersal." *Evolution* 9: 347–349 (1955).

T, I Bowman, Robert I. "Morphological Differentiation and Adaptation in the Galápagos Finches." *Univ. Calif. Publ. Zool.* 58: 1–302 (1961).

T, I Carlquist, S. "*Trematolobelia:* Seed Dispersal; Anatomy of Fruits and Seeds." *Pacific Science* 16: 126–34 (1962).

T, I ——. "Ontogeny and Comparative Anatomy of Thorns of Hawaiian Lobeliaceae." *Amer. Jour. Bot.* 49: 413–19 (1962).

G, I Carolin, Roger. "Pollination of the Proteaceae." *Australian Museum Magazine,* Sept. 1961: 371–74 (1961).

T Dawson, John W. "Unisexuality in the New Zealand Umbelliferae." *Tuatara* 12: 67–68 (1964).

G, I Erickson, Rica. *Orchids of the West.* Perth: Paterson Brokensha Pty, (1951).

G, I Evans, A. H. *Birds* (The Cambridge Natural History). London: The Macmillan Company (1922).

T Godley, E. J. "Breeding Systems in New Zealand Plants. 2. Genetics of the Sex Forms in *Fuchsia procumbens.*" *New Zealand Jour. Bot.* 1: 48–52 (1963).

T, I Gosline, William A., and Brock, Vernon E. *Handbook of Hawaiian Fishes.* Honolulu: University of Hawaii Press (1960).

T Gray, Netta E. "A Taxonomic Revision of *Podocarpus*. XII. Sect. *Microcarpus*." *Journ. Arnold Arboretum* 41: 36–39 (1960).

G, I Hatt, Robert, et al. *Island Life: A Study of the Land Vertebrates of the Islands of Eastern Lake Michigan*. Bloomfield Hills, Michigan: Cranbrook Institute of Science (1948).

T Lewis, D. and Crowe, Leslie K. "The Genetics and Evolution of Gynodioecy." *Evolution* 10: 115–125 (1956).

G, I McKeown, Keith C. *Australian Spiders*, 2nd ed. Sydney: Angus & Robertson (1952).

T, I Mertens, Robert. *"Die Inselreptilien, ihre Ausbreitung, Variation, und Artbildung."* *Zoologica* 32(6): 1–209 (1934).

T, I Oliver, W. R. B. *New Zealand Birds*, 2nd ed. Wellington: A. H. & A. W. Reed (1955).

T, I Rattenbury, J. A. "Cyclic Hybridization as a Survival Mechanism in the New Zealand Forest Flora." *Evolution* 16: 348–363 (1962).

G Rupp, H. M. R. "A New Australian Subterranean Orchid." *Victorian Naturalist* 49: 102–4 (1932).

G ———. "Notes on New South Wales and Queensland Orchids." *Proc. Linnaean Soc. N.S.W.* 58: 223–28 (1933).

G, I ———. "The Habitat, Character and Floral Structure of *Cryptanthemis slateri* Rupp (Orchidaceae)." *Proc. Linnaean Soc. N.S.W.* 49: 118–22 (1934).

G, I Schimper, A. F. W. *Plant-Geography on a Physiological Basis*, reprinted edition. Codicote, England: Wheldon & Wesley (1960).

G, I Schultz, Leonard P., and Stern, Edith M. *The Ways of Fishes*. New York: D. van Nostrand Co. (1948).

T Skottsberg, Carl. "The Arboreous Nyctaginaceae of Hawaii." *Svensk Bot. Tidsk.* 30: 722–43 (1936).

T, I ———. "On the Flower Dimorphism in Hawaiian Rubiaceae." *Arkiv för Botanik* 31A(4): 1–28 (1944).

T, I Virot, Robert. "La Végétation Canaque." *Mem. Mus. Nat. Hist. Nat. (Paris)*, Ser. B, Bot. 7: 1–400 (1956).

G Wallace, Alfred R. *Natural Selection and Tropical Nature*. London: The Macmillan Company (1895).

G, I Warner, H. H. *"Angraecum* and *Xanthopan."* *Amer. Orchid Soc. Bull.* 3: 42–43 (1934).

G, I Welty, Joel C. *The Life of Birds*. Philadelphia: W. B. Saunders Co. (1962).

G, I Zimmerman, Elwood C. *Insects of Hawaii. Introduction*. Honolulu: University of Hawaii Press (1948).

Chapter 11

G Barrett, C. *"Menura*—Australia's Mockingbird." *N. Y. Zool. Soc. Bull.* 30: 207–16 (1927).

G Darwin, Charles. *The Descent of Man and Selection in Relation to Sex* (1871). Various editions available.

G, I Editors of *Life*, and Barnett, Lincoln. *The Wonders of Life on Earth*. New York: Time, Inc. (1960).

G, I Gilliard, E. Thomas. "The Evolution of Bowerbirds." *Scientific American* 209(2): 38–46 (1963).

G, I Iredale, Tom. *Birds of Paradise and Bower Birds*. Melbourne: Georgian House (1950).

G, I Marshall, A. J. *Bower-Birds*. London: Oxford University Press (1954).

T Mayr, Ernst, and Gilliard, E. Thomas. "The Ribbon-Tailed Bird of Paradise (*Astrapia mayeri*) and Its Allies." *Amer. Mus. Nat. Hist. Novitates* 1551: 1–13 (1952).

T, I ———. "Birds of Central New Guinea." *Amer. Mus. Nat. Hist. Bull.* 103(4): 311–74 (1954).

T   Mayr, Ernst, and Rand, A. L. "Birds of the 1933–1934 Papuan Expedition." *Amer. Mus. Nat. Hist. Bull.* 73: 1–248 (1937).

G, I   Pratt, Ambrose. *The Lore of the Lyrebird.* Sydney: The Endeavor Press (1933).

T   Rand, Austin L. "On the Breeding Habits of Some Birds of Paradise in the Wild." *Amer. Mus. Nat. Hist. Bull.* 73: 1–248 (1938).

T   ——. "Breeding Habits of the Birds of Paradise: *Macgregoria* and *Diphyllodes.*" *Amer. Mus. Nat. Hist. Novitates* 1073: 1–14 (1940).

G, I   Ripley, S. Dillon. "Strange Courtship of Birds of Paradise." *National Geographic* 97: 247–78 (1950).

Chapter 12

T   Allen, J. A. "Notes on *Solenodon paradoxus.*" *Amer. Mus. Nat. Hist. Bull.* 24: 505–17 (1908).

T, I   ——. "*Solenodon paradoxus.*" *Mus. Compar. Zool. (Harvard) Mem.* 49: 1–24 (1910).

T   ——. "*Zaglossus.*" *Mus. Compar. Zool. (Harvard) Mem.* 49: 253–307 (1912).

T   Annandale, N. "Fauna of the Inlé Lake, India." *Rec. Indian Mus.* 14: 1–214 (1918).

G, I   Bergamini, David, et al. *The Land and Wildlife of Australia.* New York: Time, Inc. (1964).

G, I   Blanchard, Frieda C. "Tuatara." *National Geographic* 67: 649–62 (1935).

G, I   Burrell, Harry. *The Platypus.* Sydney: Angus & Robertson, Ltd. (1927).

T   Calman, W. T. "On the Genus *Anaspides* and Its Affinities with Certain Fossil Crustacea." *Trans. Roy. Soc. Edinburgh* 38: 787–802 (1896).

G, I   Conrad, G. M. "By Boat to the Age of Reptiles." *Natural History* 45: 224–31 (1940).

T, I   Cooke, C. Montague, Jr., and Kondo, Yoshio. "Revision of Tornatellidae and Achatinellidae (Gastropoda, Pulmonata)." *Bishop Mus. Bull.* 221: 1–303 (1960).

G   Darlington, Philip J. *Zoogeography.* New York: John Wiley & Sons (1957).

G   Dawbin, W. H. "The Tuatara in Its Native Habitat." *Endeavor* 21: 16–24 (1962).

G   Fleay, David. *We Breed the Platypus.* Melbourne: Robertson & Mullens (1944).

T   Germain, Louis. "Études sur les Faunes Malacologiques Insulaires de l'Ocean Pacifique." In *Contribution à l'Étude du Peuplement Zoologique des Iles du Pacifique, Société de Biogéographie* (4: 89–153). Paris: Paul Lechevalier (1934).

T   Gregory, William K. "The Monotremes and the Palimpsest Theory." *Amer. Mus. Nat. Hist. Bull.* 88: 1–52 (1947).

T, I   Günther, Albert. "Description of *Ceratodus.*" *Philos. Trans.* 2: 511–71 (1871).

T, I   Hill, W. C. O. *Primates. II. Haplorhini: Tarsioidea.* Edinburgh: Edinburgh University Press (1955).

G, I   Kozhov, Mikhail. *Lake Baikal and Its Life.* The Hague: Dr. W. Junk (1963).

G, I   Le Souef, A. S., and Burrell, Harry. *The Wild Animals of Australasia.* London: George G. Harrap & Co. (1926).

T, I   McDowall, R. M. "The Affinities and Derivation of the New Zealand Fresh-Water Fish Fauna." *Tuatara* 12: 59–67 (1964).

T   McDowell, Samuel B., Jr. "The Greater Antillean Insectivores." *Amer. Mus. Nat. Hist. Bull.* 115: 113–214 (1958).

T   Manton, S. M. "Notes on the Habits and Feeding Mechanisms of *Anaspides* and *Paranaspides* (Crustacea,

Syncarida)." *Proc. Zool. Soc. London* 1930: 791–800 (1930).

T   Patterson, Bryan. "An Extinct Solenodontid Insectivore from Hispaniola." *Mus. Compar. Zool. (Harvard) Breviora* 165: 1–11 (1962).

T   Prashad, B., and Mukerji, D. D. "The Fish of the Indawygi Lake and the Streams of the Myitkina District (Upper Burma)." *Rec. Indian Mus.* 31: 161–223 (1929).

G, I   Sanderson, Ivan T. *The Monkey Kingdom.* Garden City, New York: Hanover House (1957).

T, I   Schmidt, Karl P. "A Visit to Karewa Island, Home of the Tuatara." *Fieldiana (Zoology)* 34: 153–64 (1953).

T   Simpson, George G. "Zoogeography of West Indian Land Mammals." *Amer. Mus. Nat. Hist. Novitates* 1759: 1–28 (1956).

T   ———. "Historical Zoogeography of Australian Mammals." *Evolution* 15: 431–46 (1961).

T   Stebbins, Robert C., and Eakin, Richard M. "The Role of the 'Third Eye' in Reptilian Behavior." *Amer. Mus. Nat. Hist. Novitates* 1870: 1–40 (1958).

T   Stephenson, N. G., and Thomas, Elsie M. "A Note Concerning the Occurrence and Life-History of *Leiopelma* Fitzinger." *Trans. Roy. Soc. N.Z.* 75: 319–20 (1945).

G, I   Troughton, Ellis. *Furred Animals of Australia.* New York: Charles Scribner's Sons (1947).

T   Turbott, E. G. "The Distribution of the Genus *Leiopelma* in New Zealand with a Description of a New Species." *Trans. Roy. Soc. N.Z.* 71: 247–53 (1942).

G, I   Van Tyne, Josselyn, and Berger, Andrew J. *Fundamentals of Ornithology.* New York: John Wiley & Sons (1959).

G, I   Whitley, Gilbert. *Native Freshwater Fishes of Australia.* Brisbane: The Jacaranda Press (1960).

Chapter 13

T   Axelrod, Daniel. "The Evolution of Flowering Plants." In S. Tax, ed., *Evolution after Darwin,* pp. 227–305. Chicago: University of Chicago Press (1960).

T   Bailey, I. W., and Nast, Charlotte G. "The Comparative Morphology of the Winteraceae." *Jour. Arnold Arboretum* 24: 340–46; 24: 472–81; 25: 97–103; 25: 215–21; 25: 342–48; 25: 454–66; 26: 37–47 (1943–45).

T   ———. "Morphology and Relationships of *Trochodendron* and *Tetracentron.* I. Stem, Root and Leaf." *Jour. Arnold Arboretum* 26: 143–54 (1945).

T, I   ——— and Smith, A. C. "The Family Himantandraceae." *Jour. Arnold Arboretum* 24: 190–206 (1943).

T, I   Bailey, I. W., and Smith, A. C. "Degeneriaceae, a New Family of Flowering Plants from Fiji." *Jour. Arnold Arboretum* 23: 356–65 (1942).

T   Bailey, I. W., and Swamy, B. G. L. "*Amborella trichopoda* Baill., A New Morphological Type of Vesselless Dicotyledon." *Jour. Arnold Arboretum* 29: 245–54 (1948).

T, I   ———. "The Morphology and Relationships of *Austrobaileya.*" *Jour. Arnold Arboretum* 30: 211–26 (1949).

T, I   Carlquist, S. "Morphology and Relationships of Lactoridaceae." *Aliso* 5: 421–35 (1964).

G, I   Chamberlain, Charles J. *The Living Cycads.* Chicago: University of Chicago Press (1919).

T, I   Eames, Arthur J. *Morphology of the Angiosperms.* New York: McGraw-Hill Book Company (1961).

T, I   Florin, Rudolf. "The Distribution of Conifer and Taxad Genera in Time and Space." *Acta Horti Bergiani* 20: 121–312 (1963).

T, I   Foster, Adriance S., and San Pedro, Manuel R. "Field Studies on *Micro-*

cycas calocoma." Mem. Soc. Cubana Hist. Nat. Felipe Poey 16: 105–21 (1942).

T Money, Lillian L., Bailey, I. W., and Swamy, B. G. L. "The Morphology and Relationships of the Monimiaceae." _Jour. Arnold Arboretum_ 31: 372–404 (1950).

T, I Nast, Charlotte C., and Bailey, I. W. "Morphology and Relationships of _Trochodendron_ and _Tetracentron_. II. Inflorescence, Flower and Fruit." _Jour. Arnold Arboretum_ 26: 269–76 (1945).

T, I Sarlin, P. _Bois et Fôrets de la Nouvelle-Calédonie._ Nogent-sur-Marne, France: Centre Technique Forestier Tropical (1954).

T, I Skottsberg, Carl, ed. _The Natural History of Juan Fernandez and Easter Island._ Stockholm: Almqvist & Wiksell (1953).

T Smith, A. C. "The American Species of _Drimys." Jour. Arnold Arboretum_ 24: 1–33 (1943).

T, I ———. "Taxonomic Notes on the Old World Species of Winteraceae." _Jour. Arnold Arboretum_ 24: 119–64 (1943).

T, I Swamy, B. G. L., and Bailey, I. W. "The Morphology and Relationships of _Cercidiphyllum." Jour. Arnold Arboretum_ 30: 187–210 (1949).

Chapter 14

G, I Allen, Glover M. _Extinct and Vanishing Mammals of the Western Hemisphere._ New York: American Committee for International Wild Life Protection. (1942).

G Anon. "Queer Vipers." _Time,_ Oct. 19, 1959: 534 (1959).

T, I Archey, Gilbert. "The Moa. A Study of the Dinornithiformes." _Bull. Auckland Inst. and Mus._ 1: 1–119 (1941).

G, I Bailey, Alfred M., and Sorenson, J. H. _Subantarctic Campbell Island._ Denver: Denver Museum of Natu-

ral History. (also Wellington: A. H. & A. W. Reed) (1962).

G, I Elton, Charles S. _The Ecology of Invasions by Animals and Plants._ New York: John Wiley & Sons (1958).

T Gill, Edmund D. "The Problem of Extinction, with Special Reference to Australian Marsupials." _Evolution_ 9: 87–92. (1955).

G, I Greenway, James C., Jr. _Extinct and Vanishing Birds of the World._ New York: American Committee for International Wild Life Protection (1958).

T, I Hagen, Yngvar. "Birds of Tristan da Cunha." _Results of the Norwegian Scientific Expedition to Tristan da Cunha_ 20: 1–248 (1952).

G, I Harper, Francis. _Extinct and Vanishing Mammals of the Old World._ New York: American Committee for International Wild Life Protection (1945).

G, I Melliss, John C. _St. Helena._ London: L. Reeve & Co. (1875).

T "Modification of Biotic Balance of Island Floras and Faunas (a Symposium)." In J. L. Gressitt, ed., _Pacific Basin Biogeography,_ pp. 485–61. Honolulu: Bishop Museum Press (1963).

T, I Oliver, W. R. B. _New Zealand Birds,_ 2nd ed. Wellington: A. H. & A. W. Reed (1955).

G, I Rice, Dale W. "The Hawaiian Monk Seal." _Natural History_ 73(2): 48–55 (1964).

Chapter 15

G, I Beebe, William. _Galápagos—World's End._ New York: G. P. Putnam's Sons (1924).

G, I ———. _The Arcturus Adventure._ New York: G. P. Putnam's Sons (1926).

T, I Bowman, Robert I. "Morphological Differentiation and Adaptation in the Galápagos Finches." _Univ. Calif. Publ. Zool._ 58: 1–302 (1961).

T   Chesterman, Charles W. "Contributions to the Petrography of the Galápagos, Cocos, Malpelo, Cedros, San Benito, Tres Marias and White Friars Islands. *Proc. Calif. Acad. Sci.*, 4th Ser., 32: 339–62 (1963).

T   Chubb, Lawrence J. "Geology of Galápagos, Cocos and Easter Islands" (including Richardson, Constance: "Petrology of Galápagos Islands"). *Bishop Mus. Bull.* 110: 1–67 (1933).

T, I   Dall, William H., and Ochsner, W. H. "Landshells of the Galápagos Islands." *Proc. Calif. Acad. Sci.*, 4th Ser., 17: 141–85 (1928).

G, I   Darwin, Charles. *Voyage of the Beagle.* London: J. M. Dent & Sons (1906). Ltd. (Many other editions available.)

G, I   Editors of *Life,* and Barnett, Lincoln. *The Wonders of Life on Earth.* New York: Time, Inc. (1960).

G, I   Eibl-Eibesfeldt, Irenaus. *Galápagos.* New York: Doubleday & Company, Inc. (1961).

T, I   "Galápagos Islands. A Unique Area for Scientific Investigation." A Symposium from the Tenth Pacific Science Congress. *Occasional Pap. Calif. Acad. Sci.* 44: 1–154 (1963).

T   Garman, Samuel. "The Galápagos Tortoises." *Mus. Compar. Zool. (Harvard) Mem.* 30(4): 261–96 (1917).

T, I   Gifford, Edward W. "The Birds of the Galápagos Islands." *Proc. Calif. Acad. Sci.*, 4th Ser., 2: 1–132 (1913).

T   ———. "Field Notes on the Land Birds of the Galápagos Islands and of Cocis Island, Costa Rica." *Proc. Calif. Acad. Sci.*, 4th Ser., 2: 189–258 (1919).

T, I   Harling, Gunnar. "On Some Compositae Endemic to the Galápagos Islands." *Acta Horti Bergiani* 20: 63–120 (1962).

G, I   Howell, John T. "Cacti in the Galápagos Islands." *Cactus and Succulent Jour.* 5: 513, 515–18, 531–32 (1934).

T   ———. "The Genus *Scalesia.*" *Proc. Calif. Acad. Sci.*, 4th Ser., 22: 221–71 (1941).

T   Kroeber, A. L. "Floral Relations among the Galápagos Islands." *Univ. Calif. Publ. Bot.* 6: 199–220 (1916).

T, I   Lack, David. "The Galápagos Finches (Geospizinae)." *Occasional Pap. Calif. Acad. Sci.* 21: 1–151 (1947).

G, I   ———. *Darwin's Finches.* Cambridge: Cambridge University Press (1947).

G   Melville, Herman. Las Encantadas. In *The Complete Stories of Herman Melville.* New York: Random House (1949).

G, I   Slevin, Joseph R. "An Account of the Reptiles Inhabiting the Galápagos Islands. *Bull. New York Zool. Soc.* 38: 2–24 (1935).

G, I   ———. "The Galápagos Islands. A History of Their Exploration." *Occasional Pap. Calif. Acad. Sci.* 25: 1–150 (1959).

T   Snodgrass, Robert E., and Heller, Edmund. "Birds" (Papers from the Hopkins-Stanford Galápagos Expedition, 1898–99). *Proc. Washington Acad. Sci.* 5: 231–372 (1904).

T, I   Stewart, Alban. "A Botanical Survey of the Galápagos Islands." *Proc. Calif. Acad. Sci.*, 4th Ser., 1: 7–288 (1911).

T   Swarth, Harry S. "The Avifauna of the Galápagos Islands." *Occasional Pap. Calif. Acad. Sci.* 18: 1–299 (1931).

T, I   Van Denburgh, John. "The Snakes of the Galápagos Islands." *Proc. Calif. Acad. Sci.*, 4th Ser., 1: 323–74 (1912).

T   ———. "The Geckos of the Galápagos Archipelago." *Proc. Calif. Acad. Sci.*, 4th Ser., 1: 405–30 (1912).

T, I   ———. "The Gigantic Land Tortoises of the Galápagos Archipelago."

Proc. Calif. Acad. Sci., 4th Ser., 2: 203–374 (1914).

T   —— and Slevin, Joseph R. "The Galápagoan Lizards of the Genus *Tropidurus.*" *Proc. Calif. Acad. Sci.*, 4th Ser., 2: 133–202 (1913).

T   Van Dyke, Edwin C. "The Coleoptera of the Galápagos Islands." *Occasional Pap. Calif. Acad. Sci.* 22: 1–181 (1953).

Chapter 16

T   Angel, F. "*Reptilia et Batrachia.*" In A. Gruvel, ed., *Faune des Colonies Françaises.* Paris: Société d'Éditions Géographiques, Maritimes, et Coloniales (1931).

G, I   Attenborough, David. *Zoo Quest to Madagascar.* London: Lutterworth Press (1961).

T, I   Capuron, R. "*Rhopalocarpacées.*" In H. Humbert, ed., *Flore de Madagascar et des Comores.* Paris: Muséum National d'Histoire Naturelle (1963).

T, I   ———. "*Contributions à l'Etude de la Flore de Madagascar.*" *Adansonia* 3: 370–400 (1963).

T, I   Carlquist, S. "Pollen Morphology and Evolution of Sarcolaenaceae (Chlaenaceae)." *Brittonia* 16: 231–54 (1964).

T, I   Cavaco, A. "*Chlénacées.*" In H. Humbert, ed., *Flore de Madagascar et des Comores.* Paris: Muséum National d'Histoire Naturelle (1952).

T, I   Choux, Pierre. "*Les Didiereacées, Xerophytes de Madagascar.*" *Mem. Acad. Malgâche* 17: 1–71 (1934).

G, I   Evans, A. H. 1922. *Birds* (The Cambridge Natural History). London: The Macmillan Company (1922).

G, I   Grandidier, G., and Petit, G. *Zoologie de Madagascar.* Paris: Société d'Éditions Géographiques, Maritimes, et Coloniales (1932).

T, I   Hill, W. C. O. *Primates.* Vol. I, *Strepsirhini.* Edinburgh: Edinburgh University Press (1953).

T, I   Humbert, H. Les Composées de Madagascar. Caen: E. Lanier (1932).

G, I   Jacobsen, Hermann. *A Handbook of Succulent Plants.* London: Blandford Press (1960).

T, I   Jumelle, H. "*Aponogetonacées.*" In H. Humbert, ed., *Flore de Madagascar.* Paris: Muséum National d'Histoire Naturelle (1936).

T, I   Milne-Edwards, A., and Grandidier, A. "*Histoire Naturelle des Mammifères.*" In *Histoire Physique, Politique, et Naturelle de Madagascar.* Paris: Imprimerie Nationale (1 vol. text, 3 vols. plates) (1876).

T, I   ———. "*Histoire Naturelle des Oiseaux.*" In *Histoire Physique, Politique, et Naturelle de Madagascar.* Paris: Imprimerie Nationale (1 vol. text, 3 vols. [1878, 1879, 1881] plates) (1885).

T, I   Perrier de la Bâthie, *H. La Végétation Malgache.* Ann. Mus. Colonial Marseille, Ser. 3, 9: 1–266 (1921).

T, I   ———. *Biogeographie de Madagascar.* Paris: Société d'Éditions Géographiques, Maritimes, et Coloniales (1936).

T   Rand, Austin L. "The Distribution and Habits of Madagascar Birds." *Amer. Mus. Nat. Hist. Bull.* 72: 143–499 (1936).

T, I   Rauh, Werner. "*Morphologische, entwicklungsgeschichtlicher, histogenetische und anatomische Untersuchungen an den Sprossen der Didieraceen.*" *Akad. Wiss. Lit., Abhandl.* (Math.-Nat. Klasse) 1956 (6): 1–104 (1956).

T, I   ———. "*Weitere Untersuchungen an Didieraceen.*" *Sitz. Heidelberger Akad. Sci.* (Math.-Nat. Klasse) 1961(7): 1–118 (1961).

T, I   ———. "*Didiereacées.*" In H. Humbert, ed., *Flore de Madagascar et des Comores*. Paris: Muséum National d'Histoire Naturelle (1963).

G, I Sanderson, Ivan T. *The Monkey Kingdom*. Garden City, New York: Hanover House (1957).

T Straka, Herbert. *"Über die mögliche phylogenetische Bedeutung der Pollenmorphologie der Madagassischen Bubbia perrieri R. Cap. (Winteraceae)."* *Grana Palynologica* 4: 355–60 (1963).

T, I Vaillant, Léon, and Grandidier, Guillaume. *"Histoire Naturelle des Reptiles."* In *Histoire Physique, Politique, et Naturelle de Madagascar*. Paris: Imprimerie Nationale (1910).

Index

DR. SHERWIN CARLQUIST is Associate Professor of Botany at Claremont Graduate School in Claremont, California. Educated at the University of California at Berkeley and at Harvard University, he has been primarily interested in insular plants. His studies and field trips have taken him to Hawaii on several occasions as well as to many islands of the Pacific, and on these trips Dr. Carlquist has studied firsthand many of the plants and animals discussed in this book.

The author of numerous papers that have appeared in botanical journals, Dr. Carlquist wrote a text, *Comparative Plant Anatomy*, and, with Mrs. Helen Bauer, *Japanese Festivals*.